The
Crowded
Sky

The
Crowded
Sky

HANK SEARLS

Harper & Brothers, Publishers
New York

To Shirley

contents

PROLOGUE   9

part one: 13
    CLEARED TO VICTOR
    ONE-FIVE-ONE-EIGHT

part two: 103
    CRUISE AND MAINTAIN . . .

part three: 185
    MAYDAY AT TWENTY
    THOUSAND . . .

    GLOSSARY   253

prologue

Mid-air collisions will always occur. So will railroad accidents, bus tragedies, and collisions at sea.

It is seven times safer to fly commercially than to drive; two bees are less likely to collide in their three-dimensional world than two beetles in their terrestrial one. But wherever men trust their safety to the understanding of other men, there is room between intellects for a barrier.

Sometimes a barrier to understanding is mechanical. Sometimes it is psychological—a sign of mental inflexibility. Few airline captains are inflexible, but some are. So are some doctors and judges.

Few experienced military pilots press their luck. Some, when sufficiently motivated, will. . . .

The swarming east-west airways crawl jerkily across the map from range station to range station like the courses of determined but erratic ants. To a pilot or a ground controller they have names as familiar as highway numbers to a trucker; the old airways: Green Two, Red Three, Amber Three; the newer "omni"* airways: Victor One-Five-One-Eight, Jet Route Seven-Eight, Victor Sixteen; military routes Jet Two Victor, Jet Four Love, Jet Six Victor (often, unfortunately, merely alternate names for the civil routes).

* See Glossary, page 253, for unfamiliar terms.

The airway is not a highway, but an invisible alley, sometimes of infinite height. Day or night, its traveler depends for safety not as the motorist does on keeping right or left of a center line, but on holding a promised speed and an assigned altitude. If he speeds up, he will overtake his predecessor; if he climbs or descends inadvertently, he is suddenly in an opposite stream of traffic approaching with the speed of sound.

The pilot boring along an airway on instruments sometimes envisions his portion of the alley as shrinking to a low, narrow tunnel. He reports to the controller as he passes over range stations, trusting entirely to the man on the ground to see that the tunnel ahead is clear. The importance of being where he says he is, when he says he is there, is usually very much in his consciousness, secondary only to the mortal necessity of keeping his altitude so that he does not climb or descend the thousand (or at high altitude two thousand) feet that will put him in a tunnel of opposite flow. It is so especially in bad weather at night, when the "tunnels" teem not only with airliners, which almost always use airways anyway, but with military and private aircraft availing themselves of the controlled facilities.

The controller in the busy Memphis, or Albuquerque, or Fort Worth Center ("Amarillo Center" is a fabrication as is "Clark-Chennault" Air Force Base) begins to visualize the airways not as alleys or even tunnels. To him they are routes along which processions of imaginary blocks of space, stacked vertically, move through his area at varying rates in alternately opposite directions. Each block has in its center an airplane. The controller's task is to see that none of the controlled aircraft penetrates the block of space protecting another.

The controller on some airways has a little electronic help. His own recently installed surveillance radar can aid him, if he can find time from his traditional control board to scan it, or enroute information accurate enough to interpret it, but its "blips" can only give him an aircraft's position, not its altitude. Military radar in the Ground Control Intercept system can assist him with rough altitudes at certain times in certain areas. But until recently it was exclusively a defense net. Its line of communication with him is often frail.

So ultimately the controller must depend on each pilot to confirm constantly that he is over the station he should be, when he was told to be there, and that he is at his assigned altitude. Pilots do not, and usually cannot, communicate with each other.

Only the man on the ground can change the instructions, or clearance.

And between the man on the ground and the man in the air stretches of course only the thread of a radio frequency. Sometimes the thread becomes knotted with too many transmissions. Sometimes distance strains it or thunderstorms snarl it with static.

Sometimes, as in simpler communication between human beings, the thread snaps. . . .

part one

CLEARED TO VICTOR
ONE-FIVE-ONE-EIGHT

one:

NAVY JET 3255
SAN DIEGO, CALIFORNIA

Strapped in the quiet, gently swaying cockpit, Dale Heath climbed southward on instruments through the afternoon fog. He pushed from his mind his doubtful radio—it had after all received clearly his air traffic control climb-out instructions on the ground a few moments before.

He throttled back slightly, listened to the whisper of the jet engine behind his passenger. Unless the note changed he would not notice it again. Now he centered his attention on the tiny airplane poised under glass on his instrument panel. It rode above a horizontal bar, an artificial horizon that would always parallel the real one hidden beyond the murk outside.

He knew that he was rusty on instruments, that he might be halfway to Albuquerque before his skill was repolished. The immovable white shroud outside his bubble canopy, glimpsed subconsciously while his attention was on the artificial horizon, planted an illusion of stillness, of lack of motion. For a moment he felt that he was suspended fixedly in a void. Recognizing the delusion as a forerunner of vertigo, he nevertheless had to glance at his airspeed indicator to prove to himself that he was moving.

But then vertigo struck in earnest, with his inner ear screaming falsely that he was in a diving, graveyard spiral, the seat pressure crying with visceral certainty that the turn was tightening. Although he knew rationally that he was climbing on course, it took all his will power to trust in the little airplane on his panel, all of his strength to battle the instinct to pull up from a dive he was not in.

Dale Heath knew that he was too experienced an airman to surrender to the mortal swindle of vertigo, but its shadow added to the vague unease he had felt since morning.

The aerologist had increased it when he spoke of the front over Denver; the line chief when he passed off the questionable radio with a shrug; but Cheryl had seeded it before she even arose.

He had been edging from his bed, not wanting to awaken her. Outside, in the bright California sunlight, children were playing on the street. He could hear the faint chime of a Good Humor truck. The room was stale with the smell of cigarettes she had smoked the night before, reading one of her fashion magazines long after he had dropped to sleep. This morning, if she awakened at all, she would be jumpy, tired, and irritable. She breathed evenly now, and if neither the children nor the ice-cream truck had awakened her, perhaps he'd be out of the house before she stirred.

The sound began as a wild whistle in the direction of the Silver Strand, lowered its pitch to a steadily increasing roar. An F4D, he thought, and if he's low he'll wake her up, and there goes Sunday morning. . . .

The F4D *was* low, the pilot was slow in detecting it, and he added throttle directly over Coronado. The blast of his engines reached into the house, squeezed the bedroom in pure noise, shook it, and released it as the plane shrieked over the air-station boundary. A windowpane continued to rattle. Outside, the children had not stopped their play.

"Oh, God," his wife murmured. She clawed a hand down her face, glaring at him as if he had been flying the plane. There were shadows under her eyes. "When are you leaving?"

"Not until this evening. I told Anne I'd take her to the zoo. . . ."

"The zoo?" She suddenly sparkled and lost ten years of age. "I want to go."

A few months ago the idea would have cheered him. Now he felt nothing, but he owed it to Anne to try. . . .

"Swell," he said cautiously. "I'd like that."

"No you wouldn't," she shrugged. "You'd rather be alone, the two of you. . . ."

"No," he said.

"The hell with it. Go to the zoo."

She had been momentarily teased, perhaps, by a picture of the three of them, hand in hand, strolling past the cages, and then lost the vision in the practical problem of make-up and dresses. Or had she been testing him?

"When will you be back?" she asked disinterestedly.

"By three."

"I mean from Washington."

"One week, as I said."

"I still don't see what you're going to do back there next weekend. Or are they working weekends in the Navy Department now?"

He shook his head.

She reached into the bedside table and took out a nail buffer.

"Why can't you come back Friday?" she persisted. "Are you going to see Jean?"

The feeling of discomfort that had plagued him all day had begun there; the conviction that within the next day or two he must act, and that in acting he would change all of their lives: Cheryl's and Anne's and Jean's. . . .

"Yes, Cheryl, I am."

She smiled distantly, working on her nails. "You *do* love her, don't you?"

A few weeks before, not long after his discovery of the terrified lieutenant, she had proposed the same theory, calling him a hypocrite and no better than she. Then he had simply refused to discuss it. But he *did* love Jean, although God knew how Cheryl had guessed; had loved her unconsciously, perhaps, even before he knew that Cheryl was cheating.

He hated scenes, especially with Anne in the house, but now an evasive answer seemed hardly worth the trouble.

"I think so. Yes."

She giggled unexpectedly. "The widow of your best friend! And for a month you've been making me feel like a cross between Flaming Mame and Suzie Wong. Honest to God . . ."

"At least," he flared, "I haven't been sleeping with her."

She looked up from her nails. "You haven't been sleeping with anybody much lately, have you?" she yawned. "Well, give her my love. Not," she added dryly, "that you won't. . . ."

He moved to the bathroom and began to run his snarling razor over features stamped with wind and sky and sea. He shaved closely, for an oxygen mask on a stubble of whiskers irritated his face. And he might not have time to shave again before he saw Jean.

He thought of her cool gray eyes and the swirls of her short brown hair. His spirits lightened. Still shaving, he walked to the end of the cord and glanced out at the clock in the bedroom.

"You can hardly wait to see her, can you?" Cheryl murmured, still buffing her nails. "Why don't you leave earlier? You could get back there in time for dinner."

Cheryl's green eyes were laughing. He pondered the eternal mystery of their marriage—her almost psychic perception of those of his thoughts she wanted to understand, and the drawbridge that rose in her mind when he tried to reach her with some idea that she did not believe or wish to hear.

"Frankly, because I'm taking Anne to the zoo."

"How noble," she said. "See if you can get her to bring me a cup of coffee and some toast."

Now that she wanted something, even a cup of coffee, she was grinning companionably. She had been, still was when she tried to be, a lovely, radiant girl.

He shook his head in wonder.

"I'll ask her."

"Good show," she said, closing her eyes.

Anne sat at the table with her chin on her hands, reading a book, waiting for him. She wore blue jeans and a plaid shirt. A pony-tail cascaded upward from her blond head like a fountain of gold. He stood for a moment, watching her, while the familiar, almost excruciating love subsided in his chest. Then he moved behind her and tugged at the pony-tail.

She put her hand on his in a gesture so adult and womanly that he was almost shocked. *God,* he thought, *the guy that gets this girl ought to spend his life burning candles.*

The table was laid neatly for two. By the stove five eggs, four sausages, and a mixing bowl of pancake batter were lined up in methodical procession toward waiting skillets so that nothing would be forgotten. She turned on the stove and Dale sat down. At his place lay the folded Sunday paper, undisturbed, or if read at least rearranged.

"Set for the zoo?" he asked.

She turned, not a woman cooking breakfast for a man but an excited child. "Can we, still?"

"Of course."

"I thought maybe we couldn't."

"First we go to the zoo, *then* I go to Washington."

Expertly, with one hand, she broke eggs into the skillet. *Now where in the hell did she learn that?* Dale wondered. *Her mother can't do it right with both hands and a table knife.* He sighed and began to read the paper.

"How long will you be gone?" she asked, elaborately busy.

"A week."

She turned from the stove. "Are you going to see Jeanie?" Their eyes met. "Yes."

"Tell her I gave Sloppy the vitamin pills. He's much better. She'll know what I mean."

Sloppy was a ludicrous, primitive rag rabbit with flopping ears that Jeanie had given her when she was six. Dolls were far beneath her now, except for Sloppy.

"I'll tell her."

"I'm glad you're seeing her, Daddy," Anne said carefully.

Who are we kidding? Dale asked himself. *She knows the score and the inning and the batting averages of all the players.*

He steered to safe water. "Before I forget, your mother would like some of your super-duper coffee and some toast."

Anne grinned at him, drew herself up to her full five feet, and tossed a salute in the direction of the bedroom. He wondered, as he so often had, to what sort of armed truce his daughter and his wife had adjusted during his long overseas absences in the last twelve years.

The zoo was magnificent. The hyenas chortled, the parrots screamed, the apes seemed charged with dramaturgic electricity. Anne and he gobbled popcorn, two hot dogs each, and several Cokes. He shuddered to think of the gaseous torture his stomach would endure, even in a pressurized cockpit, at thirty thousand feet.

But rumbling onto the ferry in the battered station wagon that Cheryl hated so much, Dale sensed that Anne was sinking rapidly. They abandoned the car for their favorite spot topside. The San Diego fog was slithering in from the ocean on schedule. It would be an instrument flight, apparently, all the way.

Anne, standing in his lee, shivered and drew closer to him. Without much hope she said, "Maybe they won't clear you."

He smiled down at her, aching at the loneliness in her voice. "Maybe not . . ." He changed the subject. "Do you still want to go to boarding school?" he asked. She was entering high school in June, knew his tour in Coronado was drawing to a close, and had sounded him out. With the pay raise he just might swing it.

She nodded.

"Why?"

"When you go to sea again, I'd just as soon, that's all."

"Your mother would be lonely," he said automatically. Then he wished he had not said it.

She shot him a cynical glance that made her look a good five years older than she was. "Daddy . . ." she said reprovingly.

Anger at the woman who had thrown away this incredible child's friendship flared in him briefly.

"Well, she would," he said lamely.

She shrugged. "Let's face it, Daddy. She and I just don't dig each other. Not at all. No, I'd like to go to boarding school."

"Where?" he asked carefully.

Promptly: "Back in Washington."

He was slated for Atlantic duty. That was part of it, but not all.

"So you could be near me?"

She nodded.

She's written off her mother, he thought, *completely; does she know how close I am to throwing in the sponge? Or does she know something I don't?*

"What about your mother?"

There was no malice in her voice: "She couldn't care less."

"But if I got the Atlantic, she'd move East too and then you wouldn't have to go to boarding school."

"She would?" The hazel eyes held steadily to him.

He was dangerously close to pumping her, and that he must not do.

"Well, but honey, assuming she didn't want to move East, you'd have to have somebody around. Nearer than the Mediterranean, I mean. To kind of look after you."

"I'll bet Jeanie would. She's my godmother."

Jeanie, Dale thought, *would show you more simple, intelligent love in a month than Cheryl has in thirteen years. . . . She would break her neck to take care of you.*

Jean and he had even discussed it on his last trip East—academically, "if anything happens to me." For he, like all fliers, dwelt in the accepted shadow of sudden death, and the thought of Anne unbuffered by himself from the shocks of Cheryl's amorality, now that he knew of it, was chilling. Although he was no businessman, although he was too direct for ordinary slyness, inspiration had somehow come to him, and he had acted swiftly and quietly to protect her. Even Jean knew nothing of it. . . .

"I think," he said, "when we get home, I'll mention the school to Cheryl. I'll see what she says. It might be good for you at that."

"I want it more than anything in the world," she said simply.

He gazed down at his daughter's small, pony-tailed head in

wonder. Whatever else he had done, at least he had carried his daughter to the firm ground of adolescence.

He squeezed her shoulder, and together they watched the approaching Coronado ferry slip.

There would be practically no room in the TV-2 jet trainer for luggage, so he selected from the closet the tiny leather overnight bag that had been Sal Porter's and that Jeanie had given him in Hawaii. He began to pack. Cheryl, in an exquisite slip, was sitting on her unmade bed applying make-up.

He selected three unfrayed khaki shirts from the drawer.

"Anne says," he continued cautiously, "she'd really like to go."

There was no use emphasizing how *much* Anne wanted boarding school; it would simply raise the price.

"Where does she want to go to school?"

"Back East."

"Washington?" There was a hint of amusement in her voice. "Yes."

"Do you suppose," she asked innocently, "that she expects us to let Jean look after her?"

"Probably," he answered cautiously. "Why not?" He could feel a familiar throb of anger beginning in his chest. *Steady*, he warned himself, knowing that she was baiting him.

"I don't think a lonely widow's apartment is the place for an adolescent girl. Especially a nurse's—you know how promiscuous they are. . . ."

He was suddenly facing her, his hands shaking. "You bitch," he gritted, wanting to smash the immaculately groomed face. "You foul-mouthed bitch!"

She grinned up at him. "Simmer down, Buster. I was just kidding."

He returned to his packing: "I'm going to send her to boarding school. She wants to go, and I'm going to send her. There isn't a damn thing you can do about it."

There was a long silence. Then Cheryl said, "Just yank her out. You'll be gone."

He forced down his anger. "You haven't stated your objection. What's wrong with it?"

"Oh, I don't know," he heard her yawn. "Money, maybe. I don't see how we can afford to send our daughter to boarding school when I can't even afford a little old Thunderbird."

So that's going to be it, he thought. The injustice of the situation clawed at his throat. He had not once allowed himself, after that night, to allude to it again. Except that he couldn't bring himself to physical intimacy with her, it had remained a closed subject. But now the bitterness forced itself out.

"You're in a hell of a spot," he grated, "to be bargaining."

Her face shone triumphantly. "Ah ha," she lilted. "The veneer cracketh. I thought you'd forgotten. . . . Or something. Are you going to start bringing that up now?"

"Maybe."

She returned to her nails. "You shouldn't have come back afterward, my sweet. Any lawyer could have told you that."

Their glances met in the bureau mirror. She winked at him without malice, and for a moment there was between them almost a bond; the bond of two antagonists who have fought over the same ground for an eternity and sense that the end is approaching in a draw.

He finished packing, shrugged into his green aviator's winter uniform, placed the golden wings with care, and went to the living room.

Anne was sitting on the floor, dispiritedly playing records. "No soap?"

"I don't know. Are you ready to go?"

"Yes."

But it was Cheryl, as he swung the station wagon into a parking place behind the Operations Building at the air station, who brought up the subject again.

"Anne," she said, "run into Operations and get me a pack of cigarettes."

When the girl was gone she faced Dale. "Well, my love to all the admirals. Say hello to Jeanie with the light brown hair. And Dale?"

"Yes?"

"About the school. Let's settle it now."

She really wants that car, he thought.

Mentally he ran over his savings. It would be close, but at twelve thousand a year if they financed the damn car he might just make it.

"All right. Order the T-bird." He hesitated. He had never been able to live with a lie, and ever since he had made what at the time had seemed an inspired provision for his daughter's protection, it had gnawed at him. "There's one thing. . . ."

"Yes?" she asked cautiously.

"There's another stipulation. Next month I'll be operating off a carrier again."

"Operating is right," she murmured.

She had always assumed that he and all other naval aviators behaved overseas like bulls loosed on a herd of cows. It was useless to argue the point.

"I didn't tell you, but off Quemoy last year I damn near got killed."

"Oh?" she asked without much interest. "What happened?"

"A cold cat shot—it dumped me ahead of the ship. But I put in a fast five seconds thinking. Of you and Anne . . ."

She smiled grimly. "Mostly Anne, I'm sure. And?"

"Cheryl, you two just don't get along."

She shrugged. "We manage. We have to."

"Suppose I got killed next year in the Med. . . ."

She shifted uncomfortably. "Oh, for God's sake . . ."

"Suppose I did." He took a breath. "Would you voluntarily leave Anne in the school?"

She stared at him. "Now listen! Who'd pay for it?"

"My insurance, but I'm coming to that." He paused. "I don't expect to get killed, you know."

"I don't expect you to."

"In five years she'll be on her own anyway . . . and you're not happy with her."

"I'm her mother."

Don't, he pleaded silently, *see yourself as a lonely widow.* . . .

But she was too honest for that.

"This is ridiculous," she said suddenly. "Nobody's going to get killed."

"Then?"

"Sure," she said cheerfully. She stuck out her hand.

She had never broken a promise, with the exception, he thought wryly, of a few she had made before a Navy chaplain fifteen years before. It was the one small passage of common understanding inviolate to her. She seemed to sense it as a narrow gate in the barrier between them, to know that if it was locked there would be nothing.

"First," he said, steeling himself for her anger, "I'll tell you something. When I went to Washington I called the Mutual agent. I changed my beneficiary. On all but the ten thousand government insurance. You get that."

"Oh?" she asked evenly. "And who gets the rest? Jean?"

"Not exactly. Twenty thousand to Anne, with Jean as trustee. The other twenty to you, *if* you give Jean custody."

"And if I don't?"

"Jean's trustee of that too, and Anne gets it at twenty-one."

The storm didn't break. She studied her fingernails. "Well, weren't you clever."

"I was pretty mad."

"You think I'd sell my daughter for twenty thousand dollars?"

"I think you'd welcome a chance to hunt alone, to put it bluntly."

She grinned suddenly. "Maybe you're right." She shrugged. "Why ask me to promise, if you've got it squared away anyway?"

He ran his hand through his hair. *Why indeed?*

"Because I don't want it that way. I'd rather change it back. I'd rather have you do it voluntarily."

"So I won't be 'selling' her?"

"Maybe that's it. . . ."

"How noble! Oh, what difference does it make? All right."
She put out her hand again, and he shook it.

"O.K., kid." He opened the door. "Stick around till I take off,
will you?"

"Why? You know I hate the sound of those things."

"Because," he explained angrily, "Anne will want to. Is that
all right?"

She shrugged. "I'll wait in the car. Dale?"

"Yes?"

"Don't leave mad."

She was looking at him with what he classified as her troubled
look. Or was there sincerity in it?

He grinned. "O.K., Cheryl. I'll see you a week from Monday."

She held up her lips and he brushed them with his. She shook
her head and took his chin in her hands. She kissed him more
firmly.

"Don't sweat it," she said cheerfully. "It all counts toward
twenty years."

He shook his head helplessly. "You're something," he said.
"You are really something. . . ."

Anne returned with the cigarettes and followed him to the
ready room. From previous experience he knew that she would
dog every step until he turned up his engine. He took his nylon
flight suit from his locker, his oxygen mask and hard-hat, and
his en-route high-altitude charts, compact airways maps made
up for the cramped cockpits of modern jets.

He pulled his bright orange flight suit over his clothes—there
would be no room to hang up his uniform anyway. Then, tailed
by Anne, he went to the operations desk.

The operations duty officer, Lieutenant Kramer, sneaked a
glance over the counter as Dale began to fill out his flight plan.

"Plane's all set, sir. What route do you plan?"

When Dale had phoned aerology from home, a low-pressure
area near Denver was grinding slowly eastward over the Rockies.
He would fly the southern route and miss the turbulence to the
north. Besides, there was less jet airline traffic to the south. . . .

"Jet Four Victor, I think."

The lieutenant nodded. "That's what I figured. There was a guy trying to get a hop to Albuquerque, but I'll tell him. . . ."

Dale hesitated. "Who is it?"

"A seaman first, named . . . Just a minute. McVey. On leave. He's off a tin can. The U.S.S. *Hailey.* He's been trying to get home since yesterday."

Dale thought of some lonely seaman watching the precious moments of his leave tick away. "Emergency leave?"

"I don't think so."

Kramer beckoned to a tanned young man in blues, sitting on a leather couch by the wall. "McVey?"

The young man was instantly at the counter. "Yes sir?"

"You on emergency leave?" asked Kramer.

"No sir," the boy said desolately. Dale had the feeling that the young man would have liked to plead, to beg, that he was desperate for the ride, but that some inner discipline held him back.

"Well . . ." Dale spread his chart on the counter. He could join Jet Six Victor at Prescott, Arizona, ride it to Albuquerque and drop the kid at Kirtland Air Force Base. It was just as short a route, most of the flight simply a high-altitude airway coursing the same aerial river bed as the transcontinental Victor One-Five-One-Eight, using the same navigational facilities. And what difference did the weather make? He was a good instrument pilot, if somewhat rusty. Why not?

He glanced again at the boy. He read intelligence and frankness, and some vague pain and trouble in the shadows under his eyes.

"O.K., Mac." He stuck out his hand. "I'm Commander Heath. Get a hard-hat and mask from flight-gear issue and meet me at the line shack."

McVey almost sagged in relief. "Thank you, sir." He smiled, but none of the worry left his face. Whatever was drawing him home was not pleasant.

Dale drew a new flight plan from the stack and began to fill it in. He was finishing as a swarthy Marine major in disheveled flight clothes, chewing a cigar, paused at the desk. He glanced at Dale's flight plan.

"You eastbound, Commander?"

Dale nodded. "To Washington."

"I don't envy you. I just come in from New Orleans. Man, you got traffic. I never heard such traffic. Every Air Force jockey and airline pilot in the country must have filed I.F.R. tonight."

"Bad, huh?"

"I had to wait an hour in the line at El Paso for clearance," the major complained. "Strictly for the birds . . ."

Dale, still trailed by Anne, made his way to the line shack. Chief Comstock, a bulging aviation mech with whom he had served on two ships, stirred himself and found his aircraft's yellow sheet.

"One-One-Three-Two-Five-Five," the chief said. "Here it is."

Dale looked over the last five pilot reports. An item snagged his eye. On the third flight preceding, a pilot had written "U.H.F. radio cutting out intermittently." He had not grounded the plane, and the note from the radioman who had later checked it read "U.H.F. O.K."

Had he fixed it, or found nothing wrong? Dale turned to the rest of the "gripe sheets."

On the last flight, Ensign Flanger had noted trouble again: "U.H.F. occasionally garbled."

Again a radioman had written: "U.H.F. ground check O.K."

Dale looked at the chief. "What about this radio?"

The chief shrugged. "Couple of ensigns getting in their four hours a month, Commander. You know how it is. Radio cuts out a little, they hit the panic switch."

Dale studied Flanger's report. Flanger worked for him. He was a careful young man. Although, of course, the chief was right—Flanger had a paperwork job that allowed him little time in the air.

"We got a spare airplane?"

"No sir. Four-Eleven's in for check, and Five-Six-Six has a brake change."

Dale considered the yellow sheet for a long moment. Then he signed it, accepting the plane.

He turned to Anne. "I think you better stay off the line, Princess. So I'll just say good-by to you here."

She looked disappointed, but nodded. He squatted by her and she flung her arms around his neck. Out on San Diego bay a foghorn moaned sadly. He felt her shiver.

"Oh," he said suddenly, "you're going to boarding school. Back East, if you want."

She looked at him incredulously. "Oh, Daddy! Oh, Daddy, I'm so glad!" She hugged him again and smiled at him through the tears in her eyes.

"You're the greatest," she said. "*The* greatest."

He started to turn.

"Daddy?"

"Yes?"

"Be careful."

She had never said that before.

"Yes, honey. Don't worry."

The TV-2 trainer squatted on the line, garish but sleek under the white and orange paint that was supposed to make it easy to spot from other aircraft. Like all jets, it seemed to Dale to be straining at an invisible leash, animate even on the ground and impatient to fly.

With the chief, Dale helped McVey settle in the rear seat, and gave him a five-minute check-out on the ejection procedure. Then he preflighted the plane. Finally he squeezed into the front cockpit. It smelled as always of oil and fuel and sweat. And the armrests were damp with fog. He buckled himself in and cinched on his mask.

The jet starting unit plugged under the wing awoke with a shriek.

He flicked on the radio, checking to see that it was on the tower's channel.

"Navy North Island Tower, Navy Jet One-One-Three-Two-Five-Five, ground check. How do you read me?"

The answer came back clearly and quickly: "Five by five, loud and clear. How me?"

"Five by five."

So far, Ensign Flanger's concern for the radio was baseless. "Do you have my A.T.C. clearance?"

"Wait one . . . Affirmative. Are you ready to copy?"

Apparently the major had been wrong about the wait to be expected. Or maybe Dale had simply picked a lucky altitude. He adjusted the pad strapped to his knee. "Ready to copy."

The tower cackled swiftly: "A.T.C. clears Navy Jet One-One-Three-Two-Five-Five to Kirtland Air Force Base. Climb on a heading of one-eight-zero degrees to sufficient altitude to cross the Coronado Radio Beacon at one-eight-thousand. Re-cross Coronado Radio Beacon at flight level three-three-zero. Maintain flight level three-three-zero via Coronado direct Thermal, direct Rice. Jet Route Seven-Eight, Jet Route Six Victor. Over . . ."

Dale repeated the clearance and went methodically through his starting procedure. When he had sped his turbines to 10 per cent r.p.m., he lit off with a solid thump and listened as the whistle of his jet drowned that of the starting unit. He signaled away the unit and his chocks, released the brakes, and taxied the screaming, bobbing aircraft to the head of the runway. On the way he completed his take-off check list, and, cleared for departure, swung down the long strip without pausing.

As the plane gobbled the runway hungrily, he tore his eyes from the white center line and sneaked a glance to the left toward Operations. He picked out Cheryl, apparently motivated to stand by the car and wave.

And at the other end of the operations line he saw a tiny blond figure, pony-tailed and dwarfed by the hangar behind her. Her hands were jammed in her pockets, but before he shifted his attention he saw one of them wave passionately. Then he was airborne, cut off from his daughter by dirty-gray fog.

The sudden transition left him empty and forlorn. He shivered inexplicably and forced his attention to his artificial horizon. He heard the tower, lost in the murk below: "Navy Jet One-One-Three-Two-Five-Five, off at two-zero. Have a good trip, sir."

He rogered for the message. The radio was still five by five, loud and clear.

two:

FLIGHT SEVEN
WASHINGTON, D.C.

First Officer Mike Ruble lay clothed on his bed in the Washington Statler Hotel. He was a solid, dark young man with a face ordinarily cheerful and friendly, but shadowed now with impatience and boredom.

He was leafing through the last few pages of a sketchbook. They were landscapes he had whisked off to keep busy yesterday; lifeless, stereotyped views of tourist Washington. Now he ripped them out, left them on the desk in case the maid might want them, and walked to the window.

He peered out. Over the Capitol hung clouds sagging with snow. A horn on the street honked discordantly, too high in key for the toneless afternoon. If the layover continued, what could he possibly do tonight?

Tomorrow he might return to the National Art Gallery. There were some Goyas he had wanted to study further. But tonight?

For a moment he thought of phoning the stewardess—what the hell was her name? He had spent a whole evening with her, and suddenly he could not remember her name. Kitty—Kitty Foster. No, as he recalled, she was leaving on a flight this evening.

He turned from the window. Why they wouldn't let him deadhead back to L.A. he couldn't imagine. He would rather work on a flight, but to break the monotony of winter in Washington, he would gladly walk. The phone suddenly rang, and the afternoon brightened. It could only mean a hop. Unless it was a local to New York, which he disliked more than Washington, it would have to be a move for the better.

It was the dispatcher, and it was a flight, and it was back to Los Angeles. "Are you available?"

"I hope to tell you I'm available," Mike said. "What time?"

"You better catch the three P.M. limousine. It's Flight Seven, departing at . . ." There was a pause. "Departing at five. O.K.?"

"Roger, wilco, over, and out," Mike chortled.

Quickly he stuffed his Valpac, slipping the sketchbook in the crease. Then he shrugged into the gray tunic carrying the three stripes of a Pacific Central copilot. He hadn't asked the captain's name, but would cheerfully have flown with the most irascible pilot on the line as long as the nose was pointed west. He hadn't even asked about the equipment. But Flight Seven, he recalled, was nonstop, and would probably be a DC-7. Things were looking up.

Bag in hand, he checked the room. How many small hotel rooms in the last four years had he languished in? How many streets had he walked, a stranger in a strange town, looking for somewhere to pass the time?

He was a single man, but friendly, and he was tired of strange towns and strange faces. He thought of the beach near his apartment, and the laughing tanned girls he knew. His spirits lifted.

He passed down the hallway and paused at a door. He drummed on it with his fingers.

A trim blonde girl in Pacific Central stewardess uniform stood tucking her blouse into her skirt.

"Hello, Mike," she said, a little surprised. "Are you finally getting out of town?"

"Flight Seven to L.A. Is that your hop?"

She nodded and let him in.

"So I'm finally getting inside," he said dryly, with laughter in his throat.

"What do you mean? Oh . . . I see. Well, I'm sorry about last night. I couldn't ask you in. After all, we just met. . . ."

"That's the story of my life."

"Are you mad at me?"

Mike looked at her in surprise. "Of course not, Kitty. You don't have to put out to every copilot in the company to get along. This isn't Hollywood, you know."

She grimaced mechanically. "Do you have to talk like that? No, I just . . . Well, we had such a nice dinner and all and I . . ."

Her voice trailed off.

She began hurriedly to pack a few toilet articles in the standard PCA stewardess bag on the bed.

"Hell, I shouldn't have made a pass."

She shrugged. "You know what I think it is? I think it's because you're bored. You don't really give a darn about me. None of you."

Does she have to make such a production of it? Mike wondered. She was right, of course. He'd had a boring evening listening to nervous chatter of flights she had made and passengers who had not made her. And almost automatically, at her door, he had bent to kiss her. She had stiffened and turned her face away. Had there been tears in her eyes?

Now she said seriously, "Do you know I haven't had a date with a captain or a first officer since I've been in this company who hasn't tried to crawl into bed with me?"

Her eyes were dead level on his. Maybe the chatter and the trivial anecdotes were a veneer she wore. And there *had* been tears last night. Mike looked at her sharply.

She looked around the room, checking automatically to see that she had forgotten nothing.

It was so typically the glance of a transient girl, forced to leave another haven, that it lent her a certain pathos.

Mike and Kitty had the limousine to themselves, moving through the Washington traffic toward the Arlington Memorial Bridge. Passengers on Flight Seven, if any were staying at the

Statler, would take a later airport car; crew members had to check in an hour before the flight. It was beginning to snow lightly; both of them knew that Kitty might be in for a rough, bouncing trip, but neither of them spoke of it. Flight Seven was a coach, which meant that she would probably stew it alone; full to capacity as it might be with Christmas traffic, it could have as many as ninety-two passengers. He felt sorry for her.

Mike asked, "Who's our captain?"

"Dick Barnett. Do you know him?"

"I've heard of him. I never flew with him. Isn't he second senior pilot on the line? Or third?"

"Second. Twenty years, they tell me."

"How come he doesn't take the limousine?"

"I've heard he stays with Massey when he's in Washington."

Massey was board chairman of the airline, and it was said that some senior pilots had a standing invitation to lay over at his home in Chevy Chase. Was Barnett a politician?

"Is he pretty sharp?"

"He sure is. And is he ever distinguished looking!"

"That's what it takes," Mike sighed. "I'll never make captain, I guess. Does he paw stewardesses?"

"Oh, Mike, stop it." There was a smile on her lips. "Did I bore you last night?" she asked suddenly.

He was a gentle young man, careful not to hurt others, but honest, so he said now, "Yes, you did. A little."

He had not hurt her. She squeezed his hand. "I don't know what happens to me on the first date with a guy. I just can't seem to shut up. Do I bore you now?"

He smiled back at her. "Not at all, Kitty. Not at all."

The Pacific Central Airlines Washington dispatcher's office was a spacious, nervous place. Typewriters tapped out flight manifests, teletypes clacked out weather synopses, baggage supervisors in shirt sleeves spoke into the telephones that they wore like extensions of their features.

Across the room lay a long counter. Mike was standing at it, studying en-route weather, when Captain Richard Barnett strode in.

Mike glanced at him as the captain examined the crew schedule board. Kitty was right—he was certainly distinguished. He was taller than Mike, slimmer. He had silver hair and a classic profile. He radiated experience and efficiency. He reminded Mike of someone. . . . The captain turned to him.

"Ruble?"

"Yes sir."

The captain stuck out his hand: "I'm Dick Barnett. I guess my first officer was illegal. . . . He had an extra hop this month. He flew back deadhead this morning."

The Federal Aviation Agency limited flight personnel to eighty-five hours a month; if you exceeded that, to the schedule people you were a leper. Whatever miscalculation had caused it, Barnett's first officer on the eastbound flight had had to be returned deadhead, like a sack of wheat, to Los Angeles to await the coming of a new month. Mike blessed the unknown copilot's previous industry and whatever scheduler had shortsightedly stranded the man in Washington. Between the two of them, they had sprung him from the Eastern weather.

"Glad to meet you, sir," he said. He indicated the synopses. "Looks like it'll be a little rough."

The captain looked briefly at the weather, running his thumb along the "winds aloft" chart to a few key stations.

Mike suddenly remembered who the captain reminded him of. Eight years before, in a shabby, tar-paper officers' club in Korea, he had first met Colonel Vance Neilson. The man had breezed into the bar, fresh in Air Force blues from the States via Tokyo, seemingly ready that instant to take the squadron over from the tired, irritable major who had commanded it for six months.

The pilots of Mike's Sabrejet squadron were a disillusioned lot, not given to snap decisions. But Colonel Neilson had glittered with such charm, given promise of such experience, so neatly fitted into the concept of what a regular officer should ideally be, that they had almost all been taken in. All except

Splash Royce, a squat, red-haired automaton as lethal and accurate in the vastness of MIG Alley as a diamondback on the desert.

Mike remembered the colonel's first night in the bar, and how quickly he had surrounded himself with the pilots who were to fly with him. Mike said, "Seems like a real sharp guy. Thank God we got somebody to get this outfit back on its feet."

But Splash was unimpressed. "Wait," he said, chewing his immortal stogy. "Wait one, Buster. We might want the major back."

And so they had. The colonel had displayed just that slight inflexibility in action that separated the dead from the living. He had been stubborn and immutable behind the façade of good-fellowship. Two of his wingmen had died demonstrating his inelasticity, another had tested it further and parachuted to a Communist stockade, and finally the colonel had provided the ultimate proof. Just before he was to be relieved as a result of rumors in Tokyo that all was not well, one dreary day he had bet his own judgment against that of a G.C.A. radar controller on the ground and calmly and efficiently flown into a Korean ridge he apparently thought was a mile north.

Mike chided himself for comparing Barnett to the colonel. It was strange how physical appearance would type a stranger in one's mind—this man, an airline veteran of twenty years, could patently be no more like the fossilized colonel than the man in the moon.

"Captain, I guess you'll want to take Victor One-Five-Two-Two. The northern route is clobbered."

"We'll take Victor One-Five-One-Eight."

Mike raised his eyebrows. *What the hell? Hadn't he understood him?* He tried again.

"Amarillo is reporting a frontal passage. It's clearing down south on Victor One-Five-Two-Two, so I thought—"

"I think, Victor One-Five-One-Eight," the captain said. "Shorter and better winds aloft."

Good winds were fine, but turbulence meant something too. Was this character route-bound? Many captains had their favorite routes, had been accustomed to them for years, knew the frequencies of every omni-range and could fly them without glancing at a radio facilities chart. When it was a tossup, it didn't make any difference, but in this case, it *did*. Customer comfort counted too. He thought of Kitty nursing ninety airsick passengers.

There were enough milk-run locals that *had* to be routed through bad weather without deliberately planning a non-stop coast-to-coast through an occluded front.

"From the cross section, Captain, it'll be turbulent as hell up there."

The captain smiled patiently. "As I say, there's ten knots more average head wind down south."

Mike gave up. "Yes sir. What altitude?"

"Let's ask for nineteen thousand."

"Nineteen thousand? Westbound?" Westbound aircraft on the airways were usually assigned even altitudes by Air Traffic Control; it was as basic in aviation as Bernoulli's principle.

"I mean twenty," Barnett said quickly. He grinned apologetically. "I came east at nineteen thousand—it stuck in my mind."

Mike leaned over the flight plan. Apparently the captain was not only route-bound but altitude-bound. The picture of the silver-haired, handsome man, boring eternally east and west on Victor One-Five-One-Eight at nineteen and twenty thousand feet, an airborne Casey Jones wearing tracks in the sky, made him grin. *Well*, he thought, *it takes all kinds to make an airline*. And he liked Barnett already for his friendly smile.

But just the same, it was a shame for Kitty and the passengers that they had to go through the front.

He finished the flight plan and handed it to the captain to sign. Barnett read it, meticulously signed his name. His handwriting was beautiful.

Louie Capelli, a dark little flight engineer Mike had flown with before, appeared at the counter. He was a morose individual, incessantly sulking over blows dealt the Flight Engineers International Association by the Air Line Pilots Association.

"Hello, Ruble," he grunted. He turned to Barnett. "Plane's pre-flighted. Everything's O.K."

The captain smiled: "Thanks, Louie."

The dispatcher came to the other side of the counter. He posed his pencil above the flight plan. "Sure you want to go Victor One-Five-One-Eight? Wichita Office suggests Victor One-Five-Two-Two today. Why don't you go south?"

"Victor One-Five-One-Eight," the captain said firmly. "Better winds. See you at the plane, Ruble."

Mike smiled at him and waited as the dispatcher signed the clearance. Capelli, squaring his engine logs on the counter, said, "I'm sure glad they're trying to park that old bastard behind a desk."

"They are?" Mike asked noncommittally. "Why?"

"For a couple of C.A.R. violations. All he needs is an excuse to fly north. He flew the D.C.-Tulsa- L.A. run about a million years. He must be afraid he'll get lost down south."

Mike, who knew of no violations, turned to him in annoyance. "Maybe after twenty years with the company he's entitled to make up his own mind. You think?"

Capelli's eyes widened. "Don't climb on me, Buster. I just work here."

Capelli swung on his heel and walked away, every step sounding a protest at the fellowship of pilots, pilots whose union was fighting to eliminate his very profession.

Mike felt sudden compassion for him. He decided to invite him sometime during the flight to bring his family to the beach next Sunday. . . .

Patricia Benedict was snuggled warmly in the rear of Howard Kronkheist's new Lincoln between Ed's scratched aluminum suitcase and her own scuffed luggage. Reluctantly, dreading the swirling snowflakes, she glanced at the Washington National terminal building.

She had thoughtfully insisted on sitting in back so that Ed and Kronk would not have to direct their interminable medical conversation around her. But for some reason, halfway from Kronk's Baltimore apartment, the two men had fallen silent.

When she had tried to spark a conversation they had responded eagerly, brightly, a little too quickly.

She considered the special status of one who has had an operation. She had noticed it before—the aura of delicacy which seemed to cling for weeks after you were up, well, and about. Even men like Ed and Kronk, enmeshed in sickness and convalescence from dawn to dusk, treated you as a figurine when you had been ill.

Every animal but man avoided its sick. Man, she thought comfortably, treated his with a sort of reverence.

She supposed that it was because no matter how minor the ailment or how sure the cure, the well were reminded by the sick of the impermanence of life and properly grateful to the patient on recovery.

And of course, with Kronk and Ed there was a greater reason for her increased stature: to Kronk she represented another success on the operating table as well as a friend who had recovered, and Ed's love for her must have peopled even his own objective medical imagination with phantoms of doom.

She felt protected and loved and warm, but a little tired, and wished that she would not have to brave the snow for a while. But Ed was shaking hands with Kronk.

"Well, Doctor . . ."

"Doctor" used by one to the other had always induced a grin, from their days in pre-med, perhaps, when the title must have seemed impossibly distant. This time it brought none. Their eyes met across the front seat steadily. A message seemed to pass between them.

Ed's thanking him for what he did, Pat thought. She had a better way herself. As she left the car, she smiled into Kronk's incredibly ugly face.

"I'll never forget what you've done," she murmured. And she leaned across the seat and kissed him firmly and decisively.

She had always known that in a certain way he loved her. And if there was room for anyone besides Ed, she loved Kronk too. But Kronk's reaction was somehow greater than she had expected. As she drew away, a shadow of real grief passed over his dark, heavy face.

He cares all right, she told herself. *He's Ed's best friend, but he cares.*

She squeezed his hand a little self-consciously. "Thank you, Kronk. You're my favorite doctor."

Kronk smiled. "Your favorite?"

"As a doctor, that is." She smiled up at her husband. "I wouldn't let Ed touch me with a knife."

"Not even a dull one?" Kronk asked.

"Not even a dull one. He's too heavy-handed."

Ed, whose touch on a hurt fell as gently as snowflakes on the skin, smiled. "Come on, Pat. We'll miss our plane and have to walk."

Because of the snow, they sent Kronk away, although he wanted to see them off. Then, following a redcap with their luggage, they moved to the Pacific Central counter.

The budget for the Big Trip had demanded that they fly coach on this less important one, and the lines before the check-in agents were long ones. For a moment Ed stood scowling. She had noticed the same frown over and over during the past few days. He was worried about something. The children, maybe, alone with his mother, who spoiled them? Or maybe a man used to mortal decisions, deprived of a chance to make them for a few weeks, turned trivialities into things of importance just to keep in practice. She ran her finger along his set mouth.

"Smile, darling. You're on TV."

He smiled, but shook his head impatiently. "It's these damn waiting lines. You'd think they'd have a better system. Why don't you sit down and wait? I'll check our baggage through."

"I'm all right. I'd rather stay with you."

With sudden decision, he moved her past the queues to the far end of the counter. He leaned across and spoke to a pretty girl in a slate-gray uniform.

"They're holding us on Flight Seven, coach to Los Angeles. Is there any chance of changing it to a first-class flight? Leaving around this time?"

"I'll see, sir. Just a moment."

Pat looked at him quizzically. "Ed! Coach was all right. Remember the Big Trip! This could be a dozen Pernods on the Rue de la Paix."

"The hell with our budget," he muttered. "It's ridiculous, you having to stand in line this way."

She stared at him. She was well. How long was this going to go on? It could get irritating.

"Oh, Ed, quit acting as if I were a cripple or something."

The pretty girl returned. "I'm sorry, sir. It's the Christmas traffic. You'd better hold your coach seats."

Resignedly Ed picked up their baggage and fell into line. The loud-speaker in the terminal crackled suddenly and a girl's artificial voice announced: "Pacific Central Airlines Flight Seven for Los Angeles now loading at North Concourse, Gate Twelve. Please show gate passes. . . ."

Pat glanced at her watch. They had left Kronk's apartment in plenty of time. Kronk, like most doctors she knew, was a fast driver, but the snow had done them in. She knew coach flights. This one looked crowded already, and Ed liked to sit clear of the wing in the rear, where he would stare for hours in somehow touching rapture at the toylike cities and farms below.

She squeezed his arm. "I'll go wait in line at the gate. Otherwise, you won't get to sit where you like."

When she reached the iron gate she was already halfway back in line. A bored man in a gray uniform stood with his passenger manifest on a clipboard, checking passes. Past him, squatting like a tethered monster, loomed the airliner.

Pat liked crowds, and this one had a happy holiday mood that intrigued her. Obvious strangers were talking cheerfully. Everyone was laughing at a crowd of tipsy fraternity boys seeing off a pair of coeds.

A curly-haired little boy of perhaps ten, preceding Pat in line, pointed importantly at the plane.

"It's a DC-7."

Pat smiled. "Is it?"

The little boy nodded. "It'll go three hundred miles an hour," he boasted, as if he had designed the plane himself. She found herself, as always, comparing this little boy to Killer. She had to admit that this child was handsomer. She wondered if his cloak of self-reliance fell as swiftly as Killer's did when confronted with a strange situation. But this one, like Killer, was clearly an expert on all things airborne.

"It sure is big," Pat marveled.

"I'm going to learn to fly jets," announced the boy. "You ever been on an airplane before?"

"A few times. Have you?"

The child looked at her scornfully. "Heck yes. I fly all the time."

An elderly woman with him winked at Pat. Her lips moved above the little boy's head and Pat read "Once before."

At the gate she looked wildly back for Ed. There he was, hurrying down the line of passengers, the new, faintly worried lines set again around his eyes. She would find out on the plane what was bothering him.

There were no secrets between them. . . .

Doctor Ed Benedict guided his wife down the aisle. A tubby passenger, already seated, stood up suddenly to remove his coat and threatened to bump her. Ed fended him off with a hand. The two smiled automatically.

If only, Ed thought, *I could protect her from the other.* . . .

He was suddenly angry at the fat man, the stewardess, the passengers who would share this confining tube for hours now, when he wanted to be alone with her.

"Darling, there's a window seat," Pat said suddenly. They stopped by a triple chair.

"You take it, Pat," he said. "I always seem to get the window."

"No. I like to sleep, and you like to watch. You take it."

They were settled when a little boy appeared in the aisle. He was pouting. He addressed himself to Pat.

"I'm all alone, so my grandmother said I should sit by you," he said. Then hopefully: "There isn't room, is there?"

No, Ed almost said. *We have to be alone.* . . .

Pat smiled. "Of course there is. Be our guest."

The boy sighed and sat down. "Coming out, my mother didn't make me sit by anybody!"

"Oh, I'm sure your grandmother didn't mean that you wouldn't be all right. But I'd like it if you'd tell me something about the airplane."

Now where, thought Ed, *could she have met this character?* He had been with her almost every instant in the terminal. She was always making quick acquaintances. Perhaps her interest in others, her insatiable curiosity, was the source of the magnetism that could yank utter strangers, sometimes reluctantly, into her sphere. And she did it all unconsciously. . . .

But for once he regretted it.

The boy announced that his name was Joey Lafitte, the same as the pirate, and began to recite to Pat some improbable statistics about the plane. Ed, losing interest, began from habit to classify those passengers still searching for seats in terms of their physical disabilities.

The tubby passenger who had bumped Pat. Was he just a man who liked to eat, or ate from some psychological compulsion, or could it be his thyroid? Buses, trains, coach flights were clinics—remember the streetcar rides with Kronk? First-class flights were not so good, because higher-income passengers tended to have their surgery when they needed it.

The woman heading for the seat in front of them, bluish, unhealthy lips . . . "Marked cyanosis," he would have written on her medical history. Would he have allowed a patient to fly with a heart that could so starve her capillaries? Perhaps, in a pressurized cabin.

The woman two seats forward, folding her coat to hand to the stewardess—the lopsided, asymmetric thickening of the neck, that and her stolidness hinting of a nodular goiter. He wondered idly whether she knew she had one—if she did, did she know that it could be malignant? His mind shied from the specter of cancer, but he reined it sharply, forcing it to consider the stranger's prognosis.

Well, why not? Why not this woman, too? She was at least ten years older than Pat.

In sudden revulsion, he winced. *I'm trying,* he told himself, *to console myself by wishing diseases on others. Of all the morbid, crummy adjustments.*

He turned his attention to Joey Lafitte.

"On the way to my grandmother's the man let me sit by the window," Joey said pointedly.

"Oh?" Ed raised his eyebrows. "Well, Pat?"

"No," she said flatly. "You like the window. You stay there."

Ed grinned. "How can I? I'm failing a qualitative analysis."

"You stay put," Pat protested. "He's a con man in miniature."

"Just like Killer," Ed pointed out.

"What's a con man?" asked Joey.

"A miniature con man is a little boy who figures just because he's small people will let him sit by the window."

Joey digested this. "I was just trying to be thoughtful," he announced.

"Precisely," inquired Pat, "in what way?"

"Well, the lady's going to bring coffee, and dinner, and if I'm sitting here, I'm liable to bump her and it might spill on you."

"Oh, brother," breathed Ed.

Pat stared at Joey. "You're not a con man at all. You're a racketeer!"

"Millions for defense," said Ed, "but not one cent for tribute."

Joey changed his tack. He smiled winsomely at Ed.

"If you're here, it'll be easier for you to go to the bathroom. You won't have to get past her and me and—"

Ed, from the depths of his misery, found himself laughing. He changed seats with the little boy. Pat pressed his hand warmly.

"Oh," she said, "look!"

A distinguished silvery-haired man, in slate-gray uniform with four gold stripes on his sleeve, walked up the aisle. He shone with the sort of confident competence that Ed had seen on airline billboards.

"He looks as if he's been around awhile, anyway."

"He certainly does," Pat sighed comfortably. "Well, if looking distinguished can do it, we ought to have a good flight."

She settled back in her seat, the picture of contentment.

Captain Dick Barnett entered his craft through the passenger door aft, rather than through the crew's hatch in the nose. In younger, more introspective days, he had looked on this habit with amusement, knowing that it was because he enjoyed the glances of the women and the respect in the eyes of the men.

Now he took it more seriously. It did no harm to smile at passengers—he knew that he emitted confidence and charm. Besides, he had noticed that such entrances, coupled with progress reports broadcast over the cabin speaker during the trip, wrung from the flight a gush of favorable "passenger comment" cards to the main office. In the last year he had begun to think that he owed the walk up the aisle to the company as a public-relations gesture. He was, after all, more than simply a captain—he was second senior captain on the line.

As he opened the door to the flight deck, he saw through the radio compartment that Ruble and Capelli had already entered the cockpit up the baggage ramp in the nose. They were running item by item through the pre-start check list on the rolling scroll above the dash. After each item Ruble's thumb would move the script to a new one. Barnett laid a hand on Capelli's shoulder, and the flight engineer stood up, swung his chair to the side to give the captain access to the left-hand seat, and then reseated himself between and aft of the pilot and copilot. Even here in the cockpit, Capelli's perennial resentment charged the air.

Barnett, settling himself in the left-hand seat, nevertheless flashed him a smile. It was good policy to keep your flight engineer happy—the Flight Engineers International Association had strong ties with ground engineering personnel, and one never knew when some ground engineer might report excessive brake wear or gas consumption out of spite.

His copilot smiled across the cockpit at him. "Full house?"

"Always is, this close to Christmas." He narrowed his eyes thoughtfully. "What was your first name, Ruble? I'm sorry. I forgot. . . ."

"Mike, Captain."

"I'm Dick."

He leaned back in his leather seat, fastened his safety belt, and took over the responses to Ruble's check-list challenges from Capelli. His hands flashed swiftly to each lever and switch as Ruble called it, but his mind was aft in the cabin. A full house of passengers, he thought. There was an old man who looked irascibly important in the front—could he be a company wheel? No, not on a coach flight. And yet, this close to Christmas it was conceivable that some company executive might have been stuck with a coach seat. And, too, it was said that Brighton's men in customer relations were riding coaches now, checking everything from stewardess courtesy to pilot technique.

For a moment he wished that he had looked more carefully at the weather on the northern route. Massey's friendly warning came back to him: "Dick, you have to fly to please a lot more people now than we did in the old days. Passengers and Air Traffic Control, and even the goddamned stewardesses. And two civil air violations written up last year—man, if I didn't know you could fly the boxes these things came in, I'd have you up before the board, union or not!"

Then they had had a drink and dropped back to the older, happier, days.

The hell with Brighton's man, if he was one. A captain was still skipper of his own plane.

"Carburetor air direct," Ruble was saying. "Captain?"

"Oh, yeah. Carburetor air direct."

They finished the pre-start checkoff list and Ruble tested the Selcal radio. It rang musically, like a telephone. They started the engines, their hands supplementing each other in fast coordination. Ruble had strong, practiced fingers. A senior copilot, Barnett guessed—ready for a captaincy and sweating out a vacancy. He heard him call the tower.

"Washington National Ground Control, this is Pacific Central Flight Seven. How do you read me? Over."

The loud-speaker behind Barnett crackled into life: "Loud and clear. How me?"

"Five by five. I.F.R. to Los Angeles. Request taxi instructions."

The tower came back: "Pacific Central Seven cleared to runway three-six. Wind northwest ten. Altimeter three-zero-point-zero-five. I have your A.T.C. clearance. Are you ready to copy?"

Ruble, apparently surprised by the quick response, fumbled for the grease pencil he would use to jot the clearance on the window, smiling apologetically. It was a point of pride among first officers never to have to ask the tower to repeat a clearance. Ruble was obviously not ready to copy. Barnett felt a tug of sympathy, but remembering his complaint about the southern route, decided that it would be a good time to put the young man in his place.

"Go ahead," Barnett said at once into his mike.

"Roger. A.T.C. clears Pacific Central Airlines Flight Seven to Los Angeles International Airport—cleared to Montebello, direct Springfield, Victor One-Five-One-Eight, cross Springfield at two thousand."

Seemingly lost in thought, but not missing one familiar word of the clearance, Barnett sensed that Ruble was hopelessly behind.

The swift voice went on, "Continuing to climb in the holding pattern west of Springfield on the one-five-one-degree radial of the Herndon omni—to gain sufficient altitude to recross Springfield at six thousand—cross the Herndon one-eight-zero-degree radial at seven thousand, cross Casanova at one-two-thousand. Cross Montebello at two-zero-thousand. Maintain two-zero-thousand. Victor One-Five-One-Eight, Flight Plan. Read back."

Barnett looked at his copilot. Capelli, between them, chuckled. Ruble grinned wryly and shrugged, reaching for the microphone to ask for a repeat. Barnett shook his head.

He picked up the mike and quoted the clearance exactly, word for word. He caught the "all clear" salute from the mech far below on the ramp, saw the brightly ribboned landing gear pins safely in his hands, and began to taxi to the runway.

Ruble seemed properly impressed and somehow relieved. *Didn't think I could do it*, Barnett thought, a little irritated. It was a standard clearance, heard perhaps twenty times a year on Dick Barnett's favorite route; if it had changed one word, he reflected, he would have been in trouble. Well, that was the advantage of knowing a route.

They rumbled down the runway, snatched up the gear, and within a half minute were completely on instruments, lumbering through heaving storm clouds.

The seat-belt sign would stay on for a while tonight. . . .

three:

AMARILLO CENTER

Surreptitiously, because he already felt guilty at having to leave Sally on this evening, Norm Coster glanced at his watch as he laid down a chicken leg. He liked to be at the board early in bad weather so that, before he relieved, his mental gears would be whirling fast enough to mesh with the Center. It was three-fifteen.

Sally either missed the glance or accepted it, but her sister Eve did not.

"You aren't going to skip dessert again, are you? We made pie."

I'd like to have a talk, Norm thought suddenly, *with that damn woman's ex-husband. I'd like to congratulate him.* But that was unfair—he had asked Eve to Texas himself, and she had come swiftly at her own expense to be with her sister. Behind the rapier tongue, he supposed, lay a tender heart. *But, God,* he complained, *she makes me nervous. . . .*

Sally came to his rescue. "You go ahead, darling. I'll warm some up when you come home."

She stood up and shuffled to the window. To Norm she was beautiful in her awkwardness. "From the weather, you won't have time to eat your sandwiches," she said.

But because she had made them he picked them up as they left the kitchen. Passing through the dim living room, Norm stumbled into the bassinet still on display with the shower gifts.

"We'll have to move when the little monster gets to crawling," he observed. "If we can afford anything bigger."

"We'll manage," Sally said absently. "If he ever comes. False labor!"

She had had false labor pains two days before.

"Well," Norm observed, "I think you're pregnant all right."

"Maybe we're going to have a false baby."

"Even a false baby is going to need room to grow up in," Norm pointed out. He didn't want to leave. "Sally?"

She looked at him with lake-blue eyes that could reduce him to incoherence. "Yes?" she asked softly.

"Don't look at me that way. . . . God, I love you. . . ."

"No you don't," she said. "You just want a child."

"What was I going to say?"

"About room for the house ape."

"Oh, yeah. Every meathead in this town who can turn a valve over at Exell or the atom plant is making more money than me. Do you want me to quit?"

He hadn't asked her since her pregnancy. She looked out at the colorless tract.

"No, Norm. You like it, and that's all that matters."

"I liked it till now. Now, it's goddamned ridiculous."

He backed the Chevy down the driveway. For three days he had been trying to change the schedule so that he could be with Sally at night. But the Center was simply undermanned. And because Mel Carnegie had been through the same thing, or said he had, he had little sympathy.

"Norm," Mel said, "what can I do? We have twenty-four controllers. If I get one of the other supervisors to trade me a man, it might be a month before I get you back. The traffic this time of year, I can't spare you." And with a smile, "Don't *worry*. Every new father thinks the first baby is more sweat than it really is. Louise and me didn't have any trouble."

"I'm glad you weren't in pain, Mel," he said, regretting it instantly. What the heck, he would probably have come to the same decision himself. Because there really was no out—they had given up trying to swap watches for personal reasons almost a year ago. What would an air traffic controller do without a wife like Sally? Quit and sell neckties, probably.

Driving along U.S. 60 toward the outskirts of town and the Amarillo Control Center, he evaluated the weather. Cumulus was mounting in the west. It was too bad that it wouldn't snow. Snow itself meant little to air traffic—the towering shapes already indicated icing conditions aloft, so the local kids might as well have the fun of a white Christmas. But the fat-bellied clouds slid past, selfishly hugging their moisture.

He parked beside the Control Center and stood beside the door, breathing the last fresh air he would know for eight hours. There was air conditioning inside, but even in the coolness of December the heat from the surveillance radar and constant moisture of a room continually in use by two dozen men could make the place a hell. And when controlled traffic increased, nerves tensed, smoke became thicker, and the place rose in temperature as if the Center were an animate being overheated with exertion.

He opened the door and dived into the clattering fluorescence.

Norm had worked in the Amarillo Center for two years; he had come to it fresh from the controller school at Oklahoma City. He had grown to sense the Center's moods. On a clear night, a slack night, it could be benign; an airline captain calling, perhaps, with a request for a more picturesque altitude for his passengers could be met with a cheerful "This is Amarillo Center. Cleared to descend." And if the aircraft were departing the Amarillo Control area, "Good night, sir. Good trip . . ."

But the Center could be harsh, unyielding, even vindictive. The same captain cutting in with a frivolous request on a busy night would at the least be ordered off the air and at most shortly find himself facing a peevish chief pilot who had heard from the F.A.A.

The centers were almost flesh and blood.

Even the magazines, motivated after a mid-air collision to half-explain the air traffic system, tried to humanize the centers.

The usual analogy was that of a policeman at a busy intersection.

It was a poor one in some ways. A crisis at an intersection could presumably be halted with a lifted hand while the policeman made up his mind what to do. A crisis on the airway snowballed because of a simple aerodynamic fact. An aircraft stayed aloft through motion; its very speed supported it in its element. A plane approaching another could be diverted, it could be climbed, it could be made to descend. But it could never be stopped.

On the other hand, the Center had its moods as policemen presumably had theirs. It was cheerful when things went well, angry when its orders were ignored, anxious when a traffic crisis approached, relieved when it was averted.

The Center was relieved now, and Norm sensed it immediately.

The eight control boards stood like islands lying in an east-west direction along the length of the uncluttered room. Around his own board, the easternmost, clustered a little knot of men. Hal Lick, the nerveless scarecrow he would relieve, was sitting back in his swivel chair, grinning at Rocky Fontaine, Norm's own assistant. Hal's assistant was shaking his head on the other side of the board. The afternoon watch supervisor was pale. The atmosphere of relief had even reached the western control board, where the controller and his assistant were chuckling.

Automatically, as Norm approached the board, he glanced at its face. It was worse than he had expected. The board was full—chock-full. There were fourteen—no, fifteen strips of paper stacked in four vertical rows. It meant that there were fifteen aircraft in his sector thrashing blindly through the night. And on the other side of the board, in his assistant's province, God only knew how many of the narrow slips waited for their estimates to be printed on them, and then to be dropped into his stacks as they were vacated.

"You guys look like you just routed the *Columbine* through the Carlsbad Caverns," Norm observed. "What happened?"

Hal Lick shrugged, but his supervisor said, "Well, everything up to twenty-three thousand feet was in use, and from the pilot reports it's strictly instrument weather to about forty thousand, and we have eastbound traffic at seven, nine, thirteen, fifteen, and seventeen thousand. Plus an Air Force jet at twenty-three. Then we have westbound stacked solid. Poor old Hal had a United estimating Tucumcari at four-two, westbound at twelve thousand. And he had an Air Force Globemaster estimating it at four-three, eleven thousand. Guess what!"

"What?"

"We hear a Cessna executive plane call eastbound with a four-three Tucumcari estimate. Claims he's inadvertently flown into instrument weather at eleven thousand five hundred."

"Inadvertently?"

"That's what the gentleman said."

"Christ!"

"What did you do?"

"Well, I climbed United to cross Vega at fourteen thousand and tried to get the Globemaster into a holding pattern south of Adrian, only by the time he figured out the change in his clearance he was four minutes past Adrian already. So I just had to cancel the change and let him cross Tucumcari on flight plan and hold my breath and pray."

"And they all lucked through," Norm murmured.

"I haven't heard different," Hal said.

"Where's the Cessna now?"

"We haven't been able to raise him."

"Great," Norm said bitterly. "Great."

"That's one pilot," the supervisor said evenly, "who better be able to prove he was V.F.R. when he started. He just better be able to prove it, that's all. . . ." He looked at his watch. "Where's that goddamned Carnegie?"

"Boss," chided Hal Lick, "you have eight seconds yet. You want him to stand your watch for you?"

As if on signal, Mel Carnegie hurried in.

"Sorry."

The off-going supervisor shrugged. "No sweat, Mel. You're on time." He paused. "Exactly."

Mel Carnegie reddened a little. "Yes . . ." He turned to Norm. "How's Sally?"

"She's still expecting a baby," Norm said a little bitterly.

"Yes . . . Did you find someone to stay with her at night?"

"Yeah. Her sister came out from L.A."

"I'm sorry about that, Norm." Carnegie waved his hand down the line of control boards. "You can see, at this time of the year—well, I just didn't want to break up the team. I need you, buddy."

Oh, well, Norm thought, you couldn't dislike the poor guy. Mel had joined the C.A.A. just after air route traffic control had been established in '36. In those days, Norm knew, there had been no formal schooling—no nerve-twangling course at Oklahoma City, where behind each student controller stood an instructor trying only to rattle him with changes as he brought in his imaginary flights. In those days there had been none of the on-the-job training that further screened the cool from the excitable. There had been only the day-to-day routine of tracing a few slow aircraft across uncrowded, apparently limitless space.

Carnegie, like some other senior Center personnel he had seen, in moments of stress tried to apply 150-knot DC-3 techniques to the solution of 500-knot DC-8 problems. Failing, they would leave the risky decisions to their men.

He smiled at Mel. "Sally will be O.K."

Norm and Hal leaned over the board, while Hal ran his finger down the vertical rows of slips. As he did, Norm's mind opened without conscious effort, encompassing in three dimensions the whole area for which he was responsible. The slips were suddenly aircraft, each moving along its airway at its assigned altitude, surrounded by a moving block of space that must be kept free for it. A thousand feet above, a thousand feet below, ten minutes ahead, ten minutes behind—these were the inviolate limits of each of his charges. The board became a four-mile thick blanket of air encompassing parts of Texas, Oklahoma, and New Mexico, sweeping west to Albuquerque Center, north to Denver Control, east to the area under the Fort Worth and Oklahoma City Centers. Through it sped at this moment perhaps fifty aircraft, northbound, southbound, eastbound, west-bound. On Norm's own board, not including the ill-advised Cessna—where the hell was he now?—there were now seventeen aircraft—while he had talked to Mel Carnegie, Rocky Fontaine had slipped two more arrivals into his slots.

Norm's finger stopped at an eastbound MATS Air Evac holding the nine-thousand-foot level from Albuquerque to Amarillo. Both men seemed to sense it at the same time—a slight anomaly in the pattern of the traffic—and Norm's finger hesitated over it as a customer's might over a break in some expensive weave.

"You're right," Hal said, without further comment. He put his finger to the slip used by ground controllers to check pilot estimates.

The MATS plane, according to the slip, had reported over Albuquerque, had passed to Albuquerque Center an estimate over its next reporting point, Amarillo, of two minutes past the next hour. But it was two hundred fifty-five miles from Albuquerque to Amarillo. Without specifically knowing what speed would have been necessary to make good such an estimate, Norm and Hal together had sensed that the time spent was too short.

It was the speed, time, distance problem that every pilot worked five, ten, twelve times an hour—that air controllers, checking them, worked some hundred times on an eight-hour shift.

"That's some Air Evac," Hal muttered. "He's making five hundred knots." He picked up the microphone. "MATS Air Evac One-Six-Four-Eight-Niner, this is Amarillo Center. . . ."

"This is Six-Four-Eight-Niner. Go ahead."

"What type aircraft are you?"

There was a short hesitation. Norm knew that in the cockpit already the copilot would be scrambling for a new estimate—Hal's question invariably presaged the stunning news of an estimate in error.

"We are a C-54," the voice said resignedly.

"We have your ground speed over five hundred knots, Four-Eight-Niner," Hal said mildly. "We request a new Amarillo estimate."

"Roger," sighed the voice on the radio. "Wait. . . ."

Some copilot, thought Norm, is getting chewed right now. The estimate came back, corrected, and Hal stretched his bony arms.

"Well, buddy, I guess that does it. I'm going to go home, beat Vera for a while, and dive into a dry martini. . . . Have fun—"

Rocky Fontaine, wearing earphones on the other side of the board, smiled sweetly: "I have three more estimates for you. . . ."

"Oh, no," Hal said, leaving. "Let me out of here. . . ."

Rocky inserted three more slips into Norm's board. He was a ruddy-cheeked, cheerful young man Norm felt sure would be calm in a crisis. In the slack times during which Norm had allowed him to take control he had seemed to regard the sector as a chessboard and the problem of safely moving aircraft through it as a game with a slightly inferior opponent. He had made his moves with swift coolness.

Rocky was an ex-airline copilot, a victim of the technological unemployment that nibbled at the heels of junior flight personnel, now that jet airliners were allowing the individual pilot to haul in a week as many passengers as he had been flying in a month.

Rocky had accepted his drop in pay philosophically, although Norm knew that it had delayed his plans to marry a pretty little stewardess Norm had seen waiting for him after his shift. Four thousand a year, for a man who had been making perhaps ten. . . .

Norm glanced at the vertical slips and the clock. An Air Force jet was due to report over Palo Duro—should have reported a minute before. He was allowed a three-minute leeway, fast or slow. If there was no position report within two minutes Norm would call him.

He settled back to wait, thinking of Rocky's financial problem. Six years ago Norm had been in the same spot or worse, an airman first class, working the control tower at Bolling Field, adjacent to Washington National Airport. Money had not meant much then, only the crawling passage of time toward his release from the Air Force and the day-to-day excitement of the job. Money had not meant much until he had met Sally.

He remembered wandering aimlessly outside the E.M. Club on a crisp spring day, wondering whether to go in for a glass of beer or try to borrow Crowley's car for a movie downtown. And then he had seen her, sitting on a bench waiting for the base bus.

Amazingly, for he was a shy young man, he had found himself waiting beside her. More amazingly, inside the deserted bus he had sat close enough so that he could assume a certain companionship against the tide of men he knew would climb aboard at the P.X. As they bounced along, his mind darted feverishly for a spark of wit.

Blessedly it came. "Pardon me, Miss, but do you have a match?"

Startled, she jabbed a hand into her pocketbook. Was she as nervous as he? It was impossible—she must be approached twenty times a day if she worked on this woman-hungry base.

The bag slipped from her lap, scattered its contents over the floor of the bus. He chased a lipstick half the length of the deck. When she had everything replaced, she grinned at him.

"You know, I didn't have a match in the first place."

"Do you know," he said, "I didn't have a cigarette?"

"Then why did you ask me?"

"Because you can't smoke on this bus anyway," he answered.

She digested this. "That sounds," she observed, "like a shaggy-dog story, only it isn't. Are you trying to start a new fad?"

"I'm just trying to start a conversation."

"All right, let's talk."

Talk was fine—within days he was in love. But then he took sudden stock and almost let her slip away. Because he felt that she needed to be entertained, he stopped calling her unless he had money to take her to Washington; because he had so little money, his calls were infrequent; because she was so attractive, he had almost lost her to a law student at George Washington.

Suppose he had? What would life have been without her?

Suppose something happened *now?* Those things still happened. . . .

No, the doctor said there would be no trouble.

Well, what about the false labor? Nothing to worry about, as in all things she was just trying too hard.

God, he wished he could be with her. Why hadn't he reported sick?

Every night? Until she had the baby?

Norm glanced at the clock on the control board. It was time to query the Air Force jet.

But his loud-speaker came suddenly to life. "Amarillo Center, Amarillo Center . . . This is Marine Three-Two-Four-Three-Niner. Position report: Childress at zero-three, twelve thousand, I.F.R. Estimating Amarillo three-four, Dalhart. Over."

As he rogered, his eye ran down the board. The Marine plane was on Victor One-One-Four, owning the entire twelve-thousand-foot level from ten minutes in front of it to ten minutes behind it. And it was estimating Amarillo at thirty-four minutes past the hour.

But six airways spilled their traffic into Amarillo, and out again, like highways converging on a traffic circle. If there was another aircraft approaching Amarillo at twelve thousand feet on any of the other airways, estimating the Amarillo radio at any time from twenty-five minutes past the hour to, say, forty-five, the Marine plane or the other plane would have to move. And he spotted such a plane—Braniff Eight-Nine-Two on Victor One-Four-Zero, westbound at twelve thousand, estimating Amarillo only one minute after the Marine. And an eastbound Tri-State flight at thirteen thousand feet churned on Victor One-Five-One-Eight from Tucumcari. Quickly, Norm looked for an out—pilots hated to climb. There was none. . . .

He picked up the mike. "Marine Three-Two-Four-Three-Niner, this is Amarillo Center. You are cleared to climb immediately to one-four-thousand, to cross Claude Intersection at one-four-thousand. Maintain one-four-thousand via flight plan route. Read back."

The voice came back sulkily, repeating the clearance.

Rocky called across the board, his headset in his hand. "That goddamned Cessna turned up again. They can't contact it, but they got a position report over Amarillo at five minutes past, estimating Childress at thirty-five."

"What the hell! What's his altitude?"

"Thirteen thousand."

"Does he still think he's got an I.F.R. clearance?"

"Negative. Now he says he's on V.F.R. Flight Plan under I.F.R. conditions. He intends landing at Childress."

Norm's pulse raced. The Marine plane was climbing, heading toward the last reported altitude of the errant Cessna. The Cessna, at thirteen thousand, would be either too near Claude Intersection or too near the Tri-State eastbound. He felt the sweat trickling down from his armpits. Well, the Cessna could not be contacted. Tri-State could descend. "Tri-State Triple Six, you are to descend immediately to one-one-thousand feet. There is traffic at your altitude."

There was no hesitation from the Tri-State captain. "This is Tri-State Triple Six, descending immediately to one-one-thousand."

The three planes were as clear in Norm's mind as if the slips of paper on the control board before him had taken sudden life. There were three imaginary tunnels through the sky southeast and west of him to worry about—far to the south the Marine plane was reluctantly climbing northward toward the middle one, bound for the top one. Closer, on an opposite course, flew the ghostlike Cessna—twin-engined, with oxygen aboard, it was to be hoped—and he could be anywhere along the middle tunnel, on a head-on course with the Marine plane. Nibbling at his tail, presumably, flew the Tri-State airliner, just beginning its descent. Part of the problem had been solved—one could only wait for the Marine's Claude position report to know that he had climbed through the central tunnel and the crisis was past.

Almost hating to look, Norm swiveled to the green, round eye of his radar. The sweep rotated uncaringly, clearly picking out targets north and east, where there was no danger, but jumbled and grassy to the south, where there was.

Years before, in another center, two controllers had watched a strange blip, obviously a jet, speed toward an airliner, closer and closer and closer, unable to contact the airliner in time, not knowing whether the jet was at the same altitude or thousands of feet above or below. The two had waited while the two blips merged, praying for them to split as the planes passed safely. But instead the white dots had joined and grown and grown. And then disappeared as the aircraft spun crazily to earth.

One of the controllers, it was said, had gone to a sanitarium.

Mercifully, Claude Intersection was obscured. He could distinguish nothing. He turned back to his board, as in preradar days, to wait.

The Center was suddenly quiet. An assistant controller from farther down the line wandered over. At the far end an intercom announced the pending arrival of three more aircraft at the western boundary of the Amarillo Control area. Norm ignored it.

Across the table, Rocky seemed unaffected. Norm yawned nervously. He sensed activity behind him—Mel Carnegie at his desk busily shuffling papers. The desk was a retreat for Mel—he too had sensed a crisis and wanted no part of it. Norm wondered what would happen if he yelled to him for help. Nothing, probably . . . Advice, maybe, to hold everyone over their nearest intersection. Even if it was too late.

The loud-speaker on the control board burst into life. "This is Marine Three-Two-Four-Three-Niner, Claude Intersection at one-one. I have reached fifteen thousand. Over."

The Center heaved a sigh. The fourteen-thousand-foot level was clear for the errant and idiotic Cessna. How he would get down at Childress was another matter—but at least there would be a respite.

Mel Carnegie wandered from his desk. He glanced at each of the boards, shuffling slowly down the floor. When he reached Norm's he smiled.

"Everything O.K.?" he asked mildly.

"Just fine, Mel," Norm answered. "Just fine."

Now, there had been an Air Force jet due at Palo Duro. Had it reported?

It promised to be a night to remember. . . .

four:

NAVY JET 3255
THERMAL, CALIFORNIA

Dale Heath's brush with vertigo had alerted him. His senses were keyed to the slightest movement of the tiny plane riding above his artificial horizon. The little aircraft portrayed in rear view the plane he was flying. If he dropped his right wing, the right wing of the plane behind the glass would seem to drop too; if he lowered his nose—and this would be accomplished with no perceptible movement of the stick, with hardly more than a mere willing of the nose to drop—then the nose of the little plane would seem to seek the horizon of its own two-inch world. The diminutive plane was the focus of his attention, but his eyes would flick across the rest of the panel as well, not helter-skelter, but in a practiced and methodical march, checking, and rechecking. Rate of climb, ball bank, gyro-compass, radio needle, tail-pipe temperature, airspeed, and then back, always back, to the artificial horizon.

Years before he had been an instrument flight instructor at the all-weather school in Memphis. At the end of his two-year tour of duty there he had been a superb instrument pilot. Dormant now, he knew, was the ability he had polished in hundreds of hours under the hood and in bad weather.

The genius of the instrument pilot lay in an effort of will, an effort in the beginning conscious and, with more training, unconscious. The pilot on instruments had to fight down all of the jangling alarms sent him by a physiology never really adapted to flight. Even birds, deprived by fog of a frame of reference, became disoriented and landed. Man's private gyroscope was in his inner ear, but his system was designed to be stabilized by the sense of sight. He was helpless in a clammy void in which no sight was possible.

Dale had seen qualified pilots in earth-bound Link trainers completely lose control of reflex and machine and slide back their canopies in fear compounded of vertigo and claustrophobia.

Dale shifted uncomfortably.

In a few minutes he would again be at home in the cockpit, but now, climbing south through the gray blanket away from the Coronado radio beacon, the transition from stability to tottering imbalance was frightening.

For jets are inherently skittish because stability is secondary in their design to speed. They require constant attention. Even when trimmed with care, if the pilot's mind strays they wander like young horses ridden sloppily.

He had already crossed the Coronado range station south of the field, but his climb-out instructions were to cross it again at thirty-three thousand feet before joining the airways. Now, still climbing, it was time to turn north and retrace his path to the range. To continue further would put him over the Mexican Border and, more importantly, through the southern border of the U.S. Air Defense Identification Zone. If he was spotted there by radar, he could cause a "scramble" by the Navy fighters assigned from his own North Island Air Station to the Air Force's Continental Defense Command. Gently he began a standard climbing turn, banking the little plane under the glass before him, maintaining his ascent at fifteen hundred feet per minute, his airspeed at two-eight-five knots.

In one minute he was heading north. He steadied, watched the omni-needle quiver and come to rest directly ahead.

The unchanging white void outside the cockpit teased him with the feeling that he had not turned at all. And then, although the artificial horizon showed his wings to be level, his

inner ear prodded him. Was he banking in the opposite direction?

He shook his head to clear the illusion from it. He reassured
himself on the honesty of his artificial horizon with a barely
noticeable rocking of his wings. The little plane followed neatly.
He glanced at his kneepad and at the clock on the panel. Off
at three-twenty P.M.—two-zero past the hour—from North Island
—now it was only three-two past. He had been airborne twelve
minutes and already he had twice had vertigo. He simply had
to break away from the paper-work and fly oftener.

All at once, as if someone had turned on a bank of lights in
a darkened room, he burst into golden sunlight.

As far as he could see, a snow-white blanket stretched to the
north; spires from some storm to the east mounted from it like
a golden castle standing in the snow.

The touch of vertigo was swept aside the moment the cloud-
level horizon presented itself. And with the solidity of visual
flight, with the glorious cloudscape, with the engine thrusting
silently behind him and the omni-needle sniffing tirelessly for
the Coronado radio range below, he felt one of the rare moments
of euphoria that had sprinkled his flying career; an instant of
complete integration of pilot, machine, and element.

Dale was not a man who lived to fly, or could conceive of no
other life, as many pilots claimed to be. From the promise of the
sky, from the undeniable beauty of storm clouds and shafted
sunlight and brass-tipped pinnacles, the flier was too often dis-
tracted by the heat of an engine or the complexity of airway
navigation. Flying could be boring: "Years of monotony," someone had said, "punctuated by seconds of panic." Too often,
when there was time to drink in the beauty of it all, there was
no beauty—a flat, unbroken sameness of cloud or ground.

But there were moments of glory in the sky, many of them;
mostly they occurred when flying conditions were the worst.
This was one of them, and for a moment he had time to enjoy
it.

At thirty-three thousand feet he eased his throttle back to a
cruising ninety-two per cent r.p.m., saw the omni swing ex-

citedly as it sensed the nearness of the Coronado beacon buried in the clouds.

He was feeling more at home already. His mind slipped into airway procedures. The moment that the needle swung at Coronado he dialed the next station, Thermal, onto his omni. This is the way he would travel across the country, swinging himself down the airway from range station to range station as an athlete might swing along a cable.

Now he banked to the right, down the invisible highway stretching to the east.

"San Diego radar, this is Navy One-One-Three-Two-Five-Five, Coronado. Position report. Over Coronado at four-one . . . Flight level three-three-zero . . . I.F.R. Flight Plan . . . Estimate Thermal at five-two . . . Rice next. Over."

The cut-and-dried form for a position report had come easily to his lips, and he had rattled it off professionally. The rustiness was rubbing off. San Diego radar rogered cheerfully.

With the plane on altitude, on course, and on the airway, Dale had time to think of his passenger. He glanced into the mirror on his canopy. Widely distorted by the curved glass, Mc-Vey stared back at him from beneath his hard-hat and over his oxygen mask. Dale switched carefully to intercom—the lore of aviation was full of embarrassing transmissions by pilots who had inadvertently broadcast information intended for internal consumption. "How you doing, McVey?"

In the mirror he saw McVey nod. Dale shook his head.

"Acknowledge on the intercom, Mac."

"Everything's fine, Commander."

Loss of communication between a pilot and a passenger could be a murderous thing in an emergency. Knowing that it was all right, Dale relaxed.

"Beautiful, isn't it?" he asked the sailor.

"Yes sir," McVey said, without much enthusiasm. "Yes sir, it sure is beautiful."

Dale saw the boy glance at the cloud castle and then retreat into his own thoughts. How old was he? Nineteen or twenty at the most. Bright, polite, handsome, with what would seem every reason to be cheerful. Then why was he so withdrawn? What worries could a twenty-year-old airman, nurtured and protected by the government, possibly have?

But that was ridiculous. A problem was a subjective thing; there was inherently as much grief wrapped up in a shattered new Christmas toy to a boy of five as in a shattered marriage to a man of thirty-eight.

He had had his share of broken toys, and at eighteen or nineteen had probably passed over the same ground that McVey was traversing. And it was not fair to assume that the burdens of youth were always left lying by the road. Because even now he carried some: Cheryl herself, for instance.

For it had been in those sensitive years, when he was only a little younger than his passenger in back, that she had inflicted the first cuts on his psyche.

Even in those days Cheryl radiated trouble for those around her. He wondered whether the resentment he had felt at their first adolescent meeting—their infant days together could surely not count—whether his resentment had colored their relationship through the years.

His father, a regular Navy commander, had forced the meeting. Without malice, unthinkingly.

They had been living in quarters at the Vallejo Navy Yard; Dale, a freshman at U.C. in Berkeley awaiting word of his Naval Academy examinations, had been commuting. It was a grim year, tossed into a competitive school of engineering with the Navy junior's typically sporadic educational background; a year in which he had had to swim or drown in the second largest university in the world.

There was hardly a bright scene of that year left in his memory, except for the little freshman coed, Susan. . . .

Now, strangely, he could hardly make out her face. It had been a long time since he had thought of her.

Suppose things had been different? Suppose he had stayed at Cal; become, perhaps, an engineer or an architect or a teacher, settled in San Francisco, say, with the coed or some other girl. There were branches in the path you walked, and he supposed it did no harm to imagine where the branch you hadn't chosen would have led. . . .

There had been a moment here for choice, for choosing cold self-interest over sacrifice, but he had not.

He had met the coed in a bookstore shopping for texts, had buried his shyness and asked her to a malt at the little shop outside Sather Gate. Incredulously, he heard her agree.

Within hours, he believed himself in love. She was a sorority pledge, and for weeks he was part of the furniture in the Chi Omega lounge.

Then, a few weeks after thy met, tragedy struck. At dinner in their quarters, his father had mentioned the arrival of his new boss, Captain Hugh Forester. The name meant nothing to Dale, absently demolishing half an apple pie, lost in a fog compounded of Christmas finals and his new-found love.

His mother chuckled. "You remember Cheryl Forester, Dale? The little girl you used to play with at the legation in Shanghai. I hope she's changed—she was a regular little hellion."

Dimly Dale recalled a devious sprite who had tormented the community amah unmercifully and had usually succeeded in shifting the blame to some other Navy junior.

"Her dad's going to be chief of staff," his father remarked. "How old is Cheryl now?" he asked his wife.

Dale's mother looked at his father suspiciously. "Well, she was born when Doris and Hugh were at Bremerton with us. And Dale was—let me see. Just two. Sixteen or seventeen, I guess. Why?"

His father ignored the question. "When we make our official call—that'll be Thursday—why don't you tag along, Dale? You can talk over old times."

It was useless to remind his father that old times had consisted of ten or twenty American children playing in a grimy Chinese schoolyard a dozen years before. And behind the light conversation there was a plan of battle that did not elude him. He said, politely enough, "I'm sorry, Dad. I'll be studying all night."

"I wish you'd come," his father said.

"If he has to study," his mother said firmly, "he has to study."

"Look, Dad," Dale said, "I've got a mid-term in physics Friday. I flunk that and you'll be the first one to climb all over me."

"You won't flunk it," his father said confidently. And with cool irrelevance, "If you're cutting it that fine, how do you expect to get through plebe physics at the Naval Academy?"

Dale strongly suspected that the standards of the U.C. School of Engineering were higher than those of Annapolis, but he had no way of knowing then, and a slur on his father's Alma Mater was unthinkable. He shrugged and retreated a little: "If I'm caught up all right by the time you go, I'll make the call with you. O.K.?"

"Swell," his father said. "Oh, and Dale?"

His mother arose nervously and began to clear the table.

"Yes sir?" Dale asked. His stomach sank. He could guess what was coming.

"The Foresters just got on the base this week. And Cheryl hasn't had a chance to meet anybody. There's this hop at the O Club Friday. . . ."

"Oh, now look. . . ."

His father got it out. "How about dragging her?"

Keeping the emotion out of his voice Dale said, "I can't, Dad. I've got a date with Sue. I'm taking Sue to a basketball game."

"Who's Sue?" His father smiled, although Dale had mentioned her to him in a rare moment of communication days before.

He shifted uncomfortably. "She's a Chi O I know. . . ."

"Have you *seen* this Cheryl? Lately, I mean?"

"No. Why?"

"Don't quote me to the captain, but she's about the sexiest—well, that's beside the point. I told him maybe you'd take her."

His mother shook her head unbelieving. "Oh, now, look. . . ."

His father looked miserable. "I didn't know he had a date. And he asked me whether there was anybody here around her age—"

Dale was on his feet. "Listen! One, I'm not around her age —I'm eighteen and she's sixteen. And two, I have a date."

"Damn it, Dale, he's my boss," his father said. "I'm sorry I volunteered you, but I did. . . ."

"Well, you'll just have to de-volunteer me then," Dale flared. "Because I'm taking Sue. . . ."

His father had looked hurt and subsided. Then, in a day or two he had strolled into Dale's bedroom while Dale was studying.

"You put me in a bad spot, Dale."

"I did not! You did it all yourself."

"Cheryl even got a formal."

"She *what?*" Dale stared. "I haven't even met her yet!"

"Her father misunderstood me. He thought you were going anyway, and it was all set. . . ."

"What is this?" Dale's voice climbed. "I already told you I *had* a date, damn it. What about Sue?"

"Come on, Mister," his father said with false camaraderie. "Tell her we made plans for you Friday—you don't have to say what. Please? For your old man?"

"Honest to God!" He slammed shut his book and walked to the window, angry and torn. Finally he turned. "All right."

Dale Heath at thirty-eight, streaking past the Salton Sea, could feel the bitterness in Dale Heath at eighteen, in a bedroom at Vallejo.

"But darn it, I'm *not* lying to Sue. I'm telling her."

So he had told Sue, plainly and simply, and his heart had gone out in a rush of love when she had seemed to accept it. But he knew that secretly he had been eliminated neatly and permanently from the life of the beautiful Susan. And when he asked her out again, she refused. It was the normal course of any conflict with his father; sometimes hard, sometimes soft and yielding as quicksand, Dad always won in the end.

Dale even went for the call. He sat uncomfortably in the Foresters' living room while his father and the captain played the eternal Academy game of who was serving where. "Rip Collins is at Pearl on the staff of CincPacFlt. He was the first man in the class of '28 to make captain, you know. . . ."

And the mothers, their tongues pliant with Manhattans, played theirs too: "When we were stationed in Norfolk, I saw her. . . . Now that they've made admiral, she's worse than ever. . . ."

Dale, who after six months at Cal could easily have drunk any of them under the table, sat miserably nursing a Coke. Then, for the first time since they were children, he saw Cheryl.

At sixteen she was dazzling—full-breasted and slim-waisted and knowing.

She came directly across the room to him, ignoring the rest, her hand outstretched. He realized now that she had probably picked up the gesture in a movie, but it had been so adult that he had stumbled as he rose.

"It's been years," she murmured, as if they were old lovers reunited.

The next night at the dance she had gone on with the pretense that there had been something between them in the infant days in Shanghai, until he almost believed her. After the dance, in his hot-rod, she flung herself into his arms with a passion that blistered his college veneer and reduced him to a panting, bumbling schoolboy.

Her sparkle and the envy she excited among the young officers at the dance, her torrid, practiced necking after, had almost made up for the resentment he felt toward his father.

He wondered now whether any stroke of misfortune or fortune could arouse in him the unadulterated grief and joy of those days.

Could a divorce do it? Freedom to marry the girl he loved? Perhaps . . .

He glanced at his kneepad. He was due over Thermal in two minutes. He turned up the volume to check. Thermal came in loud and clear: "T–R–M, T–R–M . . ."

He looked out of the cockpit. The coastal fog had given way to desert haze, tinted by the weary sun behind him. He was flashing over a huge caldron of molten copper. Far to the east puffy alto-cumulus clouds hinted that the front was passing somewhere ahead. He banked slightly and searched for Thermal beneath the haze. The shimmering surface was impenetrable. He looked at his estimate, then at the clock. He was due at Thermal—now.

As if reading his mind, the omni-needle swung wildly and lay straining against its stop to the right. Thermal lay beneath him in the golden sea. He had passed it precisely on his estimate.

five:

FLIGHT SEVEN
MONTEBELLO, VIRGINIA

Mike Ruble stared down at the billowing clouds. It was very nearly dark. They had crossed Springfield omni at two thousand feet, as their clearance had instructed them, and had spiraled upward in a race-track pattern, never straying farther than one minute from the range. Now, at six thousand feet, they were about to recross it for the last time and, still climbing, start at last west on Victor One-Five-One-Eight.

Until this moment they had been mounting an oval staircase, and were at last about to be released at the top to crawl farther up an imaginary ramp until they reached twenty thousand feet —but this portion at least was to the west in their direction of travel—and then, reaching their chosen airway and assigned en-route altitude at Montebello, they were to begin the ride along the twenty-three-hundred-mile corridor to Los Angeles.

Neither Mike nor Captain Barnett wore earphones. The speakers behind each were singing steadily with the Arcola range. The captain was using it for a check on navigation. That was fine, but he was employing the archaic audible signal rather than trusting to the bird-dog pointer which would give him the same information.

It might imply caution, or it might imply habit; whatever it was, it was tiresome. From the speaker behind Mike's head came the strident "dah-dit" of the Arcola radio, changing to a steady beat as the plane approached the range leg. The high-pitched tone filled the cockpit with reassuring but unnecessary strength. Captain Barnett banked smoothly to the left, at last, on an airway that would lead them to Victor One-Five-One-Eight.

Is he going, Mike wondered, to leave that beam turned up all the way? No, Barnett tuned down the volume and began to fly by the needle. Just habit, apparently, to set the radio high. Mike was uncomfortable, disquieted, and he could not explain it even to himself. Perhaps it was because he had stupidly missed the clearance at Washington National; perhaps it was because of the depressing weather. But something did not feel right.

The cockpit was stuffy, and he turned down the heater control. A dissonant engine began to bother him, although they were still in the climb and Capelli could be excused for waiting until they leveled off for the final fine synchronization of the props. And yet, the beat *was* irritating—might unconsciously be felt by the passengers. And it was getting more evident.

He reached over and touched the prop control lightly. The errant propeller fell into step with its brothers, and the vibration stopped. Capelli laughed.

"Keeping you awake, Ruble?"

Mike said, "Sorry." He lapsed into wry reflection. On the ground he had been shoved politely aside by Barnett in the matter of the clearance; in the air he was being told by Capelli to keep his cotton-picking hands off the engine controls. He wondered if they would prefer him to go aft and try to help Kitty.

Mike almost smiled. The situation reminded him of the summer when a wartime shortage of help had forced his father to let him, at thirteen, pitch in at the "junk shop," as the family had always called it.

In those days the Ruble Art Store had been hardly more than that. It was before his mother had suggested the change of name to the "Dallas Salon d'Art," when it was just past the stage of having been a secondhand bookstore on Commerce Street, handling a few originals and many more prints. Mike, commissioned by his father as salesman, exhibited such eagerness to the

nouveau-riche Texans awakening to the prestige value of a Dufy
or a Fragonard, that, because they were suspicious of his enthusiasm, he had driven off more customers than he had sold.

So he asked his father: "What's the matter with them, Dad?
Some of this stuff we're getting from Phoenix—and that series
of Brueghel prints—they're just terrific. Why can't I sell them?"

His father grinned: "You're a Texan yourself, Mike. The only
way to sell a horse or a painting to a Texan is pretend that you
don't want to sell it. Then they want it."

And his father was right, though Mike was too obtuse to take
full advantage of the advice. The one Turner oil that he hoped
no one would buy, so that he might save up for it himself, he
reluctantly sold to an Alice County beef heiress for a breathtaking price. But it was his only sale.

Relegated to the embryonic *"Objets d'Art"* section of the
store, with teen-age clumsiness he managed in two days to de-
stroy a vase, a hand-painted dish, and a Dresden figurine.

At the end of the week Sam Ruble had taken him for a cup
of coffee at the Golden Pheasant.

"Mike," the old man said unhappily, "I don't know how to put
this, but do you think you might resign?"

He could still feel the flash of hurt, and it must have shown
on his face.

"Aw, Mike, I was just kidding. You stick around, you want
to."

"Gosh, Dad, I'm sorry about the Dresden."

"Forget it. It's just that . . . It's just that you're so doggone
eager. It's like you were a puppy or something."

"Or a bull in a china shop?" Mike asked wryly.

"Kind of. I was thinking," his father said, "we could maybe
get you a job in the art department at Neiman's."

"That ought to cut their stock down to our size," Mike admitted. "Maybe you're right. Maybe I should get out of the art
business. . . ."

"Not all the way." His father smiled. "Just the business end."

For even then, when Mike's work was hardly distinguishable

from that of any other high-school art student, his father's faith in his painting had been solid and tangible.

Thinking of his father, the seven-year ache came back.

The lot of a Jew in Texas was not a happy one, even when everyone knew that your mother was a Fort Worth gentile of sufficiently poverty-stricken dirt-farmer background to be acceptable. And Mike's very talent engendered a certain distrust.

Sensing the loneliness, Sam Ruble made up in companionship what he must have felt that his religion was denying his son. Not even to little Tom, harder and more aggressive, did he show the love he did for Mike.

Mike remembered camping on a hunting trip given by a customer near Palo Duro Canyon in the Texas Panhandle. He and his dad had settled a little apart from the rest, away from the fire, passing a bottle of bourbon back and forth in the sunset.

"You bring your water colors, Mike?"

"No."

"That's some mountain." He pointed to the brilliant strata of Triassic Peak, alternately red and gold in the dying sun. "You think you could catch it?"

"I don't know."

"If you can't, I don't know who can. I wish I had as much talent as you. . . ."

Mike puzzled over the words. *As much talent as you?* Why "as much," when as far as he knew his father had never touched a brush?

He wished now that he had pursued the statement further. It had not been until the hectic week after his death that Mike had found out. . . . Why hadn't he paid more attention then?

But he hadn't. . . .

His father had gone on: "Mike, you're sure you want to be an artist? You're sure there's nothing else you want to do?"

"I'm sure."

After that hunting trip there had been no expense spared. If Mike had ever thought of himself as starving in a garret, he was wrong. The following year, for a week before his birthday his father had forbidden him to go down to the store.

And on his birthday a beautifully equipped little studio, north light streaming through frosted glass in the ceiling, awaited him. On the wall was a tiny but genuine Renoir sketch, "for inspiration."

It had been almost embarrassing. For days he felt as if his mother and Tommy were standing outside, waiting for his first masterpiece. And for a week he had been unable to work there, unable to conceive of anything that would be worthy of the materials and the effort that had been poured into the studio itself.

Then he had labored earnestly on an oil—the sunset, as closely as he could remember, they had seen on the hunting trip.

It had not been a success. . . . He had never been able to work well without sketches. Blessedly, though he had hoped that his dad would hang it, Sam Ruble's integrity overcame his parental pride.

"Mike, it's not good enough yet. You've got part of it, but it's not good enough yet."

And so, instead of college, he had gone to Hollywood Art School. Ruble's Salon d'Art was by then a solid enterprise, a tradition in town, but Hollywood Art School was still no easy thing for the family to finance. His mother had bridled.

"They have art courses at the University of Texas. And you don't need to study art to run an art shop, Sam. Look at *you*. And we need at least five thousand to open up that line of art supplies. . . ."

His father, who in all things gave in to his mother, had for once rebelled.

"It's more important that Mike should get off to a good start. Some of the artists we buy here, this guy Rixey, for instance, if he'd had a little training in composition he'd be a master. So Mike's going, Belle. . . ."

So he had gone.

And, he thought bleakly, for what? So that with his training and apparently passable talent he could ride eternally through the skies, a sort of artistic Flying Dutchman? What was he doing here, anyway?

The plane began to lurch as it skimmed the bottom of a layer of stratus. There were a few soft, not unpleasant bumps, one soaring air current, and they were in the bowels of the clouds.

It was deep dusk now, the purple hour that Mike disliked in the air. It was a danger hour. In V.F.R. weather when there was uncontrolled traffic, it was an hour when eyes were not yet adapted to dark and the dusk was too deep to see well. Even now, when they owned their own chunk of sky, he was uneasy.

He glanced out, checking the anti-collision light, and then turned up the rheostat on his side of the panel. The instruments glowed redly.

Doctor Ed Benedict looked up to find the slim stewardess standing over him with an expectant smile. He handed her their tickets.

"All right, Doctor," she said, passing on.

Now that they were airborne, now that they were settled down for the long trip to Los Angeles, he had to face the problem. And it was worse than Kronk had said.

"Ed," Kronk had murmured, standing in his gown with the pathologist's report, "we talked of this before. In med school."

"I know, Kronk. I remember. . . ."

"You *don't* have to tell a patient. I don't tell my patients."

"I tell mine."

"Listen, Ed, if you have to salve your goddamned conscience, she's *my* patient. I'm telling *you*, as her closest relative, but I don't want you to tell her. Is that sufficient?"

Ed shook his head. "It's no soap, Kronk. I couldn't do it. It isn't a matter of principle, or anything else. There are no secrets between us; there never have been, and I have to tell her."

"Why? For God's sake, why? You don't have to tell her *now*."

"It's a practical matter, Kronk. I just couldn't get away with it. We're too close—she's going to find out anyway—and when she does, I don't want her thinking that I wouldn't trust her."

"When she *has* to find out, she'll know you kept it from her for her own good."

"It isn't a matter of her having to find out when the acute stage comes. It's before. I just can't keep a secret from her. I don't want to, and I won't."

"Even this one?"

"This one," Ed admitted, "I would if I could. But she trusts me, and I can't."

Kronk gave up. "Will you for God's sake . . . I'm asking *this* . . . will you for God's sake wait a couple of weeks before you tell her? Will you think it over for a while?"

It was easy to agree to that. If he could only find a further excuse for not telling her, it would be easy to accede to it again. And again and again and again . . .

Suppose he waited until they were home. Suppose he drove her to their cove, where they could watch the sunset plume the charging breakers with pink. Suppose he told her there, sitting alone on the beach, or better yet, alone in the familiar solidity of the car. Then what?

An hour or two later, when the shock had passed, they would head back for the house through the darkness of La Jolla. Passing through the streets of a town so dear to her, toward the house she loved so much, toward the children—that would be the worst of all.

How could she face the children?

He should have told her in the hospital. Kronk was wrong. He should have told her in the hospital.

But he had not told her in the hospital. Now it was up to him to decide where, and when, and how it would be the easiest on her.

He looked at her. Her head was back. She seemed a little tired. Her eyes were closed, but there was a suggestion of a smile on her face as she listened to Joey Lafitte prattle on.

She's thinking of Killer tomorrow, he thought, and he pictured him himself, egg on his face from breakfast, bursting with the voltage with which two weeks at his grandmother's could invariably charge him, followed by Nita screaming and lurching across the lawn. Yes, she was far from the little boy beside her, far from the plane bouncing through the clouds.

Why hadn't he told her when they were alone somewhere? He had to tell her before she faced the children—he should have known it—then why hadn't he told her when they were alone?

How could he tell her with the damn *kid* sitting there?

He glanced at his watch. It was 5:40. In eight hours they would be landing at L.A. International. Should he wait until then? Tell her on the trip to San Diego in the car?

No, it would leave her too little time. He must do it soon. Ask the stewardess to take the little boy forward, and tell her then.

But looking at the placid features and the quiet smile, he knew that he could not break into the reverie.

He could give her that much—a few more minutes of happiness before the eternal grief.

Captain Dick Barnett felt the DC-7's pulse through the yoke which rested his hand. Smooth, everything jake. He glanced at the altimeter. Nineteen thousand feet, with a rate of climb of five hundred feet per minute. In two minutes he would be at his assigned altitude and the increasing sensitivity of his needle to the Montebello range told him that he would cross Montebello at exactly the same time.

He guessed that flying the audible low-frequency beam rather than following the bird-dog had annoyed his copilot. He had had no real reason for using the old-fashioned audible technique—nowadays you simply identified a range station by ear and then shifted quickly to the bird-dog pointer. But his mind had wandered and he had forgotten to shift.

And sensing Ruble's unspoken irritation with the noise had made him continue. Why was he forever doing that? His wife claimed that he did it driving. "Whenever I think Dick's driving too fast," Linda would chuckle to friends, "I tell him we're late. Then he slows right down. If we're late, I tell him he's driving too fast. . . ."

Then she would smile at him with her fond, beautiful eyes, and he would feel like a small boy whose every trait is an open page to his mother. The trouble was, she was right—at least in driving. He guessed that he was, as Massey said, just a perverse old bastard at that, on the road or in the air.

But he was a good driver, and he was damn sure a good pilot. In 1950 he had been taxied by a Japanese taxi director at Haneda Airport in Tokyo too close to another DC-4. He had crumpled a wing tip—a hundred-dollar job, perhaps. Not really his fault, but of course always the pilot's fault, and rightly so . . .

It was the only damage he had ever permitted on a plane under his command—the only scratch in eighteen thousand hours. The only scratch in two forced landings and four serious emergencies.

Let somebody else try to equal that record. Let the operations boys scream to Massey about the C.A.R. violations.

He chilled. *Was Massey thinking of the violations when he offered the desk job?*

No. His safety record was a solid thing, a golden testament to skill and technique and experience.

Then why was Massey trying to kick him into a swivel chair? "Dick, it's a hell of a good job. Operations Manager for the whole Western Division— You'd be a V.P. before you retired."

And that night, watching the fog roll in over Catalina from their patio, Linda had flashed Massey a grateful smile.

You couldn't force a senior captain to quit flying before sixty-five without bringing the A.L.P.A. down on you like a ton of bricks, but why would Massey even want to? Because he was reluctant to fly jets? Or because of the C.A.R. violations?

Or simply because, as he claimed, he needed his experience more in the office?

And it *would* keep him home. As Massey said, Linda would like that. . . .

"Captain? Captain!" he heard Ruble call.

He looked at him questioningly.

Ruble was smiling apologetically. "Twenty thousand at Montebello, Captain."

Dick Barnett glanced at his altimeter. He was three hundred feet too high.

"Yeah . . . Thanks," he said, without much grace. What was three hundred feet anyway? He could have climbed that far past just to get a running start on the first leg. He shrugged.

"You want to make your Montebello report?" he asked Ruble, a little sharply.

Then, imperceptibly, so that it would not look as though he had inadvertently strayed from his altitude, he steadied on Victor One-Five-One-Eight and began to descend.

"Yes sir," Ruble answered. He made his call, but Barnett caught another glance at the altimeter and felt in his copilot a vague discomfort at the slowness of the correction.

These kids were nurtured on air traffic control—strict compliance with altitude and estimate was hammered into them from the day they got to basic training. Sure it was important, but what did he want him to do? Dive back to his en-route altitude and throw his passengers all over the cabin?

He had a responsibility to them, didn't he? A.T.C. wasn't flying this airplane.

The captain was.

six:

NAVY JET 3255
RICE, CALIFORNIA

From thirty-three thousand feet the clouds below were sheep grazing on a darkening plain. Jutting from the herd Dale could see the ridges and peaks of the Piute Range molded in copper relief by the oval sun.

His radio crackled suddenly.

"Phoenix Center, this is Air Force Jet One-Six-One-Four-Zero. Rice. Position report. Over."

Dale searched the sky ahead. He could tell by the stiffening needle of his omni that he was very nearly to Rice himself.

But the Air Force jet could well be within a few miles of him and still be invisible.

Because there was no frame of reference at high altitude, because the eye must have an object to focus on if it is to see at all, another aircraft would be absorbed in the crystal expanse, no matter how close. It was a common experience for a flight leader and his wingman, separating to begin a mock dog fight at thirty or forty thousand feet, to lose each other completely on the clearest day, simply because there was too much sky to search, and with no point on which to settle the human eye focused at three feet.

The Air Force jet, Dale felt sure, was higher than he. And if so, he should be drawing contrails. . . .

Phoenix Center answered, and the Air Force pilot came back.

"Phoenix Center, this is Air Force Jet Six-One-Four-Zero. Rice on the hour . . . Flight level four-one-zero . . . I.F.R. Flight Plan . . . V.F.R. conditions on top . . . Descending V.F.R. to flight level two-one-zero . . . Estimate Thermal at one-one . . . San Diego. Over."

Dale began to search the sky ahead. If the Air Force jet was drawing contrails, he might spot him. He should be only two minutes ahead.

"You see that joker, McVey?" he asked into the intercom.

"No sir. Should I?"

"According to his position report, he's within two minutes of us. Keep your eyes open."

Dale owned his altitude. That was the theory. But a pilot in the clear was an idiot not to be looking. Especially when from his radio he knew his speed of closure with a nearby plane was a thousand miles an hour.

Absently, because it was only half an hour to sunset and because he was a little nervous, Dale checked his anti-collision lights and flicked on his running lights. He continued to scan the sky.

Apparently the Air Force jet had cheated on his estimate, not wishing to revise it. Because, unless he had whisked by unseen, he could not have been at Rice when he said he was. Dale was almost over it now.

There was no real need for worry. The Air Force jet was probably high above. But planes in the clear were notoriously sloppy in reporting their correct altitude, simply because it didn't seem to matter. Dale tried a trick. He picked up his microphone.

"Phoenix Center, this is Navy Jet One-One-Three-Two-Five-Five. I estimate Rice at zero-three. Do you have en-route traffic?"

Now at least the Air Force jockey knew he was in the vicinity. And now they were both alerted.

Phoenix Center reported that there was indeed en-route traffic, V.F.R. on top, and suddenly Dale spotted it.

The jet was a B-52 Stratofortress directly in his path, but higher, painting four golden contrails across the sky.

Dale, suddenly relieved, rocked his wings in greeting.

The bomber did not reply. Perhaps he had not seen him. . . .

Dale relaxed. "You see him, Mac?"

"No sir."

"Look straight up. See four double contrails?"

"Oh, yeah . . . Golly, how'd I miss him?"

"Well, there's a lot of sky up here."

"As fast as everything's moving, I'm glad there is."

"That's right. But, in this kind of weather, everybody's channeled onto the airways. It's the only way to control everybody, but it makes things kind of crowded."

"I'll keep my eyes open."

"Roger."

It would do no harm to tell him the story of Stub Baker. Or would it perturb him on his first jet ride? No, he would tell him. It would alert him, and might even keep his mind off whatever was bothering him.

"With all this sky, it doesn't seem possible that two jets could collide, but they do. There are three or four near-misses reported every day—and don't forget that the ones that neither pilot sees aren't reported. And neither are the ones where a guy figures he might have been wrong and doesn't want to stir things up."

"Holy cow!"

"And there are lots of actual collisions that only cause minor damage, ones where both planes are able to land, that you never read about in the paper."

McVey's voice was incredulous. "You mean two of these things can actually collide and stay up?"

"If the damage isn't too extensive—sure. There are survivors of mid-airs. I have a friend—Stub Baker. A commander. You hear about that mid-air over El Toro last month?"

"No sir."

"Well, he was in it. He was churning along at thirty-five thousand in a Cougar. He was keeping a sharp lookout—and this you can believe, because he's got about ten thousand hours and he's one of the sharpest pilots in the Navy. He looked down for about three seconds to check the fuel gauge, and when he looked back up here was this B-66. Head on, same altitude, closing at about a thousand knots. He still doesn't know where it came from."

"What happened?" McVey asked. There was finally a note of interest in his voice.

"Well, there wasn't time to avoid it. He couldn't swerve out of the way—the wingspan on those things is half a city block. He had to make up his mind whether to climb or dive. He says he knew if he dived he'd jam his canopy on the belly of the bomber, and if he climbed the bomber would knock his tail off."

"What'd he do?"

"He climbed," Dale said quietly. "It knocked his tail off, but at least it didn't jam his canopy, so he ejected."

"What happened to the bomber?"

"It crashed."

There was a moment of silence. Then, "Did the men get out all right?"

"No. Their canopy was jammed."

Dale tuned Prescott into his radio. It was faint behind a wall of static. He would wait and try when he was closer.

McVey said, "Commander?"

"Yes, Mac?"

"How many men were there in that bomber?"

"Three."

"I see. . . ." The voice sounded thoughtful.

So, Dale reflected, even this untrained kid thinks that Stub might have saved the bomber crew by diving. And maybe he could have.

He was sure that the same question, of course unspoken, had occured to everyone at the O Club bar the night that Stub had first told the story. Standing with the Band-aid across his nose hiding the cut his hard-hat had made when his chute had yanked him erect, he had toyed with his drink and held fascinated the crowd of fellow pilots.

"Man," Stub said, "you do some mighty quick thinking in a head-on situation—mighty quick."

It had occurred to everyone suddenly (for who thought these things out before?) that this glancing blow of a fighter plane on a bomber or transport could be handled in two ways. If one had time to handle it at all . . .

Should the fighter climb, he left his canopy free to eject; should he dive, he left the bomber crew alive and sacrificed himself. . . .

It had been on Stub's mind, too, that night. But he hadn't been defensive. Nobody expected you to jam your canopy, to slam your life out on another plane's belly just because there were more people in the other plane. Stub had even been a little proud of his quickness. And if he was a little callous, quoting the old safety poster, "A mid-air collision can ruin your whole day," he was a friendly man, a popular man, and it was easily forgotten.

But now the question came back to Dale. Should Stub have sacrificed himself? It was a moral question, really. It was something like that posed the pilot of a plane forced to land in a city where the only clear area that can save him turns out to be a playground. Less obvious, with fewer precedents, perhaps, but something like it . . .

Did Stub, who must have thought of this by now, lie awake?

Dale doubted it. It was after all a question of each pilot trying to survive as best he could.

And yet, there *were* more men in the larger plane.

It was not for him to worry about. He liked Stub and was glad that he had survived. Perhaps there had really been no choice.

"I think," he told McVey, "that you probably act instinctively. I don't think there's any decision to make at all."

But he was vaguely uncomfortable and decided in loyalty to Stub not to tell the story again. He forced his thoughts to other, more pleasant things. He glanced at the clock on the panel. It was just after four, Pacific Coast time. Seven in Washington. What would Jeanie be doing?"

Very possibly waiting for his call. He'd make it at Albuquerque.

He was over Rice, and he called Phoenix Center.

The reply came back on waves of dissonance. He caught his number, and then the voice faded. Apparently the Rice relay transmitter was weak.

Or was it his own radio?

He would have it checked at Kirtland. If he could find a radioman who knew the navy gear. . . .

seven:

FLIGHT SEVEN
COVINGTON, VIRGINIA

Captain Dick Barnett, Mike had to admit, might have forgotten
to level off at his assigned altitude, but he was one smooth pilot.
In the heaving turbulence at twenty thousand feet, he was anticipating each lurch with almost psychic presentiment. His
slim hands on the yoke moved hardly at all, but the big plane
answered to their pressure like an extension of his brain.

Not that the captain could do much. It was still bumpy. The
right running light cast a diffused green glow on the wing, but
Mike could not see the light itself. It was hidden from him by
fifty feet of fog, the wing tip riding invisible in the clammy
whiteness.

If this kept up, they would fly manually all the way. It could
be a tiring trip, but an autopilot was no substitute for a pilot's
touch in turbulence.

Kitty Foster slipped through the door behind them, bringing
their dinner on the covered plastic hot tray colored, as all else
was colored, in the slate gray of Pacific Central Airlines. It's a
wonder, Mike thought idly, that they don't make us dye our
hair gray—stewardesses and all.

Kitty gave Capelli the tray and he set it on his lap, taking off
the top. It was fried chicken.

"Is it going to get any better, Mike?" she asked.

"I don't think so. Not for a while."

Dick Barnett cut in: "What's the matter, Kitty? You got urpy passengers already?"

"No sir. But I was wondering about serving dinner."

"You might as well. Like Mike says, it's probably not going to get any better."

At least, Mike thought, he agrees with my forecast. Kitty turned to go.

"Say, young lady," Barnett said.

"Yes?"

"That gray-haired fellow in seat 2C. What's his name?"

"I'll look it up when I get to my station, sir."

She left and Dick Barnett waved his hand at Mike.

"You want to take it awhile?"

Mike patted himself on the head in the age-old signal. "I got it, sir."

The yoke was solid in his hands, throbbing with life. Some of the melancholy he had been feeling slipped from him as he began to meet the dips and sways of the plane.

Captain Barnett picked up his phone and Mike heard his voice over the P.A. system.

"This is your captain, Richard Barnett. We've climbed to our cruising altitude. We'll probably remain on it throughout the rest of the flight. We're at twenty thousand feet, although the cabin altitude is only seven thousand because the cabin is pressurized. We've just passed Montebello, Virginia. Montebello is a little town in the Blue Ridge Mountains—" He chuckled companionably. "Maybe you remember the song, 'In the Blue Ridge Mountains of Virginia.' It's too bad that the weather is so soupy, or you could see the lights. We're taking the northern route, because even though there are head winds up here, there are worse head winds down south; so we'll get to Los Angeles International quicker this way. Our estimate for Los Angeles is 11:15 P.M., Pacific standard time."

Mike winced. So many things could affect their estimate—a change in head wind, en-route traffic, and the very good possibility that they would have to hold over Los Angeles before letting down in the stack. He thought it poor public relations to make an estimate this far in advance. Then he looked at his flight log.

It was not such poor public relations after all. The captain had added a good half hour to their actual estimate. Now if things went normally the passengers would land early, grateful to be there ahead of time and sure that it had somehow been due to their captain.

Barnett noticed him looking at the log and winked at him. He spoke again into the microphone.

"I'd like to apologize for the bumpiness, but it's unavoidable. I'll report to you along the route again. Meanwhile, don't hesitate to ask Miss Foster, your stewardess, for anything you may need. Thank you for your attention. . . ."

He hung up the microphone as Capelli said in a voice clearly audible to Mike, "Horse manure."

Mike felt a flush climbing his neck. The flight engineer was either on better terms with the skipper than he seemed or almost psychopathically brazen.

He sneaked a glance at Barnett. Barnett had not heard, or was pretending not to have heard.

There were plenty of easygoing young captains on the line who asked no particular respect. Maybe Barnett asked none, but somehow Mike doubted it. He sensed a friendly man, but one whose dignity could be easily wounded, and anyway you just didn't talk to a fifty-year-old expert that way.

Well, Mike thought, Capelli was known as a first-class flight engineer; perhaps his skill brought special privilege.

Mike was not so sure that he wanted Capelli and his family at the beach after all.

And yet, the guy had a million kids—Mike had met them once after a flight—why deprive them of a day at the beach because of a chance remark of the father?

The intercom phone dinged musically, and Barnett lifted it. "Yes, Kitty?" He rubbed his chin thoughtfully. "Robert C. Morrison, huh? You ever hear of him? No, me either."

He thanked her and hung up. "You ever hear of a Robert C. Morrison on the line?" he asked Capelli.

Capelli shook his head.

"How about you, Mike?"

"No sir."

"I guess he's just a passenger. . . ." Barnett said comfortably.

Well, I'll be damned, thought Mike. *With all his seniority, he was worried because he thought we might be hauling a wheel!*

Barnett took over the controls so that Mike could work out the Bluefield estimate.

When Mike was through, he sat back thoughtfully. Was it his imagination, or was Barnett's flying less polished than it had been? He seemed somehow now not to be putting so much effort into outguessing the bumps. Was it because the passenger in 2C had turned out to be only a passenger?

The servility of the second senior pilot of his line disturbed him. Was this the pot at the end of the pilot's rainbow?

What was he doing here anyway?

Pat Benedict listened to the captain's report. She was pleased that his voice matched his looks; that he was thoughtful enough of his passengers to speak to them.

She had been on flights where the captain had not bothered. Then, because so seldom did you see your pilot anyway, the cockpit became a place peopled in your imagination with cold and impatient men.

And she had been on flights where the captain gave surly position reports to his passengers, as if required by company rules to do so. And that was even worse—you felt as if you were taking up his time from more important things.

It took so little communication between human beings to establish rapport. Why didn't more people try it?

Between Ed and her lay a bond of understanding as strong, she supposed, as that between any two humans on earth. And if some tiny spot was corroding it now, she would wipe it off with a few words. Not now—this was somehow not the time. But she could wait. . . .

She leaned over Joey Lafitte and tried to peer down at the

ground. But as Barnett had said, they were in the clouds. She sat back, a little disappointed.

She would have liked to see the lights of the little town in the Blue Ridge Mountains. She would look it up in her worn Rand-McNally's atlas tomorrow. What was the name of it? Montebello, Virginia, the captain had said. Wasn't that where Thomas Jefferson had his estate?

She asked Ed. He seemed to come back from a long journey.

"No, I don't think so. Jefferson's home was Monticello, wasn't it?"

At least he had told her instead of pleading ignorance. He was perfectly capable, not from perversity but modesty, of watching her delve desperately for one of the little facts that had always had such unbearable fascination for her, and then, when she had honestly failed, laying it deprecatingly at her feet as if he had just remembered it himself.

Or he might let Killer—for Killer had the same insatiable drive —scrabble mightily through the encyclopedia for some elusive trivia, and when Killer brought it glittering to the light, show the most intense interest even though Pat would sense that he had known it all along.

"Daddy"—this had been when he and Willy Carter were planning the trip to Pago Pago—"which way does the wind blow on the Pacific?"

Ed, who loved the ocean as much as she did, surely knew the answer. But he said, "Let's find out."

And the two of them had gone to the library to study wind charts.

"When you have to research something, it sticks in your mind," Ed claimed. "If I told him everything he asked me he'd forget it in two minutes."

Maybe that was what was wrong with her. She would become overwhelmed with the desire to learn a fact, or even a whole subject, and flutter ecstatically from one bit of it to the next, and six months later she would have forgotten half she learned.

All right. This time it would be different. Before they started on the Big Trip she would begin a systematic study of each country, each tiny town they would visit. Then when they came to some obscure monument or chapel, before Ed even had the guidebook out she would say casually, "Oh, I've heard of him! He was a general under the Doges. He defended Venice against the Duke of Ravioli in 1690. . . ."

"What are you thinking of, Pat?"

His voice was soft and seemed to come from a long distance. She realized that she had almost fallen asleep. She turned her head on the seat and smiled at him.

"The Trip."

He looked away quickly. "You were?"

His voice had lost some of its depth. Now it had a harshness that was jarring.

That was odd, when they were talking about the Trip. She was suddenly wide awake. Could he be losing interest? No, not after the years of planning. He was steady, not like her. . . . And yet perhaps the two weeks away from his practice had convinced him that he would be unhappy to be gone for a whole year. Perhaps he was afraid of losing it. . . . But they had already decided that the practice meant nothing if its income couldn't get them the things closest to their hearts.

"Do you want to talk about the Trip?" she asked cautiously.

He shrugged. "Well—whatever you want."

A little hurt, she subsided. She forced herself to think of the possibility that they might not make it. But this was impossible. In eighteen months they were leaving. The maps were drawn, the money was budgeted, Killer was signed up a year hence at a good military school, and perhaps not averse to the idea of being on his own. Ed's mother had offhandedly agreed to keep Nita for the year they would be gone and then almost collapsed in impatience.

Ed simply could *not* be losing interest. It must be something else.

Was there anything about the operation that might have gone wrong?

And yet that could not be it, either. She remembered the

94 • *THE CROWDED SKY*

long struggle toward the surface of consciousness, the night-marish figures of Kronk and the nurse at the foot of her bed.

"Hello, Kronk," she had murmured.

"Hello, patient."

Kronk was smiling. She shifted in bed and turned her head on the pillow. And there, as she had known he would be, was Ed, looking out the window. He moved swiftly to the bedside.

He looked down at her so tenderly that two weeks later the memory of his face could tighten her throat.

"Am I all right?" she had asked Ed. No one had ever mentioned it, but she knew that there had been a question of a further malignancy.

From the head of the bed Kronk's voice had cut in cheerfully, "You're damn right you're all right. And you're getting up tomorrow!"

She had wanted to believe it, of course, and besides, the amazing news that she could leave her bed so soon after a major operation had so intrigued her that she had not given the other much thought.

But now she found that it had been lurking in her subconscious like an evil thing. But no . . . it was an impossibly morbid thought. Kronk might conceivably have softheartedly lied to her, but Ed, who had not one pocket of deceit in his being, would never evade her.

He would not lie to his own patients. He would never lie to her. . . .

Ed Benedict turned away from Pat. He had been on the very verge of telling her. He had steeled himself to proceed as he had learned to proceed with patients.

He had been criticized, he knew, by other medical men, by nurses, even by the families of patients, for his views on this very thing. He had once had a young nurse, with tears in her eyes, tell him that he was inhuman.

But it wasn't inhuman to tell them. It was the most human thing of all.

"You wouldn't tell a child, would you?" the nurse had sniffled.

"No, Jan."

"Then why did you tell that old lady?"

"She's not a child. She's entitled to know how long she has to live and to make plans. She may have things she wants to do. I can't cheat her of them. She may have things she wants to tell her children—things that people keep putting off. Suppose it were a man. Suppose I didn't know if he even had a will. I think they should be told."

Most doctors, Ed knew, would tell a relative and leave the responsibility up to him. But relatives always decided that the patient should not be told.

In ten years of general practice you faced slow, known, and inevitable death perhaps fifty times. Some of the dying were moribund—and they knew it—and this was easy. You were simply confirming their beliefs.

Five or six had been senile, and there was obviously no more reason to tell them than to tell a child.

As for the rest—well, you told them in the easiest way for them. You tried to evaluate the personality.

A courageous man, or a devout one, was best approached almost bluntly. Then at least you were honoring bravery or faith before you left the patient to whatever private hell he must endure.

The weaker, more emotional, needed preparation as much as a patient about to undergo general surgery. There was no way to avoid hysteria with some of them, nor any need to. In a way, the emotional were luckier—their tears were a release.

With the highly intelligent, perhaps, it was best to sit quietly in your office and explain the pathological facts. You told them what had already happened to their bodies and what *would* happen to them, in medical terms, paying tribute to their intellects and hoping that by removing some of the mystery you could remove some of the fear.

Of men and women, women were the hardest to tell. Instinctively you wanted to protect them. And their basic characters were shrouded from a man behind a veil of femininity.

And he had been wrong so often with women. . . .

"Mrs. Brown, I have the laboratory report here."

In her ward bed, Lilly Mae Brown had been a mountain of dark cheerfulness, waiting with childish anticipation for morning rounds and Doctor Ed.

Now her black eyes, usually peeping in mirth from behind her fat cheeks, pleaded with him across the desk. He took a deep breath and began gently to explain what the report meant, donning meanwhile his professional armor against the tears he knew would come when he finally hinted at the truth.

But long before that time she knew. She showed it with an involuntary motion of her hand to her lips, and then drew her fingers away.

She interrupted him: "How long will it be, Doctor?"

He took a breath. "Six months to a year, Lilly Mae."

She nodded. She spoke swiftly, in a monotone, as if to herself. The hysteria would doubtless come later, but now she spoke almost calmly.

"That poor man . . . that poor man . . . oh, that poor, darlin' man . . ."

For a moment he had stared at her blankly. Then he had realized that she was talking about the flashy, defensively arrogant Negro he had seen wearing his Sunday blue suit by her bed, a truck driver with his own rig. "This goin' to kill him, Doctor. Just kill him . . . And he will drink again, I know it. So now we must think of the babies. . . ."

The voice went on in a queer, almost rhythmic chant. "So now we must think of the babies . . . and we must think what to do with them. . . . We must think where to put them. . . . Before it's too late."

And if the dam had ever burst, it had not been in the clinic. Lilly Mae Brown had hidden her fear and her grief behind cheerfulness as she had hidden her bones behind fat, and waddled in smiling dignity from the hospital to her husband's car while Ed waved good-by from the steps and her ward nurse wept beside him.

Yes, at telling the dying that they were dying he was an expert, he supposed. He knew the rules. You tried to use your experience to cushion the blow, and you told them yourself because it was part of your job and because they had to be told by someone.

But how in the name of God did you tell the woman you loved?

Mike Ruble finished his Bluefield estimate and glanced out of the cockpit. His spirits lightened. They were above the starlit overcast. The cloud layer below showed a terrestrial glimmer as some Virginia farmhouse sent its glow through a hole in the blanket. There were towering cumuli about, but they were growing more scarce. And the air was smoother.

"I guess we were wrong," Dick Barnett said. "It looks like it's clearing up."

Mike nodded. This was not the front that had looked the worst on the weather cross section—that one was centered near Amarillo—but there was no use being pessimistic. And it was, temporarily anyway, smoother. . . .

For that he was sincerely glad.

Mike Ruble was himself a good instrument pilot. He enjoyed the constant mental exercise that instrument flying gave one. And flying in the soup *could* be as smooth as flying in the clear —and that was enjoyable indeed. But flying with the airlines was different from flashing about in a fighter alone. After seven years you began to put yourself in the place of the passengers. And then, when it was rough and turbulent, you could be almost as unhappy as they.

In the clear, his spirits lifted.

He was bending over to pick up his coffee when he felt it: a sharp, solid and all too familiar little bump, much less violent and more frightening than the heaves and bounces of the turbulence that they had just endured.

He heard Dick Barnett curse. "God *damn!*"

But by this time Mike was already bolt upright, searching the quadrant of sky to his right. He caught a glimpse of a flashing light far in the distance and the telltale cherry-red glow of a jet tail pipe.

Then he lost sight of it in the distant clouds.

Barnett was still searching his own sector. "You see anything?" he asked again.

"Yes sir. I think it was a jet."

The captain turned back to his instruments. "Son-of-a-bitch," he said with feeling. "Log the time and altitude, Mike. At least we can make a near-miss report. Not that it'll do any good."

Mike logged the time and position and altitude. They had flown through the other plane's slip stream. Or, more accurately, the *border* of his slip stream. It was for both of them too familiar a shock to have been mistaken.

Mike burned with anger at the pilot who had passed so close.

"At night you can't get their numbers, either," Barnett complained. "Buzzing an airliner!"

It was a familiar argument, and one that led nowhere, and one that Mike had promised himself he would never get into again. He was shaken and raging inwardly himself, but some vestigial loyalty to the military made him object. He hated the careless in the sky with a passion, but to buzz was a criminal act.

"I don't think he tried to buzz us, sir. He's probably up here V.F.R. with his eyeballs caged."

Barnett looked at him knowingly. "He buzzed us, all right. He knew we couldn't get his number, and he buzzed us." He smiled bitterly. "Were you Air Force?"

"Yes sir."

"You guys sure stick together. You flew jets, I guess?"

Mike nodded. "F-86's."

"And you never buzzed an airliner?"

There was a constant war between the airline pilot and the military aviator; a war of numbers. The dispatches of this war were streams of letters to the F.A.A. giving the "side numbers" of the enemy who had passed too closely. It was a total war; military pilots cited commercial fliers as fervently as the airline captains cited them. And Mike knew that many airline captains sincerely believed that jets had deliberately made runs on them.

He had flown with one who had suggested that his passengers write their congressmen when a B-47 passed close.

It was the old debate, and he had sworn off, but he felt honor-bound to declare himself.

"No sir. I never buzzed an airliner. I never knew anyone who did buzz an airliner, and I don't think any Air Force, Navy, or Marine pilot has buzzed an airliner since the hot-rocks left after World War II."

Well, he thought, *I got that off my chest. And I've probably alienated the second senior captain on the line.*

Barnett colored a little but smiled. "I didn't figure you had, personally, Mike. But I was buzzed by one two trips back. I couldn't get his side number, but he buzzed me sure as hell."

Mike knew from experience that it was useless to point out to a man whose entire training apparently had been commercial that the military pilot in his own way was as professional a man as any airline captain, as dependent on his job for survival, that those who would risk court-martial for the doubtful pleasure of a run at a slow-moving passenger plane had been weeded out long before.

You couldn't really blame a man like Barnett for bitterness. In his flying career he must have seen such elemental dangers as structural failure and weather conquered, only to find when these things had been licked the even greater danger of too many men in the swarming void.

You couldn't really blame him for resenting interlopers in a shrinking sky.

The pilot of the jet which had passed so close ahead of them, if it was a jet, had probably been in the wrong. He must have been on a V.F.R. flight plan. He had a simple lookout problem. He need only search a thirty- or forty-degree cone ahead; obviously no one was going to overtake him and hit him from the rear. Whereas a lumbering airliner had a danger zone that extended all around it, even if its pilots could not see three-quarters of the area.

And the jet, on V.F.R., had been obligated to be watching; Barnett and he were theoretically relieved of the task by the air traffic control system.

But you watched anyway, when you could. You watched, day and night, and you joked about having glass-bottomed coffee cups. You kidded about the greatest anti-collision device ever invented, the Mark I Eyeball. But when you entered the area of a field like Los Angeles International, with the oblivious little Cubs and Tripacers in suspension in the smog, you jested no more. You were in a state of eye-straining, neck-craning panic.

"I thought those guys," Barnett grumbled, "promised to stay off the airways when they were V.F.R."

"They did."

"It's hot-rocks like that that make this whole lousy traffic control system necessary. What they ought to do, they ought to ground all the private planes and sell them for scrap, and take all the military planes and make an air-space reservation for them somewhere out on the Nevada desert, and fire all the air traffic control people, and then see how many mid-airs we'd have."

"I'll go that," said Capelli suddenly. It was the first time Mike had heard him agree with anyone.

"How big a reservation would you give the military?" Mike grinned at the captain.

"Oh, about a thousand yards on a side."

"That's right," said Mike. "They could taxi around in that for practice. But don't you think they might get a little rusty in their airwork?"

Barnett shrugged. "Well, Mike, they keep running into each other in the air and there won't be any of them left anyway."

Behind Mike the speaker had been almost constantly alive with position reports and clearances and all of the swift corpuscles of information feeding through the arteries of the air traffic control system. A pilot disregarded that which did not pertain to him. But his subconscious did not, and a part of Mike's brain had been busy with a situation that was developing ahead.

He had heard position reports from an Eastern airliner going north on Victor One-Zero-Three. And its altitude was theirs

—twenty thousand. Victor One-Zero-Three and Victor One-Five-One-Eight, he knew from his chart, intersected at Covington. Unconsciously he had been expecting A.T.C. to change their own altitude or that of the Eastern. So he was not surprised to hear the call.

"Pacific Central Flight Seven, this is Washington Center."

"Washington Center, this is Pacific Central Flight Seven. Go ahead," said Mike.

"This is Washington Center. We have a new clearance for you. Climb immediately to two-two-thousand. Reach two-two-thousand by Rand."

Rand was the last fix before Covington. Mike had jotted down the clearance, and he was about to read it back, when he heard Barnett.

"Wait, Mike. Just a second . . ."

He looked at his captain. Barnett was rubbing his jaw, lost in thought.

"We got another ten, fifteen knots of head wind up there at twenty-two thousand. Why the hell does it have to be us instead of Eastern?"

Mike smiled at him, a little puzzled. It was too bad that it had to be them, but it was as unarguable in his mind as a law of nature. Two bodies could not occupy the same space at the same time, so A.T.C. was moving one of them out of the way. He reached for the mike again.

"Wait. What's our Rand estimate?"

"Two-three. We've got eight minutes."

Dick Barnett picked up his own microphone. "Washington Center, this is Pacific Central Seven. I don't think I can climb to two-two-thousand by Rand. Over."

Mike stiffened. Obviously they could climb two thousand feet in eight minutes. And easily . . . And if the Washington controller had time to work out their Rand estimate himself, he would know it. But with themselves and the Eastern approaching at some four or five hundred knots, he would be unlikely to check. It was a dirty trick to pull on the Eastern flight,

and a much dirtier one to pull on the controller, and possibly
a dangerous one besides.

There was an expression that Mike had heard controllers use
toward planes that had refused an altitude: "Use it or lose it."
In other words, take what we give you, or we'll make you hold
somewhere until we can fit you in again.

But Dick Barnett's gamble paid off. There was probably no
time for a punitive measure.

He heard the speaker crackle: "Roger, Pacific Central Seven.
Eastern Six-Thirty-Four, can you accept a climb to two-two-
thousand, to reach two-two-thousand by Mecca?"

Mecca was Eastern's last fix before Covington. The Eastern
captain's voice came back resignedly: "Affirmative, Washington
Center. Commencing climb to two-two-thousand."

Barnett relaxed. Now that he had won his altitude, he seemed
a little defensive.

"Eastern's heading north," he explained. "A west wind won't
hurt him a bit."

Then he smiled ingratiatingly.

Mike returned to his log. *You're a nice guy, Barnett*, he
thought. *You're a nice friendly guy, and I know you know this
beast inside out, and it seems like if you wanted to you could fly
it through a hurricane with a cargo of raw eggs.*

*But brother, I don't like the way you fly. . . . I don't like the
way you fly at all.*

Some of the discomfort had returned. Mike shifted uneasily
and checked his Bluefield estimate.

part two
CRUISE AND MAINTAIN . . .

one:

THE SWARMING VOID

The storm had started with a howl of anger along the Aleutian Chain, calling its forces to a bagpipe shriek of wind off Umnak. But it attacked like a band of raiding Highlanders that lacked a good leader. Its squalls and eddies were never well concentrated.

So it was not a virulent storm, but it dumped rain on San Francisco, then, falsely scenting victory, sang across the passes of the Sierras in swirling kilts of snow, then deployed in a thin line to sweep across the plains and swing southward to the Texas Panhandle.

Even when it had focused its forces on San Francisco, it had never been powerful. Now its diffused center was a low-pressure area a hundred miles in diameter. Almost nowhere on the ground did it cause trouble. Even in its own aerial element it was weak. Light planes could have run its lines anywhere along the front without structural damage.

The battle line was a front seven hundred miles long. It was weakly shoving a mass of cold air eastward across the United States. The storm had been preceded by a stronger storm and might be followed by another.

But weak as it was, everywhere it went it caused trouble for the men in the air traffic control centers—Oakland and Salt Lake City and Albuquerque and, now, Amarillo.

It hindered air traffic, not in any active way but simply because it lay there, a tattered blanket covering the southwestern United States with clouds from a thousand to fifteen, twenty, thirty thousand feet. Almost nowhere could a pilot move from one place to another and depend on his eyesight to avoid other aircraft; not without taking risks, whether he knew it or not, of great magnitude.

Some pilots, as always, tried to fly Visual Flight Rules. A few light planes followed the iron compass at low altitude, skimming the underside of the overcast. And one or two others, as always, illegally and in a sense immorally, sneaked through holes to fly uncontrolled above the overcast, hoping that their destination would be clear and that the blanket would not rise in front of them to an altitude at which they could not survive.

A Phoenix salesman with two hundred solo hours took off from Tucson to skitter under the clouds to his daughter's birthday party, and made it. A rancher from Waco tried for Fort Worth in his Swift, settled for Love Field in Dallas, and cut a cursing non-sched cargo pilot neatly from the traffic pattern.

A man and his wife heading for Ardmore became lost, entered the overcast with only his four hundred hours of contact flying and a ball-bank indicator, spun and crashed in the desert.

But with these foolhardy exceptions, there was very little V.F.R. traffic flying.

So the airways themselves swarmed with craft. The intricate air traffic control system swelled with planes. In Oklahoma City an airliner waited two hours for a traveling block of space for the half-hour trip to Tulsa. In Dallas a Boeing test pilot sweated two hours for clearance to Wright-Patterson Field. At Biggs Field, Texas, a jet idled on the runway, waiting so long for a change in his clearance that he ran low on fuel and had to cancel his request and return to the line.

On an average day, over a hundred thousand aircraft would take off in the United States. If the weather was clear, only part of them would be under the control of men on the ground—the remaining, mostly military and private planes, would avoid what clouds there were so that they could see and be seen.

They would be no problem to A.T.C., for flying Visual Flight Rules, they generally knew that they must not wander into anything which would obscure them.

On this cloudy night, ten thousand aircraft swam through the ocean of air over the United States. Like certain creatures of the sea, they carried lights, but the ocean was murky; so they did not for the most part depend on their lights to make them seen. They swam blindly, their faith in those who directed them from the ocean floor—the ground controllers of the air traffic control centers.

Airline pilots usually filed instruments anyway. No more or no less of them would crowd the airways than on any other night. But military and civilian pilots who might on another night have filed V.F.R. found that if they were to fly at all they must use the controlled airways.

And this was sometimes unfortunate. In theory, anyone holding a civil or military instrument ticket was equally qualified to fly the airways on instruments whether he was a private, military, or transport pilot. Airline pilots were highly qualified, through training and constant practice. But there were some military pilots, reservists and regulars, and many more civilian pilots whose qualifications were not up to their tickets.

There were many who filed on a wing and a prayer.

All of them should statistically get where they were going, more safely than if they were driving. Statistically there would probably be fewer near-misses in the air than there would be on a cloudless night—the average was three per day, but a mid-air collision involving a plane controlled by A.T.C. was a very unusual thing.

Statistically the airways were as safe on this night as on a clear one.

The price that the airways paid for the not-so-qualified and the out-of-practice would ordinarily not be in blood or tearing metal. It would probably be instead in time lost when a green or a rusty pilot misunderstood a clearance. It would be in the rasp on an air controller's nerves when an inexperienced flier complained by his tone of a delay he should have known was a penalty for the extra craft using the pathways in the sky.

Swarming above the prop-driven columns, of course, were the columns of jets. Into the jet engine poured a given weight of fuel per second to mix with the weight of air it gobbled in that second. Since the *ratio* of fuel to air must remain constant, if the weight of the air decreased, as it did with altitude, so did the weight of the fuel required.

But even slicing for best endurance at the highest altitudes the traffic would bear, jets gulped fuel prodigiously.

The jets, at least, must have their way. . . .

The nerves of the men in the control centers were overstrained. The men were used to it, but their nerves were overstrained. . . .

In the Amarillo Center, Norm Coster had solved three problems.

A plane off on its estimate from Garden City to Las Vegas, New Mexico, crowded to within three minutes of its predecessor —too close for comfort—but this was a simple problem to solve by holding it in orbit for a few minutes. And an Air Force jet bomber low on fuel over Wichita Falls, wanting Dyess Air Force Base, had given him a few minutes of anxiety. Then some inexplicable breakdown in communications in which Fort Worth Center had failed to pass the estimate on a westbound cargo plane to the Amarillo Center had stirred the board. In a few months an I.B.M. machine would be passing estimates, but that was slim comfort tonight.

Compounding it all was the static born of an electrical storm somewhere to the north.

But now there was a lull.

Norm instinctively thought of using it to eat—it might be the last. But he was not in the least hungry. Sally's late-afternoon dinner sat heavily on his stomach. Or had Eve cooked it? No, if Eve had cooked it it would have been a crusty, light thing; a real work of art. Sally, although he would never admit it, was a poor cook.

Sally tried too hard. Eve was relaxed and casual in the kitchen, but Sally tried too hard.

Three years before, on the porch of the Army-Navy Club in Washington, D.C., General Peter B. Chase had warned him of his daughter's cooking. And other things as well.

They had sat on the patio of the club in the cool of the evening, watching the last foursome finish on the links below. The general wore civvies, but he wore them like a uniform, emitting an aura of command even sitting in a porch chair with a martini in his hand.

"I guess you wonder why I asked you out here alone, Norm."

"Yes sir," Norm said. He had lived in Washington all of his pre-service life, but the Army-Navy Club to the son of a Commerce Department clerk was a hallowed place. He had learned poise in the service, but hardly enough to deal with even so friendly a general as Sally's father. His best civilian suit felt tight.

But his own martini helped.

"Yes sir. I was wondering."

"Well, Norm, Sally is obviously going to marry you. And I like you myself. I don't see how she could have done better."

Norm, who had half-expected the general, once they were alone, to explode in classic choler at an enlisted man who would dare marry his favorite daughter, was suffused with a warm glow.

"Thank you, sir."

"I'll admit when she told me she was going with an airman first, I about dropped my uppers. With all the rank around Bolling, I wonder if you know how lucky you are?"

"I know how lucky I am, sir," Norm said devoutly.

"Then she said you were a temporary-type soldier. . . . You *are* getting out, aren't you?"

"The minute my obligated service is up, General."

The general studied the backs of his fingers, smiling. "This isn't very complimentary to my service, but I've got to admit I'm glad. Can you imagine Sally kicking around some Air Force base as the wife of an airman first?"

"I can't imagine her marrying me anyway, sir. Like I say, I'm the luckiest guy in the world."

"Well . . . yes and no."

The general nodded pleasantly at a Navy captain who seemed disposed to linger, but the movement was one of complete dismissal. The captain passed on.

"Yes and no, Norm. What do you expect to do when you get out?"

"Well, sir, I like aviation. I'd like to get some sort of a job in A.T.C. I've learned a lot in the tower, and it's interesting work, and it's steady."

"It's steady, but do they pay anything?"

"My old man's a civil servant. He doesn't make much money, but he's happy. It's what I'd like to do."

"Does Sally know about this?"

"Of course."

"I see. . . ." The general sipped his drink. "Do you know much about her?"

What was this, anyway?

"I'm nuts about her, General, that's all," Norm said cautiously.

"Well, everybody is. That's where you may run into trouble. She's spoiled."

Norm laughed in relief. "Aren't all pretty girls spoiled?"

The general shook his head. "She's different. She's not selfish —most spoiled girls are. She's just helpless. In that way, she's probably spoiled worse than most. She's not only pretty, but she's so doggone warm and soft and feminine that without even knowing it or trying to she makes a monkey out of everybody. So she's never had to learn to *do* anything."

That was certainly true. Sally could fumble in her pocketbook for the keys to her home and Norm's immediate reaction was to want to kick down the door.

"And she's the baby sister, of course. Compared to the way we've treated her, Eve must feel like an orphan child." He shrugged. "But that's the way it's been. And her husband is going to have to learn to live with it."

"It'll be a pleasure, General."

The general faced him blandly. "Frankly, Norm, as you may have suspected, I had you out here to try to talk you out of marrying her. Until you knew her better, anyway. Money apparently doesn't mean anything to you, and I've always thought of her falling in love with an older guy—somebody in the chips, maybe. Who could keep babying her. But talking to you, I think it'll work out. . . ."

"It'll work out, sir."

"I'm sure it will. Just remember that people have been knocking themselves out for her all her life. Even Eve—and that's one for the psychologists. Sally's bright, but she's way up on cloud nine."

Then the general enumerated the things that Sally would do: she would run out of gas once a month, regularly; she would undoubtedly spend the grocery money to buy him the most expensive smoking jacket in town; she would try to cook crepes suzette when he wanted pancakes.

And the general had been right, but Norm would not have traded one of Sally's fallen cakes for a Betty Crocker masterpiece.

Now he looked at the brown paper bag with his sandwiches in it. He would like to bring it back at least partially empty. He could eat one on the way home, and throw the other in the G.I. can, leaving only an apple. . . .

But there was something wasteful in that, and disloyal to Sally. And this might be the only chance. . . .

He reached into the bag. Mel Carnegie called him from his desk.

"You got a second, Norm? Phone."

Norm's heart jumped. *Was it Sally?*

He looked at the board. He had four minutes before the next position report would come in. Rocky could handle it anyway. He beckoned to Rocky and went to Mel's phone.

"Norm?"

It was not Sally, but Eve. "Yes, Eve?"

"Norm, I think her pains are beginning. She won't admit it—I think she's afraid it might be another false alarm."

"Did you call the doctor?"

"She didn't want me to. Not yet."

"Well, call him! Is . . . Is she really hurting?"

"She's lying down in the bedroom. I'll ask her. . . ."

"Look, Eve, if she's lying down, never mind asking her. Call Hudspeth. She's got the number. Or it's on the pad in the kitchen."

"If he says to take her in, are you coming home?"

If there were a quiet spell—a real one, not just this moment of calm—he might be able to get off for the half hour it would take to get home and to the hospital. On the other hand, drifting through the Center were the sounds of new saturation. Norm listened for an instant to the pulse of the Center as a physician might to the heart of an overwrought patient.

It was accelerating.

"I don't know. Call Dr. Hudspeth and see what he says. Then I'll decide."

On the way back he said to Mel, standing in thought by the window, "Mel, that was Sally's sister. She thinks Sally's going into labor. If she does, I'm going to want to blow. You'll just have to take the board for me."

Mel nodded doubtfully.

"Yeah . . . Well, we'll see."

Rocky Fontaine had kept up. He was coolly doing both their jobs—inserting new strips on the front of the board and keeping track of new estimates from the Fort Worth Center in the back.

He ran his finger down the column of slips. "It's about the same. We got two more aircraft in the sector. And I had to hold United Three-Three-One at Panhandle, ten thousand. That's all. . . ."

"Thanks, Rocky," Norm said. "My wife seems to be in labor, and—"

The speaker on the board had been unceasingly crackling out position reports and receipts for them by A.T.C., and now Norm stopped as he heard their call followed by a swift position report.

"Amarillo Center—Air Force Four-Five-One-Two. Vega at

one-eight. Two-one-thousand. I.F.R. Flight Plan. Amarillo two-seven. Sayre. Over."

Rocky picked up the microphone to roger for the call.

"Air Force Jet Five-One-Two, Amarillo Center. Roger your position report. Out."

Rocky had forgotten to check his estimate against the actual time of arrival. He was cutting corners, but there was no use pointing out the omission—Norm could do it himself.

"Thanks again," Norm said, sitting down. Mel Carnegie walked over from his desk.

"Your sister's on the phone again, Norm. She says the doctor wants your wife to go on down. She's packing for her now."

Norm considered the situation. Traffic was building up, the respite was over. And if Mel was to sit in for him, it had better be later, closer to delivery, when Sally might need him more.

"Look—I better wait'll this hump gets past. Tell her to get a taxi, will you, Mel?"

Mel looked relieved. "You bet, Norm. I'll do that. . . ."

I'm sorry, baby, Norm breathed to Sally. *Just as soon as I can. Just as soon as I can. . . .*

two:

NAVY JET 3255
PRESCOTT, ARIZONA

At thirty-three thousand feet west of Prescott, Arizona, the sun held the jet trainer suspended with ruddy shafts of light long after it had abandoned the earth below, but Dale knew that darkness would come in moments.

He was beginning to flash over fluffy alto-cumulus, the abandoned rear guard of the front ahead. The clouds were tinged with pink, like the cotton candy that Anne and he had consumed at the zoo.

Soon he was avoiding the puffs in a series of gentle banks. There might be turbulence within, and there was no use shaking up his passenger sooner than necessary. Besides he had a reluctance to return to instruments until he had to. Ahead of him stretched a long eye-straining night.

But soon he was in the clouds for good.

In the last light he could see McVey, still obediently searching the sky.

A good man, he thought. Most rear-seat passengers tired and gave up after a few minutes.

"Mac, you can secure on the lookout now. We're on instruments, and you won't be able to see very far anyway."

"Aye-aye, sir."

"A.T.C. keeps our level clear for us on an instrument flight plan," Dale offered.

The plane dropped suddenly and Dale eased in back pressure. He hoped that his passenger wasn't prone to airsickness —when you were forced to wear an oxygen mask, illness could be hell. Then he remembered McVey's home station.

"You're off a tin can, aren't you, Mac?"

"Yes sir. The *Hailey.*"

"I guess I don't have to worry about you getting sick."

"I don't think so, sir. I only got seasick once, in a storm on the Atlantic. I don't think I'll get airsick."

The U.S.S. *Hailey* rang a bell, somehow.

"Isn't Spike Lawton your skipper? Commander Lawton?"

"Yes *sir.*"

McVey's voice held a note of pride. Dale remembered the gawky boy who had been his classmate at Annapolis. From McVey's attitude, Spike had grown up.

"I know him."

"He's the greatest, Commander. The *most.*"

"I went to school with him."

"You went to the Academy, sir?"

There was respect in his voice. Dale knew that it was respect for Spike and not himself, but accepted it gladly. And his own pride in Spike he recognized as class spirit, a strange offshoot of the Academy's insularity. You absorbed it almost without knowing it. It was a spirit, he was sure, much stronger than, say, the fraternity spirit in college.

You caught the bug plebe year whether you wanted it or not. It grew from the plebe system. Christian martyrs in a Colosseum, Jews in a Nazi prison camp, a Marine squad in an exposed position would engender, he was sure, the same spirit of interdependence.

When you walked the decks of Bancroft Hall as a plebe, the only humans you saw who were not potential threats physically or psychologically—and Dale had always preferred the sweat of pushups to the degrading "'tis I the Duke" quizzes—were your classmates.

Soon you developd a conditioned reflex. Classmates with whom you had nothing in common you welcomed in the corridors of Bancroft. A plebe "squaring a corner" in a passageway, marching directly in the center, hat down, eyes front, could only be pleased to meet another plebe rather than a caustic upperclassman. So, like a Pavlov dog, when you met a classmate, you smiled and winked and were glad.

And it lasted. Dale's class had started with a thousand members. He had a poor memory for faces, ordinarily, but he had never failed to recognize a classmate on the streets of Paris, New York, or San Francisco.

At Annapolis authorities were always combating class spirit. Theoretically, your loyalty was to be to the Academy itself, and to the Navy by extension. If you caught a classmate in a minor offense, you were supposed to turn him in.

But few did. And those who did were ostracized—put in Coventry.

The spirit showed in *Shipmates,* the Naval Academy alumni magazine. And the spirit of fraternity, the feeling that there was no class like your own, seemed to grow with the years as the Academy receded in a golden haze. You saw it in the clumsy tenderness with which the survivors of the classes of '08 or '10 announced in their ever-smaller paragraphs the death of a classmate. Showing through the awkward phrases was a genuine emotion that Dale had never seen in the other alumni magazines he had leafed through.

"It is with the deepest regret that our column in *Shipmates* announces the death of Admiral 'Millie' Thomas at Bethesda Naval Hospital. . . . Services were held in the Naval Academy chapel. 'Millie,' as we all know, was one of the most colorful members of '07. We remember when he tried to jump the moat after the Army game in '06. . . . He leaves a void in the class which will be hard to fill."

Years after graduation, before Dale had gone to Annapolis, his father had once put class loyalty ahead of simple charity to his son. Dale, while he could never have done such a thing to a child of his own, could as an Academy man at least understand him now.

It had been on a day that should have been a perfect one, a

California jewel of a day in the Vallejo Navy Yard, a day to treasure forever. . . .

It had been on the day he had heard from the Academy. . . .

That afternoon, when he arrived home from class at Cal, he found the franked envelope on the old-fashioned lowboy in the hallway. He froze. His hands began to shake. He had taken the Academy exams in February, results had been due for a week, and for days he had hardly been able to eat.

Afraid that when he opened it and found he had failed his mother would come upon him in his grief, he lurched down the hall to his room, clutching the envelope as a dog would carry a bone to its lair. He *knew* he had bilged, was certain he had bilged, could have done nothing but bilge. If he had only remembered the crazy formula for a geometric mean, the crazy, simple formula pasted on his mirror for months before the exam, if he had *only remembered it.* . . . He tore open the envelope.

"The Superintendent is pleased to inform you. . . ."

It was all he needed.

His father sat in shirt sleeves at his desk in Administration, the immaculate blue blouse with three shining stripes hung carefully behind him. A shipyard clanging with lend-lease work rattled the windows. "Congratulations," he said, hardly glancing at the envelope. They shook hands. "Now all you have to do is pass the physical, and the Navy has another Heath."

Something in his attitude pricked the balloon.

"That's right. . . . I . . . I'm sorry I busted in, Dad, but I guess I was pretty excited."

His father raised his eyebrows. "If I'd known you were *that* worried, I might have given you a hint."

Dale stared at him. "A hint?"

His father laughed. "Hell, Bill Simpkins in the commandant's office back there dropped me a line three weeks ago."

Simpkins was a classmate. Dale's voice rose. "You mean—you mean you let me sweat it out for three weeks when you didn't have to? Why?"

His father looked surprised.

"It's confidential information," he said simply, "until the Superintendent releases it. If you'd let it slip, Bill would have hanged higher than a kite."

The bright afternoon had dimmed a little. "I wouldn't have let it slip, Dad. . . . I wouldn't have let it slip."

But now, twenty years later, Dale could forgive him. Communication between classmates was tempered in the crucible of the toughest four years that any of them would ever endure. Communication between his father and himself had been a fragile thing, which his father had not cared to test.

Dale had never allowed himself to be tangled in class spirit as tightly as his father had been. Classmates were after all only classmates because they happened to be born around the same time and appointed in the same year. He would hear with incredulity another Academy man say seriously: "He was from '43. That was a real stupid class," or "No wonder she divorced him. The class of '39 were all psychos."

That was the freakish part, the stupid, clannish part. But there was a gain to balance it—a self-sacrificing, blind nobility that grew in a man who looked on his class as a band of a thousand brothers. Dale had seen a first classman go to the very edge of dismissal only weeks before graduation rather than identify a classmate who had hurriedly hidden a quart of whisky in his room. It was stupid, it was quixotic, it was juvenile. . . .

But it had been a triumph of self-sacrifice over a burning desire to graduate.

Dale was too rational to believe that because he had graduated from the Naval Academy in 1944 he was a member of a race apart.

But McVey's praise of Spike Lawton warmed him.

"So you think he's a pretty good skipper, Mac?"

"Yes sir."

"Why's he so popular with you?"

There was a moment of silence. Was the boy drawing back into his shell? No—simply considering the answer.

"He's always looking out for us. He's always helping us to try to get ahead. He's the one that got me going on Bainbridge. . . ."

Bainbridge was the Navy's prep school for Annapolis. Selected enlisted men were sent there for a year to study for the Naval Academy exams. McVey and he had something in common.

"You're trying to go to the Academy?"

"Yes sir."

"Are you from Albuquerque, Mac?"

"Yes sir."

"Why is it that all you landlocked people want to go to sea?"

"Did you ever live in Albuquerque?" McVey asked wryly.

Dale chuckled. He looked at his kneepad and the clock. In five minutes they should be over Prescott. He tuned up the Prescott omni, checked the identification signals, and tuned it down again.

"Have you passed your Bainbridge exams?"

"Yes sir." McVey paused. "But, I don't know now. It looks like I'm not going after all. . . ."

"Why not?" Dale asked curiously.

"Oh, something's come up. . . ."

"Gosh, if you've passed your Bainbridge exams you've just about got it made, haven't you?"

"I wish I did, Commander. I wish I did. . . ."

A young man saw his goals in Technicolor but his own abilities in more somber tones. And having no real basis of comparison, an eighteen- or nineteen-year-old could see himself as a drab black-and-white figure against the Hollywood background of West Point or Annapolis or Harvard and become discouraged. It was simply too much to hope for.

Maybe, when they got to Albuquerque, he could tell McVey what it was really like—that the Academy was a school for motivated men, but men of average health, average ability, average balance. Maybe, if McVey *saw* the place . . .

He remembered his first sight of the town of Annapolis, with orders for a physical examination in his suitcase.

He strolled along the narrow streets, his heart pounding, passed St. John's College, heading toward Carvel Hall Hotel. He knew his way as well as if he had been bred in the town.

He had studied so many maps, read as a child so many boys' books, absorbed from his father so much of the atmosphere of the town, that he could have found his way through it blind-folded.

So he had walked up Prince George to Maryland Avenue, sweat soaking his shirt beneath the Palm Beach suit, with the smell of the fish market and prosaic traffic dampening his spirits slightly, ever so slightly. . . .

He was here at last. And he was a little, just a trifle, let down. But with the feeling came the first solid hope that he would ac-tually be accepted. The midshipmen walking the streets were no healthier than he, no different from the men he had known at Cal. The midshipmen were sweating too.

But the dream burned still brightly enough, the goal was still sufficiently lofty, to make the physical exam a hell he would never forget. He thought because the Academy dream was so organic in him that he was alone in his abysmal fear. The other candidates—look at them, in their skivvies in the sick-bay cor-ridors, well muscled, glowing with health—seemed so assured and cheerful that he knew he must somehow be weeded from their smiling, joking ranks. So he smiled and joked too with strangers, and when his name was called for a dental or an eye exam he hid the start of fear and moved calmly to the room.

It took two days. A hundred times he asked himself why he had ruined his kidneys with beer at Cal, why he had given up the mile a day he had trotted in high school, why he had strained his eyes reading on the train from the Coast. And then it turned out that he was not alone. Even the hardest, the most assured, were sizzling in the same lonely inferno.

On the second day, in the lobby of the hotel, he saw Sal Porter. Sal was a rugged, unemotional commander's son, one of the few Navy juniors that Dale knew who had broken his bonds with his family early.

But they had never been close friends, and now he hesitated before walking over. It was another branch in the path of his life, he realized now. If he had not spoken to Sal then, they might not have roomed together; if they had not roomed together, he might not have grown to know Sal then and Jeanie later. . . .

Because there was nothing left of the physical but to hear the news, they descended to the bar and ordered beers. Dale had not seen Sal since Sal had starred on their high-school team in San Diego years before. Sal said, "Well, I couldn't take the old man's crap down there any longer, so when I graduated I worked on a road gang that summer and then the backfield coach at Washington heard about the All-City deal and got me a scholarship."

Sal sipped his beer meditatively and Dale marveled at the self-assured athlete beside him. Maybe some of his coolness would rub off on him. . . .

"So some retired admiral scouting for the N.A.A. sees me at Washington, and talks to me, and when they find out my old man's a naval officer they just about hemorrhage. They don't hardly even have to bribe a congressman—I can maybe get in under a presidential appointment. The trouble is, how the hell was I going to pass the mental?"

Sal smiled. "Well, they go back through my marks at Washington, and they find that with maybe a little pushing and pulling here and there I can qualify to get in on a certificate. Of course, that doesn't get me through plebe year, but I guess I can sweat it."

"Sure," Dale said. "You always did all right in school."

"I don't really give a damn. I don't know why I came here." He smiled. "Buddy, I had it made out there. I got two hundred a month for cleaning out the furnace room of a *sorority!* Two hundred bucks a month. . . ."

"And a sorority," Dale marveled.

Sal shook his head. "And I had to come to this prison. . . ."

"I guess our folks just beat it into us, Sal."

"Yeah . . . I almost hope I bilge the physical."

Dale shook his head. "Speak for yourself. If *I* bilge it, I swear to God I'll shoot myself."

Sal looked at him patronizingly. "It really means that much to you?"

"Buddy, it really does. There are only two things I want in this world. I want to go through the Academy and I want to go through flight training. After that, the Germans and the Limies can blow up the whole damn world as far as I'm concerned."

Sal smiled.

Dale lit a cigarette nervously. "Why do they have to take three days to figure out if you pass, when they're all finished the second day?"

Sal shrugged. "Maybe they don't. If you're that excited about it maybe I can do something."

"What can you do?"

"You'd be surprised what the Naval Athletic Association can do, when they're not sure they have you hooked. Let me go make a call."

Sal threaded his big frame through the closely packed tables in the dim, cool bar.

By the time he returned, Dale was near panic.

"What . . . What did you find out?"

Sal faced him, with a strange lopsided smile. "Well, you're in. You're in, buddy."

Dale felt his knees grow weak. "I passed?"

"The list is published. You passed."

Thank God! Dale breathed. *Oh, God, thank you. . . .*

Sal was staring across the bar into the distance.

Dale asked curiously, "What's wrong, Sal? *You* didn't run into trouble, did you?"

Sal's voice was high and shaky: "I don't know. I don't know. . . . They want me back at sick bay first thing in the morning."

Dale regarded him sympathetically. "Oh hell, Sal, it's probably nothing. Just paperwork."

Sal ordered another beer and began to talk, quietly and swiftly. "It could be anything. Damn . . . it could be my blood test. I picked up this broad in Atlanta about a month ago. . . . Just picked her up in a stinking bar—Christ!"

Dale winced sympathetically. He had himself the normal college man's guilty terror of venereal disease, and he understood Sal's sudden fear. Or thought he did.

But that was not what was bothering Sal. He went on with equal anguish: "Or it could have been my knee. I told them I'd dislocated my knee last season. Now why in the hell did I tell them that? I had to go and tell them I dislocated my knee . . . ."

So Sal himself, beneath his icy indifference, had wanted to pass as badly as any of them.

The next day they had walked through the main gate together, Dale carrying his suitcase in lightheaded anticipation and Sal empty-handed because he did not want to presume on the gods.

Someone in sick bay had forgotten to test Sal for color blindness. And by the swearing-in ceremony in the afternoon, he had donned again his cloak of indifference. The ceremony was traditionally in Memorial Hall, under the crudely lettered flag carried by Perry in the Battle of Erie, bearing Lawrence's words, "Don't give up the ship."

For Dale it was an emotional experience, and when the chant of the oath had been finished, he had glanced up at the flag.

Sal said, "We can start getting ready for it now."

"What?"

Sal pointed to the pennant.

"Four years of this crap, morning, noon, and night."

It had not been four years, but three, on account of the war. Sal and he had roomed together the whole grinding time.

Sal was a man set apart by athletic ability and a certain cool maturity. He underwent less hazing than any plebe in the class —it took a determined first classman indeed to face his chilling eyes and solid six feet and force him to recite the obscene and hallowed "Mr. Speaker, Mr. Speaker . . ."

Dale himself was no adolescent at the Academy; he had become immune in college to the "Die for dear old Rutgers" philosophy. But he at least could catch a touch of the Bancroft Hall hysteria before the Army-Navy game. Sal could not.

Swinging with their platoon toward evening chow across the dark terraces, with the Chesapeake wind slicing through his blues, toward the lighted wings of Bancroft outstretched to embrace the regiment, Dale could join in the guttural "Fight, fight, fight, fight for the Navy," and lose himself in a tribal prayer for victory.

Sal, marching near him, regarded the whole affair as a joke. On the field he was a ruthless automaton. Dale, high in the frenzied cascade of midshipmen, stared one year in horror as Sal dropped coldly back, back, back before a tide of gray and then, reversing his field, sliced off forty yards. Or another year as he stood under his goal post and at the very last second spiraled a lofty punt over the Army safety man.

After Sal's last game, he had stood with him in a Baltimore bar in a momentary eddy in the crowd of ecstatic backpounders.

"Sal, I lost more weight in that game than you did."

Sal shook his head. "Where you get that Navy blue and gold is beyond me."

"Aw, now Sal. Don't tell me you're not *excited*."

"Sure I'm excited. We don't go out there to lose to the bastards. But what difference it makes when you're not playing, I've never understood."

It was too much for Dale to stomach.

"Let me recall to you," he pointed out, "a summer afternoon two and a half years ago when you practically broke down and bawled at another bar like this in Annapolis, not because you thought you had a dose or anything minor like that, but because you might not get into the Naval Academy."

Sal shrugged. "That was two and a half years ago. Man, I'm tired of the 'don't give up the ship' routine. I wish to hell I'd stayed in college, except I'd probably have been drafted anyway. And if we weren't graduating in six months, so help me I'd resign. I honest to God would."

But some of it always rubbed off on a man. It was a harsh system, feudal and clumsy, and it put into the fleet officers of narrow scope.

But you could depend on them. When the chips were down, you could depend on the coldest and the least indoctrinated to think first of the ship and then of himself.

Six years later Sal Porter had chosen to fight fire in a turret off Korea rather than to follow his gun crew to safety on deck.

And this had been dutifully and sadly recorded by whoever wrote their class column in *Shipmates*.

Don't give up the ship. . . .

"Commander?" McVey's voice broke into his thoughts.

"Yes, Mac?"

"You mind if I ask you a question? About the Academy?"

"Shoot."

"Suppose you went back there, passed your exams and all, and you were already in the place, and they found out you were married."

"Yes?" Dale asked cautiously. This was, he supposed, dangerous ground. Candidates swore that they were not married and never had been. If McVey was married and contemplating fraud against the government Dale had no wish to know it.

"I'm not married," McVey said immediately. "I mean just suppose. . . ."

Dale tried to remember. While he was at Annapolis, the authorities had indeed discovered two or three married midshipmen. What had happened to them?

Well, the war was going on, but they had been forced to resign. . . .

"Where they found them, they booted them." He paused, thinking, "I knew a couple who got away with it, though."

It was an open secret that Timmy Nichols had been married and in his last year had a son. Timmy's problem was a thorny one—even after graduation and his second and public marriage. Should he carry his son on official records as illegitimate, or throw away the fruit of three years' study and resign his commission?

A kamikaze had solved Timmy's problem off Iwo Jima. Presumably his boy stood now in the ranks of the legitimate.

"Is it pretty rough to get away with?"

Dale remembered Timmy Nichols' drawn face across the table at chow. He remembered him always a little apart at hops, dropping furtively from the ranks at Baltimore football games to disappear into sidewalk crowds and sneak to secret assignations with his wife. He remembered his miserable separation when his wife was pregnant.

And he remembered a couple of others, too, secretly married.

And if Cheryl had had her way that last year, he would have been one of them. . . .

"The Academy's rough enough, Mac. You wouldn't want to complicate it any."

The omni-needle found Prescott in the purple void and fell to the side. Dale checked the time. It was twenty minutes past the hour—they were within a minute of his estimate. They had been airborne just over an hour. He worked out his Grants estimate and flicked the intercom switch back to radio.

"Phoenix Center, this is Navy Jet One-One-Three-Two-Five-Five. Prescott. Over."

From the darkness came unintelligible gibberish. And he was directly over Prescott, where presumably the relay station was. *This,* he thought, *is for the birds.* He called again.

"Phoenix Center, this is Navy Jet One-One-Three-Two-Five-Five. I read you loud but very garbled. Will you say again?"

This time it was better.

"Navy Jet One-One-Three-Two-Five-Five, this is Phoenix Center."

"This is Three-Two-Five-Five. Position report . . ."

He transmitted his position report and his estimate, received a new altimeter setting. But when he asked for the Albuquerque weather, his radio was cutting out again. So he abandoned the task.

"Phoenix Center, this is Navy Jet Three-Two-Five-Five. I read you about four by four, garbled. I'll check Albuquerque weather at Grants."

It had so far been a beautiful night. His estimates were on. His predicted wind had held good, the turbulence had not been bad. And he was once more in command of his skill.

But the radio bothered him. He shifted uncomfortably on his chute and steadied on Jet Route Seven-Eight.

three:

FLIGHT SEVEN
NASHVILLE, TENNESSEE

Mike Ruble had spent a miserable half hour. It started as a mild annoyance, irritated by a pinprick of anxiety, when he had noticed near Bluefield, West Virginia, that Captain Dick Barnett was letting the plane slip from its altitude.

Standards of precision in instrument flying varied between one man and another, and one flight condition and another. Mike had been given instrument checks by check pilots who would accept no error at all. This was unrealistic, because sometimes the job of trying to keep a plane exactly on its altitude was simply not worth the trouble involved.

But as the DC-7 lumbered westward from London, Kentucky, Mike was conscious, even when busy with his flight log and computer, of a gradual, five- or ten-foot-per-minute descent. And later, near Highway Intersection, a ten-foot-per-minute climb.

And Barnett seemed oblivious of it. He had given the plane to the autopilot as soon as the turbulence had decreased enough to make it feasible, and with only a touch on the "nose-up, nose-down" knob he could have corrected the situation. But he sat sipping his coffee impassively, a hundred feet—no, a hundred fifty feet—above his assigned altitude.

Hopefully, Mike glanced at the captain's altimeter and compared it to his own. Perhaps Barnett had failed to catch the altimeter setting over Bluefield. Then he would only have to mention it, and the captain would reset his altimeter and ease back to his prescribed level.

But no. Pilot and copilot altimeters read the same. Barnett was simply goofing, or didn't care. . . .

Mike Ruble had an image of a Marine ready room at K-1 near Masan in Korea. Returning from R and R in Tokyo, he had caught a Marine transport from Haneda and been stranded on the southern coast waiting a ride to his squadron at Seoul.

It was a grim, cold day and he had spent most of it in the half-tent ready room. For a while he dashed off surreptitious sketches of bored Marine fighter pilots leafing through *Far East Stars and Stripes.* Then he read old issues himself until his eyes ached. Finally he memorized a framed paragraph nailed to the half-wall.

"Flying, like the sea, is not inherently dangerous. But it is mercilessly unforgiving of human error."

He forgot who had written it, it seemed to be a paraphrase of some pre-aviation navigator, but it had come to embody his whole philosophy of the sky.

He was twenty-one years old when he went to Korea. He was a shy Air Force second lieutenant with skillful hands, less than five hundred hours in F-86's, and the desire of a puppy tossed into a roomful of strangers to make friends.

He was a warm and trusting man, and had been much more forgiving of error in others than in himself.

He had seen color on the palette of wartime Seoul beneath the grime and harshness and misery. He had seen movement in the rattling jeeps, scenic warmth in the squalid cities, composition in the lines of a village wedged in the crease between two ridges.

To his young eye, even the silver Sabres waiting on the drab brown strip were part of the chromatic scale.

And for the first few weeks he had seen softness of line and color even in the sky, in the pink-tinged contrail curving grace-fully toward MIG Alley, in the arc of his leader's fuselage against a puffy storm cloud.

For a few weeks, because the enemy in the sky was weak, it

had seemed an easygoing life, soft and undemanding and tolerant.

Then he had begun to see that the sky was a black-and-white element, a canvas of straight lines and acute angles, with rules of composition that it was fatal to violate.

With some of the younger captains, some of the ones he knew better, Mike would simply have pointed it out. "Hey, Skipper. You're a hundred and fifty feet high."

And that would have been that. But he had already sensed that Barnett was a thin-skinned man beneath his veneer of good-fellowship. Colonel Neilson had been; you simply didn't tell the colonel when he was wrong, because he wouldn't follow your advice anyway. You waited and hoped he'd discover his error.

Besides, it was simply too presumptuous for a copilot to tell the second senior captain on the line that he was doing a poor job. Reluctantly, he tried subtlety.

Making a great show of it, Mike craned to stare at the captain's altimeter and then glanced at his own, as if checking to see that they agreed. *That ought to wake him up,* he thought.

But it didn't. . . .

Well, there was no real danger—his annoyance was just another manifestation, probably, of the dissatisfaction he was beginning to feel with flying in general. He sighed.

In six hours they would be over Los Angeles. If the forecast held, it would be overcast, but thinly so. For a long while they would have seen thrown against the moonless sky a glow like a false sun rising from the sea. And over the city they would begin the intricate, stylized routine of an instrument letdown, sneaking fast careful searches from the windows. Finally they would break through over the glittering city, but there would be no time to admire it; they would be scanning their own level to make sure that none of the blinking neon lights on the hills below were instead approaching aircraft.

Then they would land and taxi to the terminal, climb stiffly from the aircraft and check in. Afterward there would be the lonely drive back to Hermosa Beach. Did Kitty live in that area?

Yes, in Manhattan Beach, a few miles closer to the airport. Maybe he could drop her off. . . .

They couldn't drink in uniform, but he had a sport shirt in his car and Kitty might change at home, and there might even be time to stop at Pancho's or down on the strand at the Snake Pit for a quick beer.

With Kitty along it would be better. Somehow the prospect of walking alone into the raucous little cellar bar, rocking to the boom of the surf outside and the strains of the jukebox within, depressed him.

Mike Ruble was not a drinking man. His solid body seemed to absorb liquor without effect, his intellect clung dishearteningly to reason, almost impervious to the drinks dashed against it.

Because liquor affected him so little, he hardly enjoyed it.

He could have been abstemious—was, essentially, by preference—but he was friendly too. And in the world of aviation the nondrinking bachelor was a lonely man.

So tonight, if he arrived before closing, he would probably stop off at the Pit. With Kitty, or without her . . . And he would stand in the crowd of pilots and copilots and stewardesses, sipping a drink, perhaps a little apart from the rest but joining in for the warmth that the crowd gave him. Looking himself, perhaps, a little like the painting he had presented to the Snake Pit, hanging in the place of honor behind the bar.

A year before he had been riding in an airport limousine, passing through the skid-row district of Chicago. He had been staring idly out at the bleak alcoholics when he had seen the face. His sketch pad had been in the suitcase, but as soon as he had reached the hotel he had planned the work with a few swift strokes of his pencil.

Then, back at Hermosa, he had set up his canvas. Because the face had been staring from a crowd, because he wanted to get the impression of an island in a stream of humanity, he laid the canvas horizontally. And he painted in somber grays and blacks, giving only an impression in the background of beaten loungers in front of a cheap tile-floored hotel, hurrying businessmen and shoppers.

And alone in the foreground the face was there, staring out at the street, lips turned grimly down but somehow amused, eyes bleak but knowing, cap a trifle askew, cheeks gaunt and stubbled. It was a wonderful face. It was the face of a man who has been there and back, the face of a man looking out on a passing parade without bitterness, with tolerance, but without much hope.

Now the painting hung in the Snake Pit, and Joe the bartender, an ex-pilot, had tacked on the frame a brass plate engraved "Retired Airline Captain—by Michael Angle-Ruble."

Mike knew himself to be as far removed in outlook from the man behind the cynical stare as anyone alive, but he could feel a kinship with him too, when he and his creation watched together the boisterous crowd.

The trouble with flying, Mike thought, was that it didn't keep you busy. Even in Korea, with the predawn briefings and the pressure for combat time, days hung heavily on the airman. There were only a certain number of hours you could fly in a month, or you cracked. And when you weren't flying, what did you do?

Well, you didn't write the great American novel. You didn't even write home. You didn't compose great music.

You didn't paint. Not enough, anyway.

In Korea it was so much easier to stroll over to the bar in the tar-paper O Club to see what was cooking. . . .

And here it was easier to stroll to the Snake Pit. . . .

The canvas was already stretched on the frame, the paints were ready, the sketches waiting—you might even finish Mrs. Abram's portrait and that meant a hundred spare bucks—but the Pit was probably loaded with stewardesses, and it was so damn handy. . . .

So there you were again at the bar with your friend from skid row.

Some worked on the side. It was usually an exercise in futility. Pilots and copilots were always starting up little businesses, selling cars, insurance, working deals in their spare time. Or buying things—boats, light planes, skin-diving equipment they'd tire of.

The businesses got dropped because essentially you didn't need the money. You tired of the boats and the light planes—you flew enough anyway—and you tired of the other toys too.

Some of the boys had started a "corporation." They did not really incorporate but they rented a tiny shop with a plate-glass front, got a desk and had a phone put in, had gold lettering put on the door. The lettering read: "The Corporation," and under it: "Hours 9 A.M. to 5 P.M."

They had stationery made. The letterhead read: "The Corporation."

They bought a typewriter and hired a girl. She was a very pretty girl, even though she did not type well, and she lent the slightly dingy place a touch, as they put it, of hominess.

And if she could not type, that was all right, because there was no typing to do.

They listed themselves in the phone book as "The Corporation." Only in the white section, not the yellow business section, because there was no business to list themselves under.

It was just "The Corporation," and though for a while they kept business hours religiously, and meticulous records of business losses for tax purposes, no work was ever done there, nor was any intended. They would lie back in their denims on their swivel chairs in front of the plate-glass window, sandaled feet on their roll-top desks, drinking beer and gazing out at the startled passers-by.

They had even been investigated for making book, and they had never been able to write off their tax losses, for there was no income. And finally, when the girl herself had decided that the place was a front for some underworld scheme, they had grown tired of the game and sold out.

The whole puckish idea had tickled Mike at the time.

Tonight he thought of it as a signpost on a bleak and futile road.

Capelli touched his shoulder suddenly and asked, "Where we at?"

"Approaching Nashville," Mike told him.

An experienced flight engineer could almost tell from the fuel consumption to a given check point how bad the head winds were. Mike had a feeling that Capelli would have loved to find that they were behind schedule. But Dick Barnett had been right—head winds, for a westbound trip, were proving remarkably light.

"You happy with our wind?" Barnett asked him.

Capelli shrugged. "I'd rather be late and not have my coffee spilled," he said dourly.

That guy, Mike thought, is going to end up with Barnett's yoke wrapped around his neck.

But Dick Barnett was smiling tolerantly.

And the altimeter was two hundred feet high.

Dick Barnett had had the plane on autopilot for half an hour, but now the turbulence was building up again as they approached the advance guard of the sweeping front. In a few minutes they would be at Nashville; if it was too rough there, he would go back to manual or let Ruble fly awhile.

That would be one thing, anyway, about the DC-8 jets the company was buying. They would fly above the turbulence, usually isolated from the storms below. It would make the pilot's job easier.

Outside of that, he had little desire to fly them. The DC-7 was more familiar to him than his wife, and he understood its whims much better. The jet was an unknown animal. Ruble, beside him, probably knew more about the DC-8 now than he himself would ever know. The younger pilots and copilots were wild to fly them.

Of course, there was a certain prestige on the line and in the airways that went with jet liners; high on the temporarily uncrowded jet airways, a pilot regained some of the glory that he had lost to the man in the control center.

He would probably have to fly them all right, and there would be compensations, but he had little stomach for them.

Why not take the desk job?

The door opened behind him and Kitty Foster picked up their trays, flashing him a swift smile. He smiled back.

She was a sweet girl, one of the prettiest he had seen on the line. And smarter, too, than most.

After she had left he grinned at Ruble.

"Cute girl," he said.

"Yes sir," Ruble said enthusiastically. "She sure is."

"Smart, too."

Ruble nodded.

Barnett chuckled. "You ever fly with that redhead, Woozie Susie?"

Ruble nodded. "Yes sir."

"She try to flush the john from the cockpit for you?"

Mike smiled slightly. "Yes."

Barnett yawned and stretched, remembering Susie. Three months ago Woozie Susie had reported fresh from training school at Wichita. And he had been her first captain. A new stewardess was fresh meat. This one inclined at first toward airsickness, and to Barnett (or maybe his copilot, he couldn't remember) had come a blinding stroke of inspiration.

So they had told Woozie Susie to be sure to flush the toilet after each passenger left. And they had demonstrated to her how you did it—you entered the cockpit and worked the emergency wobble pump, strenuously, ten times in each direction.

It had become the best-kept secret, from Susie, on the line. For weeks she had dropped everything when a passenger left the rest room, to hurry to the cockpit and work the pump.

Then, presumably, some other stewardess had told her.

"I'm the guy that started the whole thing," Dick Barnett said. "It got so she was really building a bicep."

He made a minute adjustment in the autopilot and lapsed into silence.

Mike Ruble turned his face away and looked out the Plexiglass window. So the second senior pilot on the line had been the one who started poor Susie on her path as the typically dumb stewardess. She was not too bright at that, but she was a sweet and warm kid, with the guts to stick out her initial queasiness, and Mike had been the one who had set her straight.

He had told her partly because he felt sorry for her.

But mostly he had told her because the cockpit of an airliner was no place for a joke.

four:

AMARILLO CENTER

Norm Coster's brown bag lay behind him on the scope of his surveillance radar, the sandwiches still untouched. With half of his consciousness he was waiting for a phone call—Eve had promised to let him know as soon as Sally was safely in the hospital. With the other half he was following the flight of an Air Force jet bomber with poor communications, heading for Altus Air Force Base.

So when Mel Carnegie spoke from close behind him he jumped.

"Norm, I just got a call. . . ."

Norm licked his lips. "From the hospital?"

Mel shook his head. "No. From Tri-State Airlines in Dallas."

"From Tri-State? What about?"

Mel looked uncomfortable. "Well, their dispatcher claims he got a complaint from one of their pilots. Says you arbitrarily dropped their Flight Triple Six from thirteen to eleven thousand a while back. He says he was fine where he was and it was rough where you put him. On Victor One-Five-One-Eight?"

So many strips had whisked through his board in the last hour that Norm had trouble remembering the incident. He glanced doubtfully at Rocky.

Rocky grinned. "Remember that Cessna? You took Tri-State's altitude away from him to clear the Cessna."

"I remember," Norm said slowly. A nerve began to throb above his eye, and he rubbed it. He swiveled and faced Mel. "Listen, Mel, I didn't *arbitrarily* take anybody's altitude. I took Triple Six's altitude because there was an uncontrolled aircraft stumbling around up there. Who do they think they are?"

Mel tried to placate him. "I thought it must be something like that, Norm. In your sector, anyway. I thought there must be a damn good reason."

Norm, ashamed of his touchiness, said, "O.K., Mel. There was." He started to turn back to his board. Mel said, "Would you call them back and tell them?"

Norm stared up at him. "*Me?* Oh, now, Mel, look . . ."

Mel held up his hand. "No, you're busy. I'll call them."

Across the board, Rocky Fontaine watched him go, shaking his head.

"Do we have to explain every clearance we change to an airline?"

"The hell with it," muttered Norm.

You learned to swallow your anger or you dropped out of air traffic control. You learned to control your voice on the air, because fear or excitement or anger could make an emergency snowball into tragedy. And you carried your control through your eight-hour shift, and perhaps, as Hal Lick said he did, you took it out on your wife at home, or perhaps you let it eat inside of you and got ulcers. But you didn't show it on the job.

Just the same, there was no reason for a pilot or a dispatcher to assume that an air controller on a busy night would frivolously change a plane's altitude.

The problem lay in poor communications, of course. If the Tri-State airliner had been on the same frequency as the errant Cessna, he would have heard a play-by-play account of the whole crisis. Understanding it, he would never have complained to his dispatcher.

The Tri-State captain in his own mind had been like a motorist on a smooth and lonely six-lane highway, forced to a bumpy detour when he could see no obstacle ahead. And by a traffic officer he was not allowed to argue with.

You could hardly blame the pilot for releasing his venom on the ground or on his private company frequency. . . . But Mel could have backed his own man more willingly. . . .

In a few minutes he heard him calling from his desk and his pulse quickened. Eve? He scanned the board. Everything was normal. He motioned Rocky to take over.

"Yeah, Mel?"

"I got a call, Norm. It's your sister-in-law again."

Norm took the phone. His hand was shaking.

"Yes, Eve?"

"Well, we're here."

Her voice was light, but strained, as if she were forcing herself to be calm. Norm was grateful for the effort, but something told him that she would not long persist in it.

"How is she? Let me talk to her."

"She's already in bed."

"Is she O.K.?"

"Well . . . Gosh, Norm, I don't know. Frankly, she hurts like mad. I can tell."

Norm's heart sank. "Is the doctor there?"

"There's a doctor here, all right. . . ."

"Is it *Hudspeth?*"

"No. It's just the regular obstetrical intern."

"Intern? Where's Hudspeth?"

"Apparently he doesn't arrive until the launching," Eve said nervously.

"He told her he'd be with her all the time. Have they called him?"

"I don't know."

His good feeling toward Eve fled. All right, he thought wildly. *Sit there and make me sweat.* . . .

"Look, Eve, make sure they call him, will you?"

"All right, Norm." There was a pause. "When are you coming down?"

Norm cupped the phone. "Mel, you ready to take over my board?"

Mel wrinkled his brow. "She's that far along, huh?"

"I don't know how far along she is," Norm said. "I'd just like to go down there, that's all."

"O.K., Norm. If you want. But I'd a heck of a lot rather wait until you *have* to go. I'm supposed to be watching our flow control, and if I have to sit at the board for four hours it's liable to get away from us."

That was certainly true, and yet . . .

Mel pressed the point. "Can't you wait until, say, ten or so? That'd only give me a couple of hours tied to the board, and things might be slacker by then."

The doctor had doubted that there would be trouble; first babies, it was said, took forever; there was undoubtedly plenty of time. Norm would *have* to be there before the delivery—to talk to Sally, to lend her strength. But it was just like Eve to exaggerate the urgency—it was doubtful that Sally needed him at all, now.

And the Center obviously did.

"Eve," he said, "call me when the doctor gets there, will you? I'd like to talk to him."

"You're not coming down before?"

"I can't come down before," Norm said. "Call me when he gets there."

Mel smiled gratefully as he left the desk. "I told Tri-State what you said, Norm. I told them you'd be the last guy in the world to grab their altitude just for kicks. Then," he added proudly, "I gave them heck for bothering us."

"Thanks, Mel," Norm said tiredly. "Thanks."

When he got back to the board Rocky was rogering for a position report. He looked up at Norm.

"How is she?"

"She's in the hospital now. The doctor isn't there yet."

Suddenly the speaker chanted: "Amarillo Center, this is Oceana Flight Four-Two-Six. Texico at zero-nine, seven thousand. I.F.R. Estimate Tucumcari two-seven. Anton Chico next. Over."

Rocky glared at one of the slips on the board. "What the hell . . ."

"What's the matter?"

"He's four minutes ahead of his estimate. And I have a con-verging American flight on Victor One-Five-One-Eight. They're estimating Tucumcari at three-five."

Norm shrugged. "Well, that's the way it goes. You can't win them all."

"Well, damn it, I had it all set up. That stupid bastard . . ."

Norm smiled. "When you were a copilot, didn't you ever miss an estimate?"

Rocky grinned. "Maybe one or two. Oh, well . . . They've still got eight minutes' separation. Let's let it ride."

Norm's heart sank. Rocky was not nearly so ready for the board as he had thought. Sure, eight minutes of separation was plenty, theoretically if not legally. And the chances of a mid-air at the converging point were probably one in a million. And it was a shame to make an airliner hold out in the boondocks even if it was his own fault.

But there were people in those planes. There were men and women and children; pilots and copilots, too, if Rocky needed to identify himself. It wasn't a mere matter of obeying rules. It went deeper than that.

"No, Rocky. We'll hold American at Adrian."

Rocky smiled resignedly and returned to his side of the board.

Norm Coster felt very much alone.

five:

NAVY JET 3255
GRANTS, NEW MEXICO

Dale Heath yawned in his oxygen mask. He looked at the knee-pad. He was due at Grants at five-four past the hour, would pass Albuquerque and land at Kirtland fifteen minutes later.

He would enjoy a cup of coffee at Kirtland. His eyes burned from ceaselessly scanning the softly lighted instruments—from the artificial horizon to the right, then down, then left, then back to the artificial horizon. A cup of coffee would go well. . . .

He wondered whether McVey was sleeping in the rear. He could barely make out his form in the glow from the rear instrument panel. They had not spoken for ten or fifteen minutes, and there was always the threat of oxygen-mask trouble, expecially for a tyro.

"Mac?"

McVey came back quickly. "Yes sir?"

"Just wanted to check. Everything O.K.?"

"Yes sir. Just fine, sir."

The boy lapsed into silence.

Dale had decided that McVey was balancing some torrid love affair against his dream of the Naval Academy. Until he turned it over in his mind, he was amused. It was too easy for a man of thirty-eight, with some drives already quieted and emotions blunted through use, to chuckle over a boy's dilemma.

The classic advice was, "Wait. If it's for real, you'll be able to wait. Then you can have your cake and eat it."

But you couldn't give such advice seriously if you put yourself in the youngster's place.

Dale had been several years older than McVey, a first classman with less than a year to graduation, when Sal Porter warned him on the steps of Bancroft Hall, "But you don't want to get married. Not now. She's a Navy junior. She ought to be glad to see you graduate."

Dale flushed. "Well, she will be. This doesn't mean I won't graduate. I've got a weekend coming next month. I think we might just sneak up to Elkton and do it. Nobody's going to know."

Sal looked at him pityingly. "Nobody's going to know? In this crummy place? A guy can't hold his drag's hand in the movie without the superintendent hearing about it. What do you mean, nobody'd know? Look at Timmy Nichols."

Sal's advice had been good. But balancing it and his own common sense was a blazing desire for Cheryl that almost consumed him physically.

It had begun on a Saturday afternoon at the beginning of his first-class year.

The plebe messenger had entered their room and snapped to attention. "Mr. Heath? You have a visitor in the lounge." He leered when he said it, and Dale knew that it was a girl. And he had expected no visitors.

It was strange, because the Academy's somewhat ludicrous wartime security measures had closed the place except to invited guests. It should have given him a clue—whoever it was had identification of her own.

He had been dressing to join Sal and a few others for beer in the kitchen of the grimy boardinghouse they frequented, and he hesitated.

"Sir, if you take my advice, you'll come down right away."

He rolled his eyes suggestively. Dale frowned. *Who would it be?*

"She's that good, huh?"

"I haven't seen the front office so shook up since Secretary

Knox came aboard that time. She's even got the O.O.D. bringing her coffee."

The last struck a chord. Suddenly he was certain that it was Cheryl, somehow arrived from California.

He had seen Cheryl on his last Christmas leave, fighting his way through a swarm of fresh, shiny ninety-day ensigns at the Vallejo Officers Club to buy her a drink. She grew more ravishing by the year, and most of the bachelor officers and half the married ones were eating out of her hand. Yes, if it was Cheryl she would have the O.O.D., bringing her coffee, white gloves, sword, and all.

At Vallejo, the reserve ensigns had been no problem—Cheryl knew a regular, midshipman or not, when she saw one. But here it might be well to move quickly.

Even though he didn't really give a damn. . . .

It was Cheryl indeed. It was Cheryl in a flaming red dress which, if it fitted just a trifle too tightly, was certainly none too snug for the staring midshipmen in the lounge. And she was indeed being served coffee by the lieutenant commander who was O.O.D.

"He served with my dad," she murmured, guiding Dale skillfully away. They moved down the wide steps toward Tecumseh, and to a bench under a sweeping oak tree.

"Well," said Cheryl, "how are things in the trade school?"

Her knee was touching his, and a thrill ran from the point of contact through his whole frame. *It's too much,* he told himself, *to dangle a girl like this in front of guys as isolated as we are.*

"Same old stuff, Cheryl. You've been here, haven't you?"

She nodded. "Daddy instructed in the Steam Department when I was ten or eleven."

Dale felt as if he were generating a head of steam himself. "Are you just here for the day, or traveling through, or what?"

"Daddy got orders." Her eyes danced. "To Washington."

His pulse raced. This girl was not only luscious; she was going to be available. A vision of himself dragging her to hops, handing her down into a knockabout at the dock, sunk in a sofa in the shadowy gloom of an Annapolis boardinghouse parlor, excited him.

Suddenly, unreasoningly, he wanted her. . . . And badly.

"So you're going to be right next door, practically. . . ."

"That's right, Dale. And I want you to take me to the first hop there is. Give me about five minutes at that one, and I'll be off your hands for the year if you'd like."

This he would not like, he knew suddenly, but he refrained from saying so. Instead, he changed the subject.

"You know, I have an idea. Have you got all afternoon?" She nodded. "All afternoon."

He imagined the expressions on the faces of Sal and the boys at Mrs. Z's if he were to walk in with Cheryl. And it would certainly shake up the weekend crop of compliant Baltimore girls who stayed there, secure in the strength of the bedroom locks and the notorious blindness and deafness of Mrs. Z. It was a pretty crummy place, but if Cheryl wouldn't mind . . .

"How would you like to go absorb a few beers with Sal Porter—remember Commander Porter's kid? And some of the other guys?"

She grinned and patted her handbag. "We don't even have to get by on a few beers."

Dale raised his eyebrows. Cheryl was showing all the makings of a perfect drag.

"Who told you to bring a bottle?"

"As I say, Daddy was stationed here."

"I know, but at ten or eleven . . ."

"I wasn't dragging, but I wasn't blind either."

This, thought Dale as they strolled down Maryland Avenue, could turn out to be a pretty good year.

She walked close to him, and the desires of a healthy twenty-one-year-old separated too long from women flared wildly. When they turned onto Prince George Street, his hands were sweating.

"What train do you have to make back?"

"I planned to stay down tonight," she said softly.

"You did?"

It was not really presumptuous of her, because she was probably staying with friends of her father in town. His feelings were torn between those of a prisoner who had just noticed the shackles hanging from the wall, and an animal desire to keep the girl near him for the weekend.

"Great," he said thoughtfully. "We can go to the tea dance at Carvel Hall tomorrow."

"It sounds wonderful."

"This place, Cheryl, we're meeting Sal—it's kind of a dump."

"It is?" she asked.

"That's right. The old gal never bellyaches, no matter what. So you'll probably see some dolls around there that really ought to be hanging out in the local saloon."

"Is that so?" Cheryl asked with a tinkle of amusement in her voice.

What, Dale wondered, *is she up to now?*

"It's just on down the street," he finished lamely.

"Mrs. Z's?"

He frowned. "That's right. How'd you know?"

"It's where I left my bag," Cheryl smiled. "I'm staying there. . . ."

Dale almost stopped to stare at her.

The shackle swung before him.

They lounged that evening in the shabby kitchen with Sal and the boys, listening to Mrs. Z spin tales of admirals she had known as midshipmen, admirals who were close friends of both of their fathers. And the more of Cheryl's whisky the old harridan slurped, the more raucous she became. She seemed to have forged a special bond with Cheryl. By the end of the evening, before Mrs. Z collapsed and had to be carried from the kitchen by Sal and Dale, Cheryl was her long-lost daughter.

When Dale returned from spilling Mrs. Z onto her shoddy chaise longue, he said, "Why did you want to stay *here?*"

Cheryl shrugged. "I always heard about it, and I always wanted to. Besides, I like the old character. Besides, we learned enough about the brass tonight to blackmail any selection board that ever sits on you, didn't we?"

There it was already, although Dale had not noticed—the "we" of a girl who is thinking in the plural.

But he had missed it then, and later in the evening she had begun a torture that was to last for months. On the couch in the living room she had teased him almost to rape. To climb the stairs with her to her bedroom, that first night, he would cheerfully have thrown his warrant in the commandant's face.

But she had played him as an angler plays a fish; then, apparently shaken herself, pushed him almost bodily from the room.

The next day had been worse, and when he grumpily saw her off on the bus to Washington he had sworn to himself that he would never have her down again. But by Wednesday he was on the phone. His heart beat madly as he waited for her answer.

Yes, she'd be down. And that weekend he got as far as her bedroom door. Weeks later he was admitted to the bedroom, but he might better have settled for less.

"I want to. . . . I want to, Dale. But I can't. I can't until we're married."

And there it had stopped.

And months later, to Sal he had said: "She's just driving me nuts, Sal. I love her, and I want to marry her."

"That isn't love, buddy," Sal had said. "Whatever love is, that ain't it."

"Well, whatever it is, I want to marry her."

"Take a run around the track," advised Sal. "The only workouts you've taken all year have been chasing Cheryl around Mrs. Z's."

He had not taken a run around the track, but his own good sense had taken over. He had less than six months to go to graduation. Maybe he could put her from his mind. . . .

For two weeks he didn't phone Washington. For two weeks he did without her, and without her presence the hot currents slackened.

Then she phoned him.

"Are you mad, Dale?"

She sounded sincerely subdued.

"No, Cheryl. I . . . I just can't stand it. It isn't so bad when you're not here."

"Let me see you next weekend? Please?"

Her voice was vibrant, and there was promise in it. Dale wavered.

He was not a promiscuous man. He was not celibate, either, but he was not promiscuous. And he considered Cheryl, so close to his family, almost as a trust.

But he was a man, after all, and a young one.

"O.K., honey," he said. "Come on down. . . ."

Dale could still peer down the corridor of the years and pull aside the veil of that weekend. He and Sal had left the grounds after their last Friday-afternoon class, shaved and shined and ready for their few short hours of Friday liberty.

Dale, who knew that Cheryl was on the verge of surrender, was in a haze of anticipation, but was still surprised when Sal said, "I wonder if Jean's here yet?"

"Jean?"

Sal seldom had girls to the Academy. He was a ruthless satyr on a weekend in New York or Washington, but he considered the restrictions on a midshipman's time to preclude sex, and had always looked with amusement on the disheveled "flying squad" leaving their drags to sprint through the streets of Annapolis for bed check at Bancroft.

Sal was a typical "Red Mike," and a secretive man as well, and had said nothing to Dale about a drag.

"Who's Jean?"

Sal shrugged. "She's that nurse I knew in Baltimore. Took care of me when I busted my arm on the road gang."

Sal was always casually bringing up such incidents from a wispy past, somehow expecting Dale to know of them.

Sal shrugged. "We've been writing each other about once a year. So this weekend I thought I'd have her down."

"I'm glad you did. I was beginning to think you were getting queer."

"You and that Cheryl character thrashing around Mrs. Z's every weekend were making me horny. Even Mrs. Z was beginning to look good."

The front door was open, and someone was playing the cantankerous piano in the gloomy parlor. Whoever it was to Dale's untrained ear played well.

Sal led him across the living room. As his eyes adjusted, he saw a short-cropped, swirling hairdo bent over the keyboard, and then the large gray eyes he had finally grown to love.

The girl sat smiling expectantly.

"Hi, honey," Sal said. "Jean, this is my roommate, Dale Heath. Dale, Jean Rand."

Jean held out her hand. Her grip was firm and warm.

"I've heard so much about you, Dale," she said. And then humorously, "Every year."

Dale grinned down at her. "He's not much for writing letters. And he doesn't talk much about girls either. Until about two minutes ago, he'd never mentioned *you*." He looked around. "You haven't seen a brunette named Cheryl around here, have you?"

Had he noticed even then the flash of surprise on her face? She had told him since that she *had* been surprised. Told him that it had taken her hours that day to tie Cheryl and him together in her mind.

But she allowed none of it to show in her voice. "Oh, yes. If she's the one I think she is, she's getting dressed."

That afternoon the shackle had been placed neatly on his leg, awaiting only the snap of its lock to trap him. It had turned out badly, but the memory of that afternoon had had the power to stir him for years.

Remembering his own drives fifteen years before made Dale feel closer to the boy in back.

He hoped that McVey, if he was balancing marriage against the dream of his future, could still the song of young blood; could go to the Academy, if that was what he wanted; could even, on graduation, wait a few years.

The Navy, and from what he had seen, the Army too, was peppered with Academy men who had married as the gates swung open, married the first girl who attracted a woman-starved boy of twenty-one or twenty-two.

The smart ones didn't. Sal hadn't, and by graduation he himself would not have, if it had not been for Cheryl.

Six weeks before graduation, Dale and Cheryl and Sal and Jean had been sitting in a booth at the Green Spring Valley Inn, near Baltimore. Dale was suffused with a glow compounded of several pre-dinner martinis, a good dinner bought for Sal and himself by the two girls, an exhilarating ride from Annapolis to Baltimore in Jean's car, and the approaching crown of success —June Week.

Because he was an only child, because he had traveled so much with his parents, he could have numbered on one hand the times he had sat surrounded by close friends of his own age. This evening was one of the happiest he had ever spent.

And characteristically, Cheryl had chosen it to drop her bombshell. Sal had been speaking of graduation.

"Half our company's getting married graduation day," Sal said. "Can you imagine jumping from *that* frying pan into the fire?"

Jean smiled enigmatically, but Cheryl said coldly, "Why not?"

"Why?"

Dale turned to Jean resignedly. "Look, Jeanie, I feel good. I don't want to have to bandage Sal all up. Would you drag him out on the dance floor away from Cheryl?"

"Aye-aye, sir," said Jean. "Come on, you lug. You shouldn't argue with girls, anyway. They're too verbal."

When they had gone, Dale stretched luxuriously.

"I have never," he said quietly, "felt so good in my life. Six more weeks . . ."

He was ashamed now, thinking back on it, but he had said it—he had certainly said it: "I wonder if it'll keep up till I get out there."

"The war?"

"That's right."

"If it doesn't you'll be an ensign the rest of your life, that's for sure. With all the reserves ahead of you . . ."

"That isn't it. When a guy spends three years in that hole—oh, I don't know. I just want to get into it, that's all."

"I think you'll get into it," she sipped her drink. "Dale?"

He had felt it coming. He loved her, sure he loved her, but why did she have to keep bringing it up when he was feeling best? Cautiously: "Yes?"

"We're still getting married, aren't we?"

He had mentioned it as little as possible since the wild flare of desire six months before. He would marry her, all right, but he wanted a year or two of freedom first. And suppose he got killed?

He took her hand. "Honey, we've been over it and over it. After the war, yes. Not right away. Not for a year or two, anyway."

She nodded. "You don't want to jump from the frying pan into the fire. . . ."

"That's right."

She faced him squarely. "Well, I hate to push you, Dale, so to speak, but something's come up."

He chilled. "What?"

She laughed dryly. "Well, breakfast for one thing, this morning, and it's been going on for quite a while."

"What do you mean?"

"I seem to have developed a touch of morning sickness."

Dale stared at her. "Oh, now look . . ."

She nodded. "I hate to have to tell you this, Dale, but I'm pregnant."

His ears roared and he felt as if he would pass out if he did not get air.

"Dale!" She giggled. "I swear . . . you look like you're going to faint!"

He was ashamed of himself. "Well, damn it, I'm not!" He took a deep breath. "Are you sure?"

"Well, I haven't been to a doctor."

"Do you mind going to one?"

She looked down.

"Oh, Dale! How could I? Suppose Daddy found out?"

"Daddy," Dale said evenly, "isn't going to find out. And you can't just guess—you have to know."

"I do know."

Dale felt stifled. "Well, what do you want to do?"

"It's up to you, Dale. I don't want to force you into anything."

Dale felt the walls of the booth close in. He loosened his tie. "Christ, honey, it's not a question of *forcing* me into anything. What do you think we ought to do?"

She shrugged. "It's up to you. I don't know how I'd ever have it stopped, but I'll try if you say."

Dale had no particular feeling toward an unborn child he had not dreamed of three minutes before. But the idea of Cheryl risking her health for him was utterly unacceptable.

"One, you're not getting an abortion. It's too risky."

Cheryl smiled. "All right."

His mind began to grope for facts, as it did in the classroom when faced with a long problem.

"Two, you're going to see a doctor. This could be all in your mind."

"It isn't. Which doctor? I won't go to one in Washington."

"We'll ask Jean about one in Baltimore."

Cheryl hesitated. "All right . . ."

"Then . . ."

Dale was stopped cold.

"Yes?" she asked softly.

"Then we'll see. . . ."

"All right, Dale. Then we'll see. . . ."

And when Sal and Jeanie returned, she spirited Sal unconcernedly to the dance floor, and he was alone with Jean.

"Dale! What's wrong? You look all shook up."

He had always found it easy to talk to her, and now he made his decision.

"I am. Jean, I think . . . Cheryl thinks she's in trouble."

Jean's clear eyes grew thoughtful.

"Oh?"

"That's what she thinks, anyway. Is there—well, with her dad in Washington and all, she doesn't want to see a doctor there. Do you think you could tell her one here?"

"Yes. Sure I can, Dale."

He squeezed her hand gratefully. "Thanks, Jean."

"And Dale?"

"Yes?"

"Please don't worry. Maybe she's wrong, and anyway, please don't worry."

He had felt that the concern in her eyes was as much for him as for Cheryl.

Two weeks later Cheryl sat across from him at a table in the gedunk shop in Bancroft Hall.

"Daddy said to say hello, Dale. And he'll be in the reviewing stand for the color ceremony. Mom and I have seats, too."

God, how could she talk of the color ceremony when he had hardly slept for a week?

"What happened?"

She raised her eyebrows questioningly. "What happened when?"

His voice was hoarse. "In Baltimore? Did you go to the doctor?"

She nodded. "I'm pregnant."

The shackle snapped shut.

He took her hand clumsily across the table. "I want us to get married, then. I don't want us to wait."

"Do you really, Dale? Or is it just because of the baby?"

In spite of himself his voice rose. "Christ, Cheryl, why go into that? You know I wanted to marry you. And I still do. It's just that . . ." He forced a grin. "This is a crummy way to propose."

"That's all right. You proposed months ago." She smiled cheerfully. "All you're proposing now is a change in schedule, isn't it?"

He laughed, feeling better now that it was settled, burying the doubt. "That's right. Now there isn't a chance that we'll be able to get the chapel, and my orders read Jacksonville on the twelfth, so after graduation why don't we run up to Elkton the way we planned in the first place?"

Fifteen years later, rocketing over Arizona at thirty-three thousand feet, the man wondered how the boy could have been so naïve.

Cheryl grinned enigmatically. "I think we can get the chapel."

He shook his head. "Not a chance. Guys have had in for that since youngster year."

"But my daddy's a captain," Cheryl said simply. "R.H.I.P."

Well, rank had had its privileges, all right. And standing with his glorious bride on the chapel steps, with Sal beside him and Jean beside Cheryl, with the arched swords of his white-uniformed classmates glittering below, it had not been so bad after all.

It had been years later, while Jean and he waited for Cheryl and Anne outside a pediatrician's office in Norfolk, that he had found out.

"I hope this doctor's better than the last one you sent us to, Jean, or Anne will be sucking her thumb for the rest of her life."

Jean smiled uncertainly.

"What do you mean, Dale?"

"Remember the guy in Baltimore? When Cheryl thought she was pregnant the first time?"

"The obstetrician? George Marks? Sure . . . Why?"

"He was a little off, wasn't he? About two years, say."

She faced him in perplexity. "Cheryl didn't—"

She broke off suddenly.

Dreading it, knowing what the answer was, Dale said, "Go on."

"Skip it."

"No, goddamn it! Go on."

"Dale, let's drop it."

He took her arm and swung her around in the seat. "She never saw him, did she?" he whispered. "She never saw him at all."

Jean wouldn't answer, but he went on. "What a lousy trick! What a crummy, stinking trick!"

Jean shook her head. "Oh, Dale. It wasn't that, I'm sure. She just thought she was pregnant. She didn't think she had to check with anybody."

"But she *told* me she'd seen him. She *told* me."

"Maybe she saw somebody else, Dale. Maybe she saw somebody in Washington."

That evening, sitting across the table from Cheryl, with Anne upstairs in her crib, the pressure had become unbearable and he had asked her.

Her eyes narrowed for an instant.

"Who told you I hadn't seen him? Jean?"

"That's right. Why'd you tell me you had?"

Cheryl had few women friends, even in the tight Navy society of Norfolk, but she and Jean were almost inseparable.

Now she said, "That bitch. That loud-mouthed bitch!"

Dale had stared at her, shocked as much as at her original perfidy.

But the amazing thing was that that finished it. As far as Cheryl was concerned, she was discovered, and that was the end.

"I knew I wasn't pregnant, Dale."

"Then why in the hell . . ."

She shrugged. "I didn't want you to get away."

There had been something flattering in this, and Dale had finally accepted it. He had been after all going to marry her anyway. What difference did it make when?

And after her own swift lash of anger at Jean, there was no more of that either. She was as friendly toward her as ever.

But her flat nonchalance bothered him. Dale, who if he had ever been caught in a minor fabrication could from sheer embarrassment never have met his discoverer as an equal again, could only regard Cheryl with wonder.

It was the first lie he had caught her in. And the last, until the ultimate deceit, the discovery of the disheveled lieutenant. But how many undiscovered lies lay between?

The needle on his omni kicked swiftly to the side, and he noted the time.

He was within thirty seconds of his Grants estimate.

He turned up the volume on his U.H.F. The A.T.C. channel was crowded with bits and snatches of position reports from military aircraft all through the Southwest, punctuated with staccato static from a storm somewhere nearby. He awaited his turn and called Albuquerque Center.

He called twice before he raised it—and when he did, the answer was garbled.

Of course, he might be twenty miles past the relay station by now, and atmospheric conditions were not good.

Finally he transmitted his report blind.

He thought he heard an answer, so he said: "Albuquerque Center, this is Navy Jet Three-Two-Five-Five. I read you three by three, weak and garbled. Out."

Perhaps he would have better luck when he actually reached Albuquerque, five minutes east.

six:

FLIGHT SEVEN
DYERSBURG, TENNESSEE

Mike Ruble moved his computer into the rosy glow of his cockpit light. It was five minutes to Dyersburg if his estimate was correct. It was time to work out the Walnut Ridge E.T.A., so that over Dyersburg he would not be "caught with his estimates down," embarrassed by having made a station passage with no E.T.A. ready for his position report.

He worked the computer carefully, setting in the latest wind to get a good ground speed. They were making two hundred fifty-three knots over the ground.

He set the index of the computer at two-fifty-three, then checked the chart for the mileage from Memphis to Walnut Ridge and returned to the computer. He ran his finger along the close-set figures, not trusting his eyes alone. It would take seventeen minutes from Dyersburg to Walnut Ridge.

Then he checked it again. Then he wrote it into his log, and calculated it again.

Only then did he slip the computer back into its leather case and relax. He was not naturally a good mathematician. He had little innate mechanical aptitude, and compensated for it by the most meticulous checking and cross-checking.

His mind ran to generalities rather than specifics, but he had cured himself of his impatience with figures because he sincerely desired to fly, and learned early that the concrete facts of the sky were intolerant of sloppy thinking.

He had always envied men with a quick grasp of mechanical things, or a sharp sense of numbers.

But perhaps a feeling for color and form and line precluded one automatically from having particular mechanical aptitude.

People seemed to think so, anyway. He was forever running into new acquaintances who seemed incapable of believing that he could be a competent pilot and an artist as well.

If he had to choose a channel for his life, which channel should he choose?

He knew himself to be a good pilot, safe, skillful, and careful in the air. He was completely at home in the cockpit of an F-86 or a DC-7.

Was he even more at home, though, standing at an easel?

His father had a poor head for figures. Had he had to make the same decision? No, it could not have been. His father was a dilettante, he had already decided that. Anything else would have been tragic.

And yet, why would a dilettante have hidden his work? Why, unless it had meant more to the old man than he could ever have said, had he hidden it from them all?

Mike felt again the sadness he had known when he stumbled across the canvases.

Thank God it had been himself, instead of his mother or Tom, or he might never have known.

He had been wearing Air Force khakis when he had arrived at Dallas. They were soiled and grimy, the same he had been wearing three days before in Seoul, because he had not stopped long enough when he got the TWX to do more than pick up a shaving kit and sprint for the Tokyo shuttle.

His emergency orders were in his hand. The grief, which he must not show until he was finally alone, lay like a lead weight in his chest.

And he had not been alone once on that whole grinding trip from Seoul to Tachikawa to Midway to Pearl to Travis to Dallas.

Not being alone had been the hardest part of all. Circling Love Field in the back of a C-45 he had hitched from Travis, he had prayed that his mother and Tom would not be there to meet him—they had not got his wire. If he could only clean up, compose himself, think of the things to say . . .

But naturally they had been waiting. His mother had even been wearing black, as he should have known she would be, but it seemed somehow ordinary, cheap, not what Sam Ruble would have wanted.

They had been waiting, and they had—even his mother, who was quite imperceptive—apparently felt that he needed more help than either of them. Their idea of help was never to let him out of their sight.

Until he had broken loose to go through the debris in the attic above the store, he had had no privacy at all. Even when he had retreated to his studio—and this was a measure of his frantic desire to escape, because every board in it reminded him of his father—even there Tom had followed him.

But in the attic above the store he had at last found solitude. It was while his mother at Tom's suggestion was reopening the place—"Mom, it's been almost a week. Unless we're going to sell out, we better get at it. He'd want us to, anyway." And his mother sighing, "I guess you're right, Tom."

And Mike agreed. At least it would keep them out of his hair for a while, give him time finally to make the trip from MIG Alley to Commerce Street.

So while his mother dusted some of the ceramic line and while Tom phoned the clerks, Mike sneaked upstairs. He stood for a moment in a dark, cluttered storeroom. An old roll-top desk—the same one that, "fired" as an embryo salesman, he had tried to work the ledgers on—sat in a dusty corner. A scaly swivel chair stood nearby, and Mike pushed it over. He tried the roll-top and found it locked. He dug his fingers into it and yanked, and it rolled up.

Then he sat down, put his head on his arms, and waited for the tears.

When they had passed he felt better, as he knew he would. He began to wander about the attic, to postpone his return to the floor.

Absently he was poking about some of the items that Sam

Ruble had consigned to the attic. They were things that for some reason he had been unable to sell, but must have felt had value. A few canvases by unknown Dallas amateurs whose names Mike could barely recall, a few clay figures by an Arizona Navajo Sam Ruble had encouraged, a few crude charcoal sketches Mike dimly remembered doing himself in high school, carefully sprayed and wrapped by Sam himself.

And then an unfinished canvas, facing several more.

At first Mike thought that it must have been one he did himself. It was a mountain peak at sunset, and something about the foreground recalled to him the camp site on the Panhandle.

But this was impossible. He *had* painted that peak—Triassic Peak, it was—but he had finished his canvas.

The truth dawned on him. His father had painted this one himself.

Mike took another of the paintings and moved under the dusty skylight. Sure enough, his father's name occupied an unobtrusive space in the corner. "Sam Ruble, 1947."

Shakily Mike went through the rest. They were not bad— they showed a certain primitive charm, a certain promise, although Sam lacked a feeling for composition.

But he had tried.

One was the best of the lot by far. It was a painting of his mother, still pretty, peering as if waiting for Sam or her sons from the flat above the liquor store in which Tom and he had both been born.

His mother had been beautiful—still was. But the painting had more than beauty. Some of Sam Ruble's love shone from its pastel serenity.

Impulsively Mike took the canvas downstairs. He showed it to his mother. Her eyes widened.

"Where did you find this?"

"Upstairs."

"I wondered. . . . I haven't seen it in years. He spent hours —*days* on it."

"I never even knew he painted."

"He quit, honey, just after you were born."

"No, he didn't. There's at least one other up there he started after that."

"I can't believe it! It got to a point where he had to either run a cheap junk shop and try to paint, or put some time in down here and make the shop into something bigger."

"So he tried to make it into something bigger."

His mother seemed strangely defensive. "Well, he wasn't *getting* anywhere! He never sold anything. He wouldn't even *try* to."

"I see," Mike said.

"And if he'd kept it up, we probably would have starved to death." She smiled placatingly. "He didn't have much talent, Mike. And he faced it." The implication was clear, but Mike ignored it.

"Can I have this?"

"Of course, honey. Of course you can. And the others too, if you want them."

Mike turned to leave.

"Mike?"

His mother was watching him curiously.

"Yes?"

"Is it good?"

His mother could remember the net profit on every painting they had ever sold, but would hardly have known a Dufy from a western by Swinnerton.

Mike nodded. "The rest aren't so hot. But this is good. I think this is very good."

And it was. It hung now in his apartment in Hermosa Beach, alongside whatever of his own canvases were currently in his favor.

Visitors were always asking to buy Mike's own canvases. No one had ever priced Sam Ruble's.

But it was very good. . . .

Captain Dick Barnett reached over and touched his shoulder. "What was our Dyersburg estimate?"

"Zero-nine, sir."

It was zero-two past the hour now. The captain looked doubtful, nodded thoughtfully, and sat back.

Doctor Ed Benedict had watched the stewardess's steady progress down the line of seats. She had started serving trays first to those nearest the galley, moving forward; now that she was through with the forward passengers, she was starting again at the galley and moving aft. The stout woman in the seat ahead —the one he suspected of cardiovascular trouble—had just been served, and their own time was coming.

He dreaded it. He ordinarily ate well. He knew that if he didn't now Pat would ask why. And as the time approached that he must tell her, he found that the idea of food nauseated him. Could he plead airsickness? No—he had never had it and she knew it.

There was no out. The stewardess served Joey, and then Pat, and him. And he had to make the effort.

Pat smiled at him. "This is as good as first class."

"Yes."

"It's better than the hospital."

"Is it?"

"Why do hospitals have such awful food?"

Ed poked tentatively at a piece of fried chicken. God, how could he eat? He nibbled at some celery.

"I don't know, Pat. Maybe they think if they make the food too good people will want to stay. And they need the beds."

Professionally, he noted that her appetite was much better since her operation.

Yes, her body would blissfully recover, now that the blight that had sapped it was excised like some evil spirit driven from a primitive by a medicine man.

The body, unaware so far of the other evil thing that could not be exorcised, would cheerfully build itself back to health. So that it could be ravaged again . . .

"I *feel* so much better," she said, attacking a chicken wing and chewing vigorously, like a hungry child. "Remember how crummy my appetite was?"

He nodded. It had been the first indication. For weeks before he took her to Schmidt, he had fought a dread that there was something wrong with her. For miserable weeks he had come home, exuding false cheer. Each night he had asked her as casually as he could what she had done that day, trying to find out if she had found it necessary to rest, trying to discover without alarming her what she had had for lunch, battling first doubt and then the knifing certainty that there was something wrong—very, very wrong.

One evening she had been so wan at dinner that he had left her at the TV set and wandered to the kitchen. He opened the refrigerator and checked a container of cottage cheese that he knew had been there for two days. She was the only one in the family that liked it, invariably ate it for lunch, and he was red-handed in the kitchen when she came in.

"Late snack, Ed? Here, I'll do it. . . ."

Then she had seen the container. "What are you doing?"

He had been unable to answer.

For a long moment she had faced him across the kitchen table. "I see. . . ."

He nodded.

"Well, I didn't have any," she said. The pallor he had noticed in past weeks was truly striking now. "I didn't have any lunch, darling. And I didn't have any yesterday either."

Suddenly she was in his arms, fighting back sobs. "What is it? What is it, Ed?"

He had known even then, he was sure. Not from classic symptoms, for one could never make even a guess from externals, but because his medical judgment was attuned to her body in some psychic way.

So he had sat with her at the kitchen table, with the children sleeping upstairs, and questioned her as if she were a patient in his office.

"You have been tired, haven't you?"

She nodded.

"Resting during the day?"

"I had to."

Professionally and flatly: "Have you noticed any blood in your stool?"

"Yes. Oh, darling . . . Oh, what is it?"

He had a sphygmomanometer in the car. It was a poor time of the night to check blood pressure, but he had to know.

He checked, and checked it again. Fear tore at his throat. He kept his head down over the gauge, not trusting himself to speak.

Finally he looked up. "I think—I think we'll take a run up to Westwood tomorrow. I want you to see Dr. Schmidt."

She nodded dully. He began to put away the apparatus.

"What is it, Ed?"

Her blood pressure had been 105/70. Now he tried to smile. "I don't know, darling. We'll have Schmidt run tests."

"Cancer?"

The word hung in the air between them, like a tangible, solid thing that he could have reached out and destroyed.

And he found himself angry, because there was no more reason to believe that she had a malignancy than that she had some dietary deficiency or temporary anemia or menorrhagia.

"For God's sake, darling! What made you think of that?"

And then she had said it. "Because that's what you're thinking."

He put the apparatus in his black bag and shut it with a snap. "That's *not* what I'm thinking."

It was probably the first lie he'd ever told her.

The next day he left her in a room at U.C.L.A. Medical Center in Los Angeles, with his old professor of medicine from Johns Hopkins, beginning what would be a three-day ordeal for her. And him . . .

On the fourth day he was back from La Jolla to pick her up. Schmidt and he sat in the noisy cafeteria drinking coffee while his old professor tore his world to bits.

"Ed, I could feel it. I knew it when I felt her abdomen. It's just a suspicion of resistance, now, but it's there. And yesterday we got the X ray on her G.I. tract. There was a definite filling defect in the ascending colon. I'll show it to you upstairs. . . ."

"Yes sir," Ed heard himself say. "How large?"

"The size of a quarter."

He somehow held his eyes steady on the chilling blue ones that used to strike such terror in his heart before a quiz. He took a deep breath.

"Early?"

"We're very early," Schmidt said. "Indications are very, very good. Who do you want to do the job?"

And there had been only one answer to that. "Howard Kronkheist."

Kronk had been one of Schmidt's students, too, and the old man nodded.

"That's a good idea. When will you be leaving?"

"She'll want to go home to deliver the kids to my mother. And pack. I guess we'll leave tomorrow. There isn't—there isn't anything else you wanted to do?"

It was a plaintive question, and he was ashamed of it before it left his lips. But the old man had been sympathetic.

"No, Ed. There's little doubt. Now I'm going to offer you some advice."

"Yes sir."

"You *have* to try to approach this case as if she were merely another patient. Be as conservative as you can, and you tell Howard Kronkheist I said that, but remember she's no more vulnerable to this than any other woman of her pathological setup. No more vulnerable." He smiled. "Now, Ed, would you be particularly worried if you caught something like this so soon in one of your patients?"

Ed studied his coffee cup. "No sir. I guess not. Not if Howard Kronkheist were doing it."

"All right. Her prognosis is good, if this hasn't spread. Don't worry."

So Ed had leaned on the old man's words all the way to Baltimore, had even managed to inculcate Pat with their wisdom. If once or twice during the week that led to the moment in the operating room he had awakened wide-eyed, he had hidden it in her room at the hospital.

If this hasn't spread . . .

The old man's confidence was a crutch on which Ed was still leaning on the morning of the operation. He had been in the anteroom of the operating suite, talking to the anesthetist when they rolled Pat in on her own bed. He helped them transfer her to the operating table.

He knew that she would never remember his being there— she had had demerol and scopolamine. She smiled up at him with the same vacant warmth that she bestowed on the nurse who had come down with her.

He knew that it was silly, that she was lost in a world of fantasy, but he bent over her face.

"How do you feel, honey?"

She smiled up at him dazedly. "Ed?"

"That's right."

"Oh, Ed, I feel wonderful! Am I all well?"

"Just about, darling," he said softly. "Just about . . ."

Then he kissed her forehead and stood aside.

Events began perceptibly to speed up, and he was like a spectator at a movie projected a little too fast. Swiftly the nurses strapped down her wrists. The anesthetist moved in, inserting a tube in Pat's vein. He bumped Ed slightly in doing so, and apologized: "Sorry, Doctor."

Ed felt very much in the way, but could not tear himself away until he saw Pat's eyelids drop as sodium pentothal coiled about her and dragged her into the dark waters of anesthesia.

A nurse adjusted a bottle of blood. The anesthetist slipped a mask over Pat's face and began pushing on the bag he would use to control her breathing.

Only then, with two nurses and the anesthetist hovering over his wife, could he force himself to leave her for the surgeon's dressing room.

Kronk and his assistants had already gone to scrub, but Kronk had left his locker open and a gown, mask, and borrowed conductive shoes on a bench for him.

It was while tying the shoes that Ed had his attack. It began as a trembling in the knees, passed as a weakness up his thighs, as a cold spasm gripping his stomach and chest, then to his arms. His fingers shook so that he could hardly tie the laces.

My God, he thought, *I'm acting like a student nurse at her first operation.*

He walked to the window and slammed it open. The cold Baltimore air slapped his face like a dash of water. He took a few deep breaths and recovered.

He knew that he would not have a chance to be alone again that day. He did not believe in prayer, although he did not reject the possibility of a Supreme Being. He did not believe in prayer, but now he found himself for the first time in years asking silently for help.

He was not afraid of the operation, but only of what else Kronk might find.

I'll do anything, anything, he promised, *if this hasn't spread. . . .*

Then he put on a cap and mask and moved to the scrub room.

Kronk's luminous black eyes above his mask gave him a look of almost religious intensity. The mask hid some of his thick facial ugliness, and his compact body radiated efficiency and economy of motion. This was Kronk's world, and though Ed was his best friend, there could be no idle camaraderie in it. But he paused a moment, smiling with his eyes.

"Hello, Doctor. I see you found the gown and shoes."

"Yes. Thanks."

Kronk turned to the youngest of his assistants, a cherry-cheeked intern of perhaps twenty-five. How could one so young be involved in this?

"Chuck, go see if her X rays are on the projection box in there. And get a stool for Dr. Benedict to stand on."

He spared Ed a few more words: "I'm going to do a right rectus, because it'll give me the best exposure. We'll do an intestinal anastomosis of the closed type—I don't want any danger of contamination. And I'm using silk. You got any questions, Ed?"

Ed shook his head and Kronk looked relieved. They passed

through the swinging doors to the operating room, and for a few moments Ed could lose himself in the familiar routine.

Deliberately he kept his eyes away from the table. He watched as the scrub nurse handed Kronk and his assistants a sterile towel to dry their hands and arms, tied on their gowns, shook powder on their hands, and held their gloves for them.

With the precision of an athletic team they went to their places, Kronk on the right side of the operating table, his first assistant across the table on his left, the two others between them and the instrument table.

They moved so swiftly that by the time Ed had climbed onto the stubby stool placed behind Kronk the square-holed laparotomy sheet had already been drawn over Pat. There was nothing of her visible but a strip of skin to the right of her navel, three or four inches wide and running perhaps a foot from the rib margin downward.

A scrub nurse rolled a Mayo table into place over her thighs, and almost before Ed had balanced himself properly on the stool Kronk had made the incision.

It was a muscle-splitting right rectus incision, and there were few bleeding points. Kronk clamped and tied them swiftly. His first assistant wordlessly clipped skin towels to the edge of the wound, clearing the operating scene. Now there was no bare skin showing anyplace.

Kronk discarded the skin knife and took a fresh one. He hesitated for a moment and spoke his first words since he had entered the operating room.

"Blood's a little dark."

The anesthetist looked up and nodded, quickly offering more oxygen to the patient.

Kronk exposed the rectus muscle fibers, split them, and clamped a few bleeders.

For a moment Ed lost himself in admiration of Kronk's hands. Long ago they had sat side by side in an amphitheater and heard a famous surgeon say, "Gentlemen, always treat tissue as if the patient were not anesthetized. Completely conscious, gentlemen, and ready to scream with pain."

Kronk and he had glanced at each other significantly. The importance of the concept had struck them both equally. It was one of the torches that a good teacher would hand you now and then as you struggled through the dark complexity of medical study. Ed knew that it had lighted his own path for years.

Ed tried to follow the precept. Kronk actually did.

His short, stubby fingers, so unlike the hands of the classic surgeon's, were as swift and accurate as those of a concert pianist.

But they were tender, too—they moved almost imperceptibly when need be.

Kronk cut the peritoneum carefully so that he would not injure any underlying viscera. He extended it carefully to the length of the skin incision.

For a moment he paused, then swiftly he glided his hand inside and began to explore the abdominal cavity by palpation, staying always away from the lesion on the colon—for they already knew that was there and would not disturb it until they were ready to remove it—and he began to speak.

He did not turn, and his voice was that of a teacher explaining to students, but Ed knew that the words were for him.

"Well, the stomach's all right and the kidneys are in place and the right size. The spleen is normal. The liver feels all right."

He paused a moment and went on.

"The pelvic organs are negative."

He straightened and turned, looking up at Ed. Ed tried to read the dark eyes.

Kronk said, "Anything else, Doctor?"

Ed managed a smile. "You're the doctor. Go ahead."

Kronk turned back. "O.K. We'll start."

For what seemed only seconds he worked in the cavity, with his second assistant retracting without a single word having passed between them. He had a team, all right, Ed thought. Kronk had got himself a real team.

An operating team began after a while to resemble the personality of its surgeon. When it was practiced, it would provide him with a half-dozen hands anticipating every thought, guided by his intelligence with hardly an order. And attuned as it was, it shared his emotions. If he was happy and hopeful, so was the group. And if he was disheartened, the room would turn dismal without his saying a word.

Even a general practitioner like himself, who did little surgery, learned the feel of an operating situation. A moment of crisis could unite the team into a fighting thing. When things went smoothly it was a relaxed, smiling unit.

There was nothing in Kronk's group to arouse anything but confidence in the mind of the sourest pessimist.

"Ed," Kronk said, "here it is. . . ."

Ed moved from the stool and stood beside Kronk.

The bowel was exposed, and on it the lesion, a tiny peak with furrowed slopes of grayish-yellow, and a base, as Schmidt had predicted, no larger than a quarter, lay as the only blemish on the shiny peritoneum of the colon.

Ed's heart began to beat. It was small. It was very small. His knees turned liquid with relief.

Kronk said, "Well, Ed?"

Ed heard himself talking as from a long way off. "It . . . it looks pretty small. . . ."

"I hope to tell you! And it doesn't seem to involve any of the regional lymph nodes."

"No."

Kronk looked at him, his eyes shining. "Gee, Ed, I think we've got it in time. I really think we've got it in time. . . ."

Ed climbed back on his stool in a haze of bliss. He felt around him the familiar sound of the operating room, and without paying much attention could almost follow the resection from the sparse words.

"Stick-sponge . . . Hemostat . . ."

It meant that he was at the point of resection of the colon. Love for the science that would save Pat flooded Ed in a rush.

Pat would lose three feet of the large bowel, hardly know it, and go on with a life that would otherwise have ended in a few months of searing pain.

He glanced again at the table. Kronk was working toward the

distal side of the bowel, and in the bright operating-room light Ed caught a glimpse of liver.

All at once Ed sensed it. It may have been a tensing in Kronk's neck muscles, or in the shoulders of his assistant. Whatever it was, it struck everyone in the room with an electric impact. The anesthetist straightened and glanced at his dials. A scrub nurse handing the third assistant a hemostat froze, the instrument glittering in the light.

On the street outside a car honked dismally.

What was it? Ed craned uselessly. *A hemorrhage? No . . . Something respiratory? Contamination?*

Kronk was staring into space, his hand in the cavity. He was feeling, feeling for something.

What is it? Ed wanted to shout. But he swallowed the words. He found himself off the stool, at Kronk's side.

Slowly, reluctantly, Kronk pushed down on the liver. He glanced at his assistant, caught a glimpse of Ed, and shook his head.

Ed looked at the liver, and his world shattered in a kaleidoscopic shower of anger and bitterness and grief.

Sitting trapped in a crowded airliner with a tray of unwanted food on his lap, the cruel injustice of it clawed at him again.

In the surgeon's dressing room he had prayed. He had asked only the one thing; he had promised anything.

And it had been savagely denied.

He would never pray again.

"What's the matter, darling? Aren't you hungry?"

Ed smiled at her, and felt as if his face would crumble.

"Yes. I'm hungry. . . ."

Captain Dick Barnett watched the needle swing at Dyersburg. He glanced at the clock.

"What was your Dyersburg estimate?" he asked Mike Ruble.

"Zero-nine, sir."

"We just had a station passage," Dick Barnett remarked. It was only zero-five past the hour. He had sensed that they would be early, felt it perhaps from the increased sensitivity of the needle over what it should have been if Mike's estimate was correct; judged it more likely in the light of all the tiny memories that years of familiarity with the route had given him. He could almost have told from the intensity of the beam signal how far they were from Dyersburg at any time for the last ten minutes.

"Maybe we dropped some head wind on the last leg," Mike suggested. "Or maybe I made a mistake. . . ."

Swiftly he checked his figures.

They were four minutes early, and theoretically were obliged to report it to A.T.C. Dick Barnett had no intention of doing so— it was much simpler to delay the position report until the estimated time arrived, and then report as if you had just reached the station."

"Damn," Mike said in exasperation. "I figured our head wind wrong. Can you imagine that? I'll report us early."

He picked up the mike and Dick Barnett made no move to stop him. If the kid wanted to admit an error to A.T.C., it was all right with him. He was so hipped on A.T.C. rules that he couldn't see the forest for the trees.

What difference did four minutes make anyway? Or a couple of hundred feet of altitude?

None, when you had ten minutes of air space ahead of you and behind you, and a thousand feet above you and below you.

None at all . . .

seven:

NAVY JET 3255
ALBUQUERQUE, NEW MEXICO

Dale Heath was steady on Jet Route Six Victor, slicing the night for Albuquerque four minutes to the east. The random radio transmissions that had been trickling into his earphones had almost ceased, and it worried him. Was it a chance diminution of traffic, or was his receiver entirely out?

As if to quiet his fears, he heard a Navy plane calling Albuquerque Center at Truth or Consequences, a good hundred miles to the south. Odd, that when his receiver worked, it was working well—and when it didn't work, it was almost dead.

"Aircraft calling at Truth or Consequences Radio, this is Albuquerque Center. Go ahead."

Dale grimaced. For years, as a young pilot flying the West, he had thought that the station Truth or Consequences was an isolated radio somewhere, named by the old C.A.A., perhaps, as a humorous warning to pilots to tell the truth in position reports. There were many such tiny places, unknown to natives a few miles away, but familiar to airmen because they were reporting points, given the same sort of disproportionate importance in a pilot's mind that some desert truck stop might have in a trucker's.

But no—on the horrible drive in '50 from New Orleans to San Francisco, with Cheryl probing at him in the front seat of the Chevy and three-year-old Anne peevish and tired in the rear, they had come across Truth or Consequences in the flesh.

It was a creditable town on the banks of the Rio Grande—a town of over four thousand. Now, when he heard the name in a radio transmission or saw it on a chart, remembering passing through it that day, he felt unreasonable but definite distaste.

Cheryl had not ceased to complain on that trip from the time he had picked orders to Korea over orders for shore duty at the Bureau of Aeronautics "where for the first time in five years you can do us some good before the next selection board."

"Listen, Cheryl, there's a war going on out there. Doesn't that make any impression on you at all?"

And she had hummed a few sardonic bars of "Anchors Aweigh."

"My hero . . . What god-awful town is this?"

"I don't know. There's a sign."

She stretched and yawned. "Truth or Consequences, New Mexico, Pop. 4,563," she read. "Is it for real?"

"I guess so." He relaxed a little. Was the battle over?

"Whoever heard of a town called Truth or Consequences?"

Dale smiled. "I have, believe it or not. I didn't know it was a town, but it's a range station on Amber Three."

Cheryl said, expansively bored, "Amber, schmamber . . . Dale, I'll tell you a truth, and a consequence."

Something in her tone told him that the battle was not over. "What's that?" he asked wearily, braking at a speed sign.

"The truth is that I'm tired, damn tired, of being alone while you live it up off some carrier swinging on the hook five thousand miles away. I'm tired of turning down dates, chasing wolves away. I've just had two years of it, and I don't want another two years."

"For a Navy junior, you talk like an idiot. You knew what you were getting into. Your dad—"

"My dad never turned down Washington duty in his life. He spent half his life angling for it. That's why he's an admiral."

Dale swung past a truck, searching the highway ahead for a hamburger stand for Anne.

Cheryl went on: "Now you've heard the truth, you want to hear the consequence?"

"Not particularly."

"The consequence is that this time I'm not."

"What do you mean, you're not?" Dale asked idly.

"I'm not sweating it alone. I'm not turning down the dates."

Dale shot her a glance. "What do you mean?"

"When somebody asks me to go out, I'm going, that's all. . . ."

There was no defiance in her voice—only a simple statement of fact.

"You do, Cheryl, and so help me, I'll paddle you as if you were . . . as if you were Anne."

"You terrify me," she murmured. "Let's stop. I'm hungry. . . ."

And so another bar to communication had fallen between them.

He wondered now whether in those long two years in the Far East she had really cheated. It hardly seemed possible, and yet . . .

There had been odd glances even in the Orient from people who knew them both. The last time he had seen Sal, at the bar in the Allied Club in Sasebo, Sal had asked after Cheryl cautiously, with just the touch of reticence that could mean he had heard some gossip of her in the surface fleet.

It happened all the time in the Navy, even when there were children. But why did it have to happen to Anne?

He was suddenly over Albuquerque, on the nose. He pressed his mike button.

"Albuquerque Approach Control, this is Navy Jet One-One-Three-Two-Five-Five. Over Albuquerque omni at zero-zero, flight level three-three-zero, I.F.R. Flight Plan. Request clearance for standard jet penetration and let down to Kirtland Air Force Base. Over."

Only static answered him. He winced. He was already a minute past the omni-range—and a minute meant five miles. He swung into a race-track holding pattern and headed back toward the omni. He tried again without success. Then, weakly, he heard Albuquerque calling him. But it was not the call of a station that has heard a plane calling *it*. It was the call of a station that is expecting one and has not heard.

Reluctantly he shifted to his emergency channel and tried

again. This time, weakly and almost unintelligibly, Albuquerque replied.

In the jumble of words he heard: "You are cleared. . . ." And it was all he needed.

As he passed the omni again, he cut his power to seventy per cent, popped his dive brakes and began a six-thousand-foot-per-minute descent.

"McVey," he said, "you ever have any ear trouble?"

"Negative, sir."

He was set now, gliding swiftly away from the omni down an invisible highway toward a U-turn as well delineated as if he had been able to see it. It was a familiar procedure, but he found himself tense. Any break in routine like the communication failure at station passage took your mind off your checkoff list and could snowball. Had he forgotten anything? You had to stay ahead of a jet, or you were like a Central Park rider clinging to a runaway with your feet out of the stirrups.

And entering the teardrop turn, it happened. It began to snow in the cockpit. It was a familiar phenomenon, caused by warm moist air at a low altitude contacting a vent system and a windshield chilled by great height.

His hand flashed to his heater control, groped for it, finally found it. He sat in a veritable blizzard, while the cockpit canopy froze around him.

His passenger must be terrified.

"Mac?"

"Yes sir?"

"Don't mind the snow. It's not unusual. . . ."

Why tell him that he had forgotten in the radio mess to preheat the system?

Now he was past the point at which he should have started his turn. He manhandled the plane into a bank, feeling the blood drain from his head as the g's built up.

Steady, boy, he warned himself. *Let's get organized. . . .*

He came out of the turn heading back for Albuquerque omni at nine thousand feet, only four thousand above the terrain, flying the little plane on his panel, leveling to brake his descent on the steep and nebulous pathway.

He looked up from his instruments. His private snowstorm had almost stopped, and he rubbed a snowflake from his eyebrow. But now the canopy was opaque with frost. He reached up with the back of his gloved hand and ineffectually scraped a clear spot on the windshield.

Of all the stupid, amateurish things to forget—and all on account of the ridiculous radio.

Through the slit he had rubbed in the canopy he could see that he was still in stratus. And he almost missed noticing the omni-needle swing as he crossed Albuquerque again. *On the ball,* he told himself. *Get on the ball. . . .*

Out of his last turn he was three thousand feet above the terrain—he hoped. He had had to leave his altimeter at its standard setting, for he had not been able to catch the Albuquerque local pressure—three thousand feet above the terrain, and less than three minutes from the base. He took up his field heading and began a groping descent, peering for the runway lights, longing for the solidity of visual flight.

He was about to yank the plane into an emergency pull-up when he spotted them, twin diamond necklaces laid out to the east, winking cheerfully through the haze.

He paralleled the runway, broke over the field, called the tower on his base leg, and heard no reply. He forced himself to recite his last cockpit check: "Landing gear down, dive brakes up, flaps down. . . ." Then he turned finally, still tense in the frosting cockpit, and groped for the strip between the onrushing lights.

They alighted with a quiet "chirp-chirp" of tires.

He called the tower for taxi instructions.

Even on the ground, its reply was weak. . . .

Kirtland Air Force Base discouraged Sunday traffic, but with the help of the duty officer Dale located a chubby radioman named Garcia. They leaned into the cockpit in the gusty New Mexico night.

"Sometimes, Sergeant, it's working fine. I heard a plane calling at Truth or Consequences from a hundred miles south. And then five minutes later I couldn't raise Albuquerque from smack over it."

And damn near snowed myself out of the cockpit fooling with it, he almost added.

Garcia smiled. He spoke with the soft, diffident lilt of the Mexican-American: "I don't know, sir. I'll see what I can do."

Dale sat at a table in the base cafeteria with McVey, munching a sandwich. McVey stirred his coffee thoughtfully.

"Thanks for the trip, Commander. I'm very much obliged. And for the dope on Annapolis." McVey hesitated and seemed to come to a decision. "Commander, I . . . I really need some advice."

Enlisted men seldom asked officers for personal advice, and Dale knew that he was being asked for it in lieu of the boy's skipper. But if he could stand in for Spike Lawton, he was glad to.

"Shoot."

"Well, sir, I got a girl here in Albuquerque. She's . . . She's really a doll. She's the most beautiful girl in town, I think. Susan's her name— Well, it doesn't matter."

McVey sipped his coffee and seemed to consider whether or not to go on.

"Well, the trouble is, I got this letter. . . ." He patted his blouse. "I got this letter, and she says she wants to get married. Right away."

Dale stared at the boy. He had felt a certain kinship, a certain rapport with him all the way, but this was almost incredible.

"I see," he said softly.

"Last leave, you see, we were together . . ." The boy groped for words. "And she's pregnant."

"Go ahead."

"Well, this is a pretty small town, you know, and this is really a nice girl. Kind of . . ." He colored. "Yes, she's a nice girl. And it isn't like Dago or L.A., you know. . . . It's not too big. And isolated kind of. This is the worst thing that can happen to a girl in a town like this."

"I see."

"The only thing is, I want to go to Annapolis."

McVey was suddenly no longer a mature, well-adjusted serviceman, but a boy longing for a shining childhood dream. "I really want to go. . . ."

"Yes . . ." Dale sat for a long while in silence. Garcia returned.

"Sir, I think I got it. I think you got a bum relay."

Dale winced. "Have you got a replacement?"

Garcia shook his head. "No sir. I cleaned it and pulled a ground check and reset your crystals, and everything's *dai jobe.* Five by five, loud and clear." He looked doubtful. "But I wish we could yank the set."

"You think it's O.K. now?"

Garcia's heavy lids dropped in concentration. Finally he said, "I think so. Of course, sir, when they heat up sometimes . . . I think so. I think it's O.K."

"All right," Dale said thoughtfully. "Thanks."

Dale strolled to the station bus stop with McVey. It was raw and windy outside, and the base was swept with blowing sand.

McVey apparently assumed that he had forgotten his problem, for he shook hands impassively.

"Well, Commander, thanks again for the ride."

"Mac," Dale said, "the Academy doesn't mean a thing. It's a dream some guys get, but if you don't go, it's not the end of the world. Forget the Academy part of it. If you've got the stuff to make the Academy—and it may not take as much stuff as you think—you'll be O.K. in the Navy no matter what happens, because believe it or not, you'll find the competition in the service isn't really too rough. You'll get ahead eventually anyway. So forget the Academy."

McVey nodded, as if he'd counted on the classic advice. Dale made a sudden decision, and it was a decision that concerned himself as much as McVey. "Do you love the girl, Mac?"

McVey looked a little surprised. For a moment he stared

through the swirling sand at the lights of the town glimmering in the distance.

Dale took a deep breath.

"If you don't love her now, you never will. And if you don't love her now, don't marry her. Support the kid or do anything you want, but for God's sake don't marry her."

McVey stared at him. "It's going to be one hell of a stink," he said thoughtfully.

"Face the stink, but *don't* marry her." He looked into McVey's clear eyes. "I know. . . ."

He turned and headed back toward the terminal.

He called collect, not wanting to delay their conversation while he poured quarters into the box. Jean answered almost immediately, her voice vibrant and low.

"Hello, darling," she said. "I've been sitting by the phone."

She had always transmitted a placid warmth to him. The tenseness that had crept into him during the landing fled.

"I'm chugging right along."

"When will you be in?"

"About three A.M. your time. Earlier if I latch onto the jet stream."

"Andrews Field? I'll meet you."

"The heck you will. I'll see you tomorrow."

"But I want to. It doesn't matter. I won't be able to sleep anyway."

He thought of the radio. Garcia notwithstanding, unless it checked out for him he could not take off. And if he had to send back for a replacement it would take hours.

"Negative. I'll see you tomorrow."

She gave in. "Can we have lunch?"

Dale laughed. "I'll call you in the morning. How have you been?"

"Fine. They're making me night supervisor, you know—and I'll make more money than I know what to do with, and my boss proposed to me yesterday, and I got three new dresses this week."

Dale felt a twinge of jealousy. "When are you going to marry him?"

"You idiot . . ."

There was a short pause. Dale felt her presence in the booth. Then she asked, "How's Anne?"

"Wonderful. She asked about you. She said to tell you that the vitamin pills were doing Sloppy a lot of good."

She laughed. "I thought they would. . . ."

"Jean?" He paused. "I'm going to send her to a boarding school in Washington. How's that sound?"

"Oh, darling . . . Can you really?"

"I am. Find a good one for her?"

"Of course. Oh, Dale, if you knew what it means to her! I'll show you some of her letters."

"You might end up with her on weekends. Can you swing it?"

She hesitated. "You know what I'll do? I'll look for a two-bedroom place as soon as you leave Washington. She'll need a room of her own."

He laughed. Of all the girls who should have had children, Jean was the most sadly deprived.

"Now wait a minute—She'll be living at school, you know."

"But on weekends. I want it to be just as if she lived here."

There was a long silence. He had intended to wait until he saw her, but the desire to tell her was too strong. "Jean, what we talked about? Last month?"

She didn't answer, and he went on. "Darling, I've had it with her."

There was genuine regret in her voice.

"Oh, Dale . . . What about Anne?"

"She's thirteen, and she's getting out from under her, and I'm not throwing away my whole goddamned life on that woman."

"Did something just happen? Something else?"

He thought of his advice to McVey.

"Well . . . No, nothing else. Jean, it's inevitable. It's just that all of a sudden it hit me—why should I throw any more time away on her? Why can't we be together?"

"Dale, you know I want it more than anything. But there's

still Anne—and Cheryl too. You can't throw all those years out the window—not without *knowing*. Really knowing."

"I *know*, all right."

"You're sure? Really sure?"

"I'm sure."

For this, at least, he should wait, but he was strangely impelled to go ahead.

"And Jean, she's bound to contest it, or something. You'll wait, won't you?"

He caught in her voice the hint of a tear.

"Yes, darling. Yes, if you're sure. . . ."

"I'm sure. I love you, Jeanie. More than I've ever loved anyone."

"I love you. Past all belief."

"And I'll see you tomorrow."

"Yes." She paused. "Dale?"

"Yes?"

"Be careful. . . ."

He hung up thoughtfully. First Anne, then Jean. Two people in the world attuned to him more closely than any others . . . telling him for the first time in their lives to be careful.

It must be the weather, the clammy fog in San Diego and what probably was snow in Washington. Like all non-fliers, they regarded gloomy skies as a menace to flight.

Sometimes they were. . . .

He checked the aerological sequences. Winds at thirty-seven thousand were good; flying that high he would have plenty of fuel to make Memphis. He requested flight level three-seven-zero on his flight plan and handed it in. Then he went to his plane. Garcia was sitting in the front cockpit, a flashlight in his hand.

"I thought I'd check it again, sir." He shook his head. "So I called the Tower and Departure Control. Everything checks out. Five by five."

Somehow the fact that Garcia had returned bothered him more than if he had been sure the first time. But the Washington conference started tomorrow, and the set, when it had worked

at all, had never really fallen below the standards of three by
three.

And Jeanie was expecting him. . . .

He would ground-check the radio himself just before take-off.
If it was all right, he would go. He leaned over the rear seat,
clamping down the seat belt and shoulder harness for empty
flight, and climbed into the front.

While airmen from the line shack trundled out an auxiliary
power unit, he switched on the radio and called the tower for his
air traffic control clearance.

His radio blasted loudly, "Navy Jet Three-Two-Five-Five,
Kirtland Tower."

Garcia was right—he even had to turn down his volume. He
pressed his switch. "This is Three-Two-Five-Five. Go ahead."

"A.T.C. clears Navy One-One-Three-Two-Five-Five to N.A.S.
Memphis via Victor One-Five-One-Eight to Amarillo. Cruise
and maintain two-three-thousand to Amarillo. . . ."

Dale's pencil hovered over his kneepad. They were clearing
him "short." And giving him only twenty-three thousand
feet. . . .

The voice went on: "Expect further clearance at Amarillo. De-
part Kirtland via Jet Departure 'Charlie.' . . ."

Automatically Dale copied the clearance, but his mind was
busy with a problem. At thirty-seven thousand, he could have
made Memphis easily, but fuel comsumption at twenty-three
thousand was vicious. Suppose they couldn't clear him to a
higher altitude at Amarillo?

He read back the clearance and hesitated.

"Am I to expect a higher altitude at Amarillo?"

There was a pause.

"Affirmative," said the tower finally. "A.T.C. asks will you accept the clearance?"

It was only two hundred fifty-five miles to Amarillo; if A.T.C.
gave him thirty-seven thousand there, or even thirty-three, he'd
have plenty of fuel. And he might wait all night on the ground
if he tried to hold out for a high altitude all the way.

"I'll accept it," he said. He signaled the ground crew to start the power unit and fired up the jet. As he reached the head of the runway, he called the tower for a radio check.

The tower came back five by five, loud and clear.

He lunged down the runway and was pleased to note that the rustiness was gone and that he was as smooth as he had ever been. And he heard Albuquerque Center clearly when he contacted them.

But at twenty-three thousand, steady on Victor One-Five-One-Eight, he thought he noticed a fade when Albuquerque Center rogered for his departure and next estimate. For an instant he considered returning. He decided against it.

If he turned back to Albuquerque and completely lost communications, he would become a "flying rock," a menace to the airways because he was not carrying out his original flight plan.

No, if he lost contact with the ground completely, the rules were clear—he must complete his flight as scheduled, so that Air Traffic Control would know at least approximately where he was at all times, projecting his flight plan along his route and using the airspeed he had filed with them. That, or with even greater risk fly a triangular distress pattern off airways and hope that Air Force radar noticed and sent interceptors to guide you through.

He must assume that he'd be able to contact Amarillo. He must complete his flight—he was already committed.

part three

MAYDAY AT TWENTY
THOUSAND . . .

one:

FLIGHT SEVEN
FAYETTEVILLE, ARKANSAS

Six hundred miles to the east, Captain Dick Barnett flew toward Amarillo at two hundred sixty-eight knots ground speed and twenty thousand feet.

Twenty thousand *approximately*, Mike Ruble would have pointed out—actually he was still a good two hundred feet above his assigned flight level.

Both of Barnett's voice radios were V.H.F. Both were working perfectly. Mike Ruble could hear a constant stream of traffic from commercial aircraft, from F.A.A. centers, and from enroute A.T.C. stations. He could of course hear no military U.H.F. traffic at all. But there was no need to. A plane in the air might politely relay a message from A.T.C. to another aircraft for the common good, if they happened to be on the same band, but aside from that, communication between aircraft themselves was unnecessary and to be discouraged.

Even though heavy radio traffic meant heavy airway traffic, Mike Ruble usually preferred such a night to one of sparse communication.

It had always given him a feeling of fellowship to hear a pilot, perhaps flying another altitude on the same route two or three minutes behind or ahead, coming up with position reports again and again over the hours. Some of the voices you came to rec-

188 • *THE CROWDED SKY*

ognize, after years—some belonged to other Pacific Central pilots or copilots you knew—others would belong to people you met at the Snake Pit over a beer.

"Was that you in Pacific Triple-Three this afternoon, crying about the approach time they gave you?"

Yes, after the years some of the disembodied voices achieved flesh and blood, and even those of the men on the ground, whom you never saw, captured a certain substance.

He heard a woman's voice on the speaker behind him. It was a familiar one, that of the girl who handled the F.A.A. communications for Sulphur Springs radio to the south. She had a warm, careful voice. Mike had always before visualized her as a pretty, conscientious young thing whose heart rode with the men in the skies, something like the WAAF's one saw in the control towers of movies on the R.A.F.

"Roger, American Four-Two-Three. Sulphur Springs altimeter three-zero-point-zero-zero. Good night."

It was almost a voice from the past. With the new "discrete" lines installed, you seldom heard a lonely operator in an outlying station any more, except as a stand-by—the busy controllers in the centers had almost taken their places.

Her voice had always comforted him before, but suddenly he pictured her as a prim, bespectacled woman watching the clock for the end of her shift.

What was wrong with him tonight? Was he getting bored with flying?

If he was, he had better quit. Flying was an ever-changing profession, the rules of which shifted month by month, requiring the dedication of a highly motivated man. If he was losing interest, he was a menace to himself and others.

Well, why *not* quit?

He had never really intended to stay with the airlines. In fact, he had never really intended to join the airlines.

If he had stuck with his original resolve, if he'd taken six months after Korea, moved, perhaps, to Carmel or Laguna, to some other little place along the California coast to free-lance, he would be established by now.

Or broke and working at the store . . .

His mother had forced it on him on his terminal leave, by the mere assumption that he would work at the salon.

"Mike, honey, I thought we'd do it this way: I'll handle the books, and Tom can handle the buying part for ceramics, and you can handle the paintings and the art supplies. How does that sound?"

Mike felt as if he were mired in the plush carpeting. He had known even in Korea, after he had returned from the funeral, that his mother assumed he would take Sam's place. And the thought of tying himself to the store had ridden like a vulture on his shoulder during the last few months of his Air Force career.

It had been one reason he had gone with Phil and Lenny to the Pacific Central Los Angeles office when they applied for jobs.

"Where we going to do better, Mike? So we spend six or eight years riding the right-hand seat. It's more dough than we'll get anywhere else, and we'll be flying."

Now in the perfumed, svelte coolness of the salon, he was glad he had. "Mom, I'll have to think it over. I'm thinking of going with the airlines."

She stared at him. "You're what?"

"I applied for a copilot job with Pacific Central."

She was stricken. "Oh, *Mike!* You're just out of the service, and this is all set up, and all you have to do is step in. We need you, honey. Everything we sacrificed to send you to art school—Tom and I don't know anything about it. We really need you. . . ."

Mike saw tears in his mother's eyes and secretly wavered. "Well, I'll think it over—"

And then she'd weakened her case. "You've got to grow up, Mike. We're not rich, you know. You can't play flier all your life. Gosh, you have to think of your future."

"It's really not a bad future. I'd be starting at five hundred a month, and within eight or ten years I'd be pulling down eight or nine hundred."

His mother raised her eyebrows. "I can't believe that, honey. . . ."

"Well, it's true. And it's the third largest domestic carrier in the country; there's all the security in the world."

His mother was impressed. It seemed suddenly not quite so important that he join the store.

"It's up to you. That's certainly more money than you'd want to take out of the business here. And it really isn't too important to even keep carrying the originals—they only brought in twenty per cent of our gross last year."

In the back of her mind, Mike knew, was the china and glassware section she wanted to open. But she said, "A third of the place is yours, Mike. You do what you want."

He pressed home his point. "I'll sure pour my surplus in, if it'll help. We could probably use a little fresh money in the business, couldn't we?"

"Yes," his mother said doubtfully. "It's just that flying seems like such a shaky sort of thing."

If she had thought that flying was a shaky sort of thing, what would she have thought had he told her of his real desire—to free-lance as an artist?

So he hadn't told her, and he hadn't felt that he was ready, anyway. And within eight years he was pulling down not the nine hundred he had estimated but eleven hundred a month. And he was ready for captain.

He had indeed at times invested his surplus in the salon and had asked for not one cent from the business. Ahead of him stretched years of steadily increasing income, of better, more senior flights. And when one got right down to it, plenty of leisure to paint.

What would he be tossing it away for? A decade of hard struggle, without any doubt—all of his savings were in the store, and he would have to support himself from artwork almost from the beginning, even if it meant rendering for a commercial art studio. He knew something of the struggle that a few of his Hollywood art-school classmates had had—poverty in a sea of plenty, frustration, the insults an artist had to endure in a pragmatic civilization.

He had it, as they said, made in the shade now. Why step into the heat of competition?

He tore himself out of his reverie. He noted the time of passage of the Flippin, Arkansas, omni and rechecked his ground speed.

They were on schedule, the new ground speed was working out well, his estimate at Fayetteville would be fine.

If only the captain would drop that two hundred feet, they would be occupying the exact center of the block of space assigned them.

He knew that Barnett had as much instinctive feel for a plane as any pilot he had ever flown with. Outside of Washington, before his attention had apparently wandered, he had held his altitude in the bumpy air far better than Mike could have done himself.

But he was still two hundred feet over his level, and seemingly oblivious of it.

Mike was on the verge of mentioning it to him when Kitty entered with sandwiches and coffee. As she placed the tray on Capelli's lap, she smiled at Mike.

"How we doing, Mike?"

It was his opportunity to make a joke of it.

"On course, on schedule," he said cheerfully, "and on—well, just about on—altitude."

Dick Barnett smiled benignly.

"I get the hint, young fellow."

He began to ease the plane back to its level. *Well*, Mike thought, *that was easy, after all. It's just a matter of jollying him along.*

Kitty left the cockpit, and he sipped his coffee contentedly. A strange excitement possessed him when Kitty visited the cockpit, a joyful, tingling anticipation of things to come.

"Station passage, Mike," said Dick Barnett. "Fayetteville."

Mike shed his reverie and reached for the microphone.

He began to intone the position report, and when he got to the altitude, he glanced at the altimeter involuntarily.

It had crept back up to twenty thousand, two hundred feet. *Damn!*

He almost reported their true altitude, just to shake up Barnett.

But he didn't. It just wasn't done.

two:

NAVY JET 3255
AMARILLO, TEXAS

Dale Heath worked his shoulder muscles slowly. His neck was cramped and he realized that he had been straining to overhear a transmission, any transmission at all.

He had managed a position report at Otto, New Mexico, but at Anton Chico, his next reporting point, had been unable to raise either the Las Vegas, New Mexico, radio that serviced it or Albuquerque Center. Then, three minutes past Anton Chico and still a hundred fifty miles from Amarillo, he heard Amarillo Center calling an Air Force jet, loud and clear. Trying to call Amarillo, he heard no reply.

Now, fifteen minutes later, he was traveling in an aural vacuum. Ocasionally he would catch the feeble, half-heard sound of a position report, press his hard-hat against his ear to try to hear, then settle back, still tense, and force his attention again to his instruments.

He was suspended in a universe of faint incoherence, as if a curtain of unintelligibility had fallen between him and those he knew were near in the sky. He was like a sane man tossed mistakenly into a mental ward of blithering, secretive imbeciles.

He was very much alone, but a specter rode with him. It was a passenger on every instrument flight: the horrendous threat of losing total communication on the airways.

What would he do at Amarillo if he couldn't get further clearance? Hold in the soup until he ran out of fuel?

To reassure himself, he turned up his navigational radios.

He had a moment of panic before he heard the reassuring beat of the Amarillo omni-range. "AMA . . . AMA . . ."

And his low-frequency bird-dog was working too. . . .

At least he was not lost; he knew where he was. And he was presumably on some A.T.C. radar scope below, as well as that of the Air Force's Ground Control Intercept Site at Moriarity; so they knew, if not his altitude, at least his position.

He toyed with the idea of turning his I.F.F. to "emergency." Built to "identify friend or foe," it would change his pip on the scopes below to a series of dashed lines spelling trouble.

But no—he was not lost. He was not in trouble.

Almost certain he'd not contact it, he called Tucumcari Radio, somewhere ahead. He heard no reply, but a few minutes later he thought he heard his call number faintly in his headset.

Tucumcari Radio or Amarillo Center, possibly, worried because they'd had no Anton Chico position report?

Knowing that it was almost useless, Dale broadcast again. Then he sat back, holding his airspeed and heading carefully. And holding his altitude too.

He was not in trouble, but he was not out of it either.

There was a margin of safety in the sky, in everything one did. Just as a construction engineer would build into a bridge the toughness to support loads it would never have to carry, those who built aircraft stressed them for g's they would never pull. Just as a highway engineer designed curves banked high enough to hug the reckless driver, those who ruled the airways ordained that there would be room for error—the size of the block of space you occupied was more than enough. Ten minutes of clearance ahead and behind could at jet speeds mean a hundred miles of unoccupied air.

But when you flew with poor communications, you strained the tolerances. Dale moved impatiently on his chute. *Why,* he asked himself, *did I take off with a radio I wasn't sure of?* And then inevitably: *Would I have done it if Jean wasn't waiting at the other end?*

He rejected the idea in horror. After all, the radio had been working when he left Kirtland. Garcia had found the trouble, cleaned the relay, checked it. He had rechecked it himself. Radios, after all, *did* go sour even unexpectedly, in the air. Suppose *this* had happened to him, instead of the slow breakdown he had actually experienced. Would he be at fault?

Hell no.

And yet Garcia's reservation persisted.

"Of course, sir, when they heat up, sometimes . . ."

He turned it off to cool it, tried again, got nothing.

If it had not been for Jeanie, if it had been only the conference drawing him to Washington, would he have stayed in Albuquerque waiting for a new set?

He had flown to her before in moments of stress. He had flown to her from Sasebo, as soon as he had heard of Sal's death, as soon as he could wangle emergency leave.

He had thought, sitting in the bucket seat of a drafty MATS plane from Japan to Pearl, that he was doing it because Sal and Jean and he, and even Cheryl, had been so close for years. But when he climbed off the plane at Barbers Point, saw her waiting sturdily at the passenger ramp, with the kona wind swirling her hair, he was not so sure.

Then he had put it down to friendship between two adults— a certain empathy—a certain rare and valuable ease of communication. But even then, he knew now, it had been more than that.

Where did you draw the line between liking a person and loving one?

It was just a matter of degree. . . .

She drove him to her quarters in Makalapa. Her house was in that familiar state of restlessness that goes with a Navy move; the crates packed and ready to go, the smell of excelsior in the warm Hawaiian air, the sound in the kitchen of a Navy packer pounding on a barrel full of dishes.

But Sal's picture remained on a table in the lanai, regarding the world coolly.

When they were seated with coffee, under bougainvillaea rustling in the moist breeze, he said simply, "I'm sorry, Jeanie."

"I am too."

"I know you loved him."

And she said simply, "Yes. And I'm so proud of what he did. So damn proud." She changed the subject. "How's Cheryl?"

He shrugged. "I don't know. I got a letter two weeks ago, but it was the usual half-page memo."

"Does Anne write you?"

He brightened. "Once a week. On the nose. I know all about *her*, anyway, from the school bell to Jerry Maloney on TV. She got all A's last report. Not that Cheryl thought it was important enough to mention. . . ."

"Does Cheryl know about Sal?"

"I wrote her as soon as I heard. I told her you'd probably drop by when you got stateside."

Jean nodded. "She liked him. Even though they fought like tigers, she liked him. And I think he liked her."

"They were kind of alike, in a way." Dale shook his head wryly. "Although I'm beginning to wonder whether that isn't kind of an insult to Sal. . . ."

"Dale!"

"Well, it's true. . . ."

He spent two days in Hawaii that time, before returning to the Far East. He had taken her out twice, as Sal would have wanted him to—once to the O Club and once dancing at the Queen Surf.

Dale had never cheated in his married life. Jean had a mind as clean and as sturdy as her body.

But there was an unspoken moment the second night, dancing over the pounding, luminescent surf to lonely Hawaiian strings, when he had held her close.

He knew now that his love had begun then. Some relationships, like his and Cheryl's, consumed themselves in violent flames. And some, like his and Jean's, glowed in embers.

Out of loyalty to Sal and Cheryl, they might have damped the fire for years if it had not been for that crazy, sickening night six weeks before.

All at once he saw the frightened lieutenant in a new light. An ill wind?

Perhaps . . .

It was a simple, ridiculous thing, without dignity but with a certain classic humor, he guessed. The traditional tale of the cuckolded husband returning early from a trip.

It had been an inspection tour with the admiral, an evaluation of new carrier techniques in an exercise off the Coronado Islands. And halfway through the cruise the admiral had asked him to fly to Washington to start to sell the new methods to the Navy Department.

Dale flew ashore in a borrowed F9F Cougar, after dark. He made a night landing at North Island and checked on flights to Washington.

He reserved a seat on a fleet logistic plane leaving the next morning, got a ride home in a Navy sedan, and by 1:00 A.M. was fishing for the keys to the front door.

The presence of a convertible at the curb had hardly puzzled him—his mind was on tomorrow—a quick breakfast with Anne before school—the trip to Washington.

The house was dark. There was no need to awaken Cheryl, so he entered softly.

Flying now over Texas, he shriveled at the picture he might have made to some all-seeing observer with a sense of humour. The hoary picture of a husband returning early, hero of a thousand jokes from Chaucer on.

And perhaps, had it not been for Anne, once the bruise to his ego had healed, he would have been able to regard it with a certain wry objectivity himself. Already, the strange chasm between Cheryl and himself had split far enough for a divorce had it not been for Anne.

Had it not been for Anne, he was sure that control would never have fled him that night. He was after all a mature man, sophisticated, and under no real illusion regarding Cheryl.

But halfway across the living-room floor he had heard a light snap on in Anne's bedroom. She was ordinarily a heavy sleeper. Well, she must have read late surreptitiously, as she had often done, and not yet fallen asleep.

He would kiss her good night. He started down the hall toward her room, and stopped as she opened the door. She stood tensely in her doorway, silhouetted by the light.

"Daddy?"

There was real terror in her voice.

"Honey," Dale said curiously. "It's me. Don't be afraid. What's the matter?"

"Oh, Daddy!" she sobbed.

And suddenly she was in his arms, trembling violently. He carried her back to her room, stroking the pony-tailed head.

"What's wrong, darling? Did I scare you? Nightmare?"

She had not had a nightmare since she was six, but she grasped the idea quickly and told him what was probably the first lie of her life.

"Yes. Daddy?"

"Yes, darling?"

"Stay in here with me."

He stared at her. "Anne! What's going on? You haven't had a dream for years."

She was unable to go on with the subterfuge. Her eyes fell. When he questioned her, she only shook her head miserably.

He gave up and decided to ask Cheryl what had happened. "Stay here, darling. I'll be back in a second. . . ."

"No!"

It was a cry of true fear.

Suddenly he had known. The enormity of the knowledge overwhelmed him. He found himself lurching down the hallway in a trance, his knees wobbling and his hands shaking.

He flung open the door to his bedroom and snapped on the light.

Half prepared for what he found, he still for the first time in his life lost command of himself. The scene had been hurled so deeply into his memory that he could still smell the sweet-sour liquor, the cigarettes that had been allowed to burn out earlier, the lieutenant's after-shave lotion.

Cheryl awakened suddenly, wide-eyed, clutching the sheets and drawing them up to her breasts. By her lay the lieutenant, a big, too-handsome ground officer Dale had seen at the B.O.Q. pool.

For a strumming instant Cheryl glared at him. Her lips moved silently, tautly, and he read, "You son-of-a-bitch."

The strength flowed back into his legs. He found himself towering over the bed. His hand was half across his chest, poised to slash her face in a backhand swipe that might have marred her beauty forever. She flinched but didn't cower. He dropped his hand with a snarl, yanked the lieutenant awake and to his feet with unknown strength.

Dale was no fighter—he had probably in his whole youth struck not three blows in anger. And now he swung only once. He split the lieutenant's cheek and his own knuckle, and the man staggered across the room and crashed into the bureau. Dale followed up, hurling him through the bedroom door.

He gathered up his clothing from a chaise longue, and threw it after him.

Then he slammed the door and faced Cheryl.

She was looking at him speculatively, cautiously. She had never seen him lose his temper. She gave the impression of a woman with not one ion of fear in her whole body, but facing a situation to be handled with prudence.

"I . . . Dale?"

Dale found that his hands and knees were shaking again. "You bitch," he murmured. "You inhuman goddamn bitch."

She shook her head. "No, Dale, I'm sorry. We were drinking. . . . I don't remember anything. . . ."

The front door closed. Dale could hear bare feet padding down the walk, then a car door slam and an engine start.

He had to fight to get the words out of a tight throat. "But what about Anne? Anne's in the house. What about Anne?"

She shook her head. "I'm sorry, Dale. I just got drunk. I don't know what happened."

Dale studied her. "How in the world could you do it? With Anne around? How could you *do* it?"

"Anne doesn't know anything about it. He'd have been out of here before she even woke up."

"You goddamned fool, she's up *now!*"

She raised her eyebrows. "Then you woke her. I didn't."

"She just tried to keep me from coming in here, that's all."

There was no regret on Cheryl's face. Only a quizzical look. "Why, the little character! I had no idea. . . ."

Another wave of anger hit him, and for a moment he could impassively have strangled her. He got control and walked to the bathroom, dashed cold water on his eyes. He took a few deep breaths and returned to the bedroom. His mind was racing with a thousand things that he must do. Gratefully he found that the quaver had left his voice.

"All right, Cheryl," he said. "All right . . . Now, you sober enough to get this straight?"

That was ridiculous. She was perfectly sober.

"I guess so. . . ."

"All right. I'm going to Washington. I'll be gone about a week. I can't get out of it, or I'd stay and get moving on this thing."

She broke in. "What are you going to do?"

"What the hell do you think I'm going to do?"

"Are you going to try to divorce me?"

He stared at her. "*Try* to divorce you? I'm *going* to divorce you, if that's what you mean."

"You need a witness."

"We'll let a lawyer worry about that."

"You'll need a witness, and as far as I know, Anne's the only one you'll have. Did you ever think of that?"

"Don't worry about Anne. Anne's out of it."

"She won't be out of it very long, if I contest it. . . ."

Dale's head began to ache. "We won't go into that now. I have to go to Washington. I'm going to ask Anne if she wants to go with me. I'll get her on a plane tomorrow, if I have to."

"Like hell you will. I'll have every cop and shore patrolman in town down here if you try to leave the state with that girl. And don't think I can't do it!"

He wrapped his bleeding knuckle in a handkerchief.

"If she wants to come, she's coming. She's not staying with you one minute longer than she wants to."

Cheryl lit a cigarette, and he was pleased to see that her hand was trembling. But she faced him again calmly enough, exhaling a cloud of smoke between them.

"Oh, Dale, let's not make a mess of it. We're both civilized people." She smiled mischievously, and the dimples at the corners of her mouth made her look like the girl he had presented twenty years before to a dazzled Officers Club in Vallejo. "Although I'll admit," she said with some deference, "I've never seen you in a fight before. That character must be halfway to Tijuana by now—"

He stared at her. *Incredible*, he thought. *Absolutely incredible.*

She went on: "Anne has rehearsals for the school play. . . ."

The school play was indeed something to reckon with, for Anne had the lead.

"I'll ask her what she wants to do. And if she wants to go with me, the whole goddamned Coronado Police Department and the Shore Patrol and the admiral himself aren't going to stop me. Do you understand?"

Cheryl looked worried. "I believe you, Dale. But don't yank her out. Not now. Leave her. You'll be back in a week, things will be calmed down by then. Then we can talk about it. All right?"

"How do I know this isn't going to be going on while I'm gone? How do I know she won't be exposed to it again?"

She waved her hand. "Oh, Dale! Don't be an idiot! One, I'm not a damn prostitute."

"I don't know."

"Well, I'm not. . . . I was drunk, and this is the first time, and you ought to know it."

"I'll bet, the first time," Dale said harshly.

"Well, anyway, do you think I'd take a chance now? For all I know, you'll be having the house watched."

"I'll ask Anne whether she wants to go or not. I'll be back in a week."

He moved to the door.

"Dale?"

He paused.

She was regarding him with eyes that had suddenly filled with tears.

"Yes?" he asked harshly.

"You're not going to leave me. Are you? Really?"

Their eyes met across the smoky bedroom. For a long while they held.

Dale nodded. "Yes, Cheryl. I am. I'm sorry, but I am."

He sat on the side of Anne's bed, holding her hand. It was on the tip of his tongue to demand that she get ready to go—he could take a commercial plane, stay at a hotel instead of the B.O.Q. at Anacostia, and she would not have to stay one more day with her mother.

But then what would he do? Let her tag with him back across the country, through whatever court fight Cheryl would dream up, through whatever murk she would stir?

The thought that he might very well, unless he acted wisely, lose his daughter, struck him like cold water.

"Anne," he said finally, "I have to go to Washington tomorrow."

She nodded as if she had expected it. "You'll see Jeanie, won't you?"

He found that he had been anticipating it since the admiral had asked him to go. "Yes, I will. But that's beside the point." There was an awkward pause. "Honey, are things too rough for you around here?"

She looked at him, puzzled. "Rough?" Comprehension dawned. "Oh, that . . ." She shook her head. "No. She goes out sometimes, that's all, and I don't think she should, because you're married, but that's all. Tonight . . . tonight never happened before, Daddy."

"Never?"

Her eyes dropped. "Hardly."

"You want to go to Washington with me? For the week?"

Her eyes lit up. "Oh, Daddy!" Then she winced. "The play!"

"That's right. There's the play."

She seemed confused, and he helped her. She had been left with her mother for thirteen years. He marveled at her stability —and another week wasn't going to turn her into a neurotic.

"It really wouldn't be worth it, would it?"

"I'd love to go, Daddy. And I'd like to see Jeanie. But it *is* kind of a bad time. . . . And you'll be back in a week."

"I'll be back in a week," he said.

So he had grabbed a nap on the living-room couch that night, and left in the morning without seeing Cheryl. And when he had returned, knowing that he loved Jean, prepared for the rocky legal road he knew he must travel to keep his daughter, it had been Anne herself and his own soft, hateful reasonableness that had diverted him.

Cheryl herself, to his surprise, met him at the ramp. She was solicitous. He kept catching her misty-eyed, inquiring glances as he guided the station wagon through the afternoon traffic.

"Why didn't you bring Anne?" he asked.

"Because I wanted to talk to you alone."

"O.K.," he said briefly. "Go ahead."

She smiled brightly. "I have a peace offering at home for you. A rolled roast, no less . . ."

Dale winced. "Oh, Cheryl, for God's sake. . . . The only reason I'm going home at all is to see Anne. I'm not staying there. As soon as I see her, I'm checking into the B.O.Q."

They drove for a while in silence, Dale inching through the 4:30 Naval Base traffic. He heard a sob and looked at Cheryl.

For the first time since he had known her she was crying. He almost ran into the car ahead. "Cheryl, for God's sake, what's the matter?"

She looked at him with such misery that he almost melted. "Oh, Dale . . . Don't leave me! Don't leave me!"

It shook him, because it was so far out of character that he had to believe it genuine. It touched him, somehow—didn't change the facts—but touched him, all the same.

But it remained for Anne, in a walk to the beach after dinner, to loose Cheryl's final arrow.

"Daddy, Mother said you were going to leave us."

"Not 'us,' honey. I'm taking you with me, if it's the last thing I do."

She squeezed his hand and said, "I knew you would, Daddy. That isn't what's worrying me. It's . . . It's Mommy."

He shot her a glance. She hadn't referred to her mother as "Mommy" since she was a baby. Now it was always "my mother" or "Mother," formally and reservedly. He had long recognized it as a natural shield against Cheryl, a reluctance to get too close and to be hurt.

"What about her?"

She stopped under a street lamp. Past the sea wall the surf boomed on the Silver Strand. There was the smell of kelp and salt in the air.

"Daddy, she's heartbroken. I'm afraid. . . . I don't know what. But she's been crying, and she's been so nice to me, and the other night . . ." She took a deep breath for control. "The other night, after I was in bed, she came in and she knelt there and she cried. She really truly cried, and she said how much she loved you, and how she always would, and how she wouldn't try to keep you, or me, but she wished she could stay with us."

Dale stared at the brimming eyes. "She *did?*" He murmured, "She really *did?*"

Anne nodded. "And oh, Daddy . . . Daddy, can't we?"

He sat on the sea wall, bringing his eyes to her level. "Do you think she'll change? You think she means it?"

Anne nodded. "I *know* it. . . . I know it."

Anne, in her young sincerity, could not have been expected to know. But when a man was thirty-eight, he should have learned, he reflected bitterly, a few things about leopards and their spots.

Within a week—less than a week, two or three days—Cheryl's sudden concern had passed. There were no more rolled roasts, there were no breakfasts unless Anne cooked them, there was in Cheryl only the same secret satisfaction that Dale had seen in the eyes of the pilots who had through their own coolness survived close squeaks.

After a staff cocktail party one night, he asked her, sitting at the O Club bar, "Why'd you do it? What were you trying to pull?"

"Hmm? What do you mean?"

"The snow job you handed me when I got back from Washington. Me and Anne."

She picked a dice cup from the bar and rattled it meditatively.

"Roll for a drink?" she asked. "If I win we'll have another?"

He shook his head. "What were you trying to prove?"

"Nothing," she said disinterestedly. Suddenly she said candidly, "I saw a lawyer while you were gone."

A tight knot of anger began to form in his stomach. "Yes?"

"He said for me to get you to come back. He said if you did, legally you'd forgiven me. That's all. . . ."

"You're a sweet kid," Dale said softly. "You're a very sweet kid. . . ."

She rolled the dice and smiled up at him. "Four sixes, Dale. That'll be a horse on you. . . ."

Well, it had been a horse on him, and a horse on Anne, and he had a feeling that it might cost him more than a few drinks at the bar.

It might cost him alimony, it might cost him time to win through in the end, but no trick that Cheryl could play was going to cost him Anne.

And somehow this morning, she had shown that she knew this. Slyness was no match for doggedness, and perhaps she knew it.

Or perhaps she didn't care. . . .

Dale Heath straightened suddenly, clapping his hard-hat close to his ear. Again, tantalizingly, he thought he heard his call. "Navy Jet . . ." And then, "Five-Five . . ." And then, ". . . rillo Center. . . ."

He was due at Tucumcari in five minutes. It would be Amarillo, and it could be he they were calling. In case his transmitter was working, he called them blind, but he knew that he was not received because he heard the call once again.

When he got closer to Amarillo, perhaps . . .

He glanced at his "fuel remaining." Five hundred sixty gallons. O.K. so far, but they had better have a good high altitude
awaiting him at Amarillo.

Norm Coster sat at Mel Carnegie's desk, waiting for Eve to
return to the phone. At least, he thought, the doctor's there now,
and I won't have to take her word for the agony Sally's in. He
decided that, traffic or not, he'd insist that Mel relieve him at
the board and go down.

He saw Rocky Fontaine swivel in the chair and signal him
urgently.

"Damn," he murmured. He hated to hang up the phone on
Eve—it would probably snap the last taut nerve and turn her
into a raging, bitter woman ranting at him for what he had done
to her baby sister.

He suddenly realized that he was a little afraid of his sister-
in-law.

But he put the phone back in the cradle.

When whatever problem was bothering Rocky was solved, he
would simply insist that Mel take over, and go to the hospital.

Rocky pointed to a flight strip. "This is a Navy jet, Norm. No
Anton Chico posit on it, and it should have reported at Tucumcari at two-seven. Estimated here in ten minutes."

A lost plane, or communication failure? Well, if it was a lost
plane, there was nothing they could do. And if it was communication failure, it constituted no menace as long as it stuck
with its flight plan.

Norm turned to the surveillance radar, set up the sensitivity.
Reception to the west was poor—a minor afterguard skirmish of
the front swirled across the screen in dark shadows. And along
each of the airways marched a procession of pips—it was difficult
except when a plane made a position report to identify which
was which. But Norm squinted at the scope. . . .

Yes, he had him. It was dangerous to make assumptions, but
he had him almost certainly. One of the pips to the west was
moving perceptibly toward the center of the screen, inching in
almost unnoticeable jumps with each sweep of the beam, but

nevertheless moving. You had to watch a prop plane for many sweeps before you noticed its progress—this was a jet. And in the right position.

Well, there was nothing to do but wait for the jet's Amarillo position report to make sure. There was no real danger—a way had been cleared for every plane on the board.

And yet . . .

Norm checked the strip quickly. A bolt of alarm shot through him. He licked his lips. "Say, this is the guy Albuquerque cleared short out of Kirtland."

He flicked a switch on his board and spoke to the high-altitude controller.

"Chuck, you still holding flight level three-seven-zero for Navy Jet Three-Two-Five-Five?"

"Affirmative."

Well, at least they had a decent altitude for him when he arrived. If they could tell him about it . . .

He picked up his handset. "Navy Jet One-One-Three-Two-Five-Five. Navy Jet One-One-Three-Two-Five-Five. This is Amarillo Center. Do you read? Over."

From the speaker came nothing but static and the chatter of other aircraft. But Norm thought he heard faintly "Amarillo Center." And then unintelligible gibberish.

Norm decided to protect the jet's present twenty-three thousand feet for forty minutes east, just in case.

Dale Heath stiffened in his cockpit. Close, very close and very clearly, he heard an Air Force jet at forty thousand feet making a position report to Amarillo Center. Was his set suddenly working again? All at once the Air Force pilot's quiet voice, comprehensible where the others had been so maddeningly unintelligible, brought him back to a sane and human world. Then it faded. . . .

He switched to "guard" and called him. His voice sounded high in his ears.

"Air Force jet calling Amarillo . . . Air Force jet calling Amarillo . . . This is Navy Jet One-One-Three-Two-Five-Five. How do you read me?"

His hands were moist. He waited and tried again. There was no answer.

He glanced at his "fuel remaining." Four hundred eighty gallons. Not bad, but if he had to hold at Amarillo while he tried to get clearance to go on, not good either.

He discovered he was close to panic. He was sweating, and a drop of perspiration ran down his cheek, under his mask, tickling him mercilessly. He fumbled with the straps securing his mask to his hard-hat, gave it up, jammed his thumb into the yielding rubber and rubbed.

Take it easy, he told himself. *This isn't the first time you've lost your radio, and it won't be the last.* . . .

He took a deep breath, settling back to continue his flight. He turned up the volume on his omni, comforted by the strong signal from the Amarillo range. As he watched the omni-needle, it jerked to the side. He glanced at his watch. He was almost exactly on his estimate.

Sure that it was useless, he pressed the microphone switch on his throttle and talked into the mask.

"Amarillo Center, this is Navy Three-Two-Five-Five. Position report. How do you read me?"

He heard a distant but glorious voice, elusive and yet almost readable. He strained, closing his eyes in concentration. "Amarillo Center clears you to . . ." he heard. His heart leaped. And then a staccato burst of static cut off the altitude.

His whole body tensed in frustration. He forced himself to relax, and tried once again.

"Amarillo Center, this is Navy Jet One-One-Three-Two-Five-Five. Amarillo two-zero, two-five-thousand feet, I.F.R. to Navy Memphis." His voice still sounded strained, and he lowered it deliberately. "Holding Amarillo at two-three-thousand. Request you say again my further clearance. . . ."

This time he heard nothing.

He felt like a beggar who had just let a diamond roll into a drain.

three:

FLIGHT SEVEN
TULSA, OKLAHOMA

Feathery cirrus rode the night sky as high as thirty thousand feet; alto-strati churned at twenty thousand. Dick Barnett guided the DC-7 undeviatingly through its tops, lurching now in and now out of the clouds.

He himself hardly felt the turbulence. A conviction was growing in him that he was the victim of a gigantic conspiracy.

He had been thinking of the desk job. It might be nice at that to be home every night, to join the bankers and engineers and doctors in the eight-thirty A.M. cavalcade winding through Palos Verdes, to walk in the evening, brief case in hand, across the lawn from the driveway, knowing that a martini awaited him on the rear patio.

It would be nice, if a little dull, to accept an invitation to a party without making a dash for the schedule to check.

And if some of the adulation and curiosity he excited in his neighbors—lawyers and stockbrokers and car dealers—and in their wives—if some of that was lost, what difference did it make? Operations Manager of the Western Division of Central was no title to be taken lightly.

And neither would Vice-President be.

It was when he thought of Linda's reaction that he had stiffened. They had first talked of it when Massey had visited them two months ago. Massey had brought it up lightly: "One

210 • *THE CROWDED SKY*

of these days I'm going to get old Dick behind a desk before he grows into that left-hand seat like a potted plant."

"That'll be the day," Dick had said.

But a glance had seemed to pass between Linda and Massey. Nothing more had been said.

Now Dick Barnett frowned. There had seemed to be an undercurrent that night, as if Massey and Linda were plotting something. They had always been on the same frequency, his wife and Massey, and were forever talking good-naturedly over his head.

But that night it had been as if they were asking a small boy to retire before bedtime—tentatively probing for resistance and dropping the subject when they found it.

The irritating belief began to grow on Dick Barnett that the idea of the desk job might even have been Linda's. The more he thought of it, the more certain he became. It wasn't the C.A.R. violations after all! It was his own wife, trying to run his life again.

He shifted peevishly. Years ago she had maneuvered him, always making it seem that it was his idea, into bidding for a billet in the Eastern Division. She was a Virginia girl, and apparently had decided that they would be happier in Arlington than in Los Angeles.

At the very last moment he had discovered that her mother had been looking for a home for them in Virginia before he had even decided to bid.

Well, he had shown her that time. They were still, eight years later, in Los Angeles.

And he was damned if even for her he was going to trade command of a silver DC-7 for the captaincy of a desk at the Pacific Central Airport office.

His wife was a lovely, warm, and gentle person—he would have been lost without her—but nobody was running his life for him.

Pat Benedict studied her husband as the stewardess removed the tray from his lap. He had eaten only half his chicken. Now he sat with a strange, set expression on his face.

He's getting ready to tell me something, she thought. There was only one thing to do—wait. He would never keep anything from her, but he would wait until his thoughts were formulated before bringing up a subject.

She wondered what it would be. He had avoided talking of the Big Trip—it must have something to do with that.

Some financial difficulty? No, that was well taken care of. An opportunity the trip might interfere with? No, they had already decided that nothing but the Trip could tempt him away from his practice in La Jolla—that he was as happy with it as he would be with a more lucrative one in, say, San Diego or even Los Angeles.

So it could only be that he missed the practice, missed the day-by-day contact with the sick and those who helped them.

But if he had grown so impatient in two weeks, how could he ever survive a whole year away?

The thought troubled her. More than anything in the world she wanted to make the Trip and she had not truly thought of its effect on a busy man.

Darn, she thought. It was always something. If they had not had to postpone it for a year because it turned out that Killer was too young to enter the military school he had chosen, they might well be starting in a few months. Maybe that was it— maybe he was *sorry* they'd had to put it off.

"Darling," she said, "you know what?"

He smiled too quickly. "What?"

"Putting the Trip off a year might be a good thing. You know what we can do next month?"

"What's that?"

"We could take a few days, days we knew there was going to be powder up at Mammoth, and get some lessons before we clobber ourselves at Cortina."

He seemed to wince. "Yes . . ." he said doubtfully. "That would seem to be a good idea, wouldn't it?"

What in the world was bothering him? The operation?

"Will the incision be O.K. that soon? For skiing, I mean?"

He seemed to grasp at the idea as a straw. "No, Pat. Come

to think of it, it wouldn't be a very good idea. I think we ought to wait awhile."

"You could ski, and I could kind of take it easy in the Inn," she suggested.

He shook his head.

She lapsed back into study. Another thought had occurred to her. He was so violently enamored of his little girl that she began to wonder whether the thought of leaving her for a year was depressing him.

At this she felt a twinge of jealousy and a tug of guilt at her own willingness to go. But that was ridiculous. In an hour Nita could lose herself in sheer joy at her grandmother's—she might forget them in a year, but she would have half-forgotten her grandmother a week after they were home.

Besides, they had promised when they were married that they would do this—that they would do it without regret, like adults, while they were still young, and that if there were children they'd simply have to accept it.

"I'll bet Nita is spoiled rotten," she offered, to bring up the subject.

"She'll be all right," he murmured.

"Think how she'll be when we come back from the Trip," Pat offered. And then, slyly: "I wonder if we really ought to make it?"

And this he seemed to consider.

Joey Lafitte, asleep in the window seat, stirred beside her. *The heck with this*, she thought. *Let's out with it.* She turned to Ed.

"Now look, Ed, something's eating you. If you don't want to tell me, O.K., but you'll have to admit you're a lousy traveling companion tonight. And if you're going to worry about whatever you're worrying about on the Trip, maybe we hadn't better go."

At this sacrilege, he came out of it. He seemed to make a decision.

"Pat," he said, "you're right. I have to talk to you about something. . . ."

The loud-speaker in the cabin spoke suddenly, "Ladies and

gentlemen, this is your captain again, Dick Barnett. I hope that the last stretch of bumpiness didn't inconvenience you—I think it may improve from now on."

Joey Lafitte stirred and rubbed his eyes. "Are we there?" he asked Pat sleepily.

"No, Joey," she said softly. "Go back to sleep."

Now why, even if it was early, would the captain chance waking up children?

Joey yawned enormously and said, "Where are we?"

The loud-speaker continued: "Our head winds have decreased a little, so we'll probably land at Los Angeles ahead of schedule. We're almost over Tulsa now, past the halfway mark. I'd like to remind you again that if there's anything you'd like, please ask your stewardess, Miss Foster. Thank you. . . ."

Joey Lafitte stretched. "Could you ask her for some milk?"

Pat nodded and pressed the button over the window. She glanced at Ed. He was lost to her again. Whatever it had been that he was going to tell her would apparently have to wait.

Ed Benedict almost collapsed in relief when the captain's voice awakened Joey Lafitte.

He found that his hands were digging into the leather armrests, that his knees were shaking uncontrollably, that streams of sweat were rolling down his sides. He was a man truly in neurogenic shock, and now the respite brought him weak relief.

He sat back, resting his head, and closed his eyes.

When he was nine or ten, living in Oakland, he had been a cub scout. One Saturday the cubmaster had taken the pack to Neptune Beach, an amusement park on the bay.

After the rides and the hot dogs and the funhouse, they had gone to the swimming pool. And a rugged, well-co-ordinated youngster—Robert Briggs was his name, as Ed recalled—one of the natural leaders that springs up in any group of boys—had started a game of follow-the-leader.

Soon they were all diving into the pool after Robert, following him under water, clambering up the side, racing down the tile.

And then Robert had apparently decided to separate the men from the boys.

He had started on the low board, with a running dive. Ed, almost last in line, had no trouble with it, but some prescience told him that the worst was yet to come.

And it did. Robert climbed the ten-foot board, and a few cautious kids dropped underhandedly from the line. And Ed should have too, for he was not a diver, but he steeled himself, took a deep breath, and raced down the board after his predecessor.

He hit askew, with a jolt that almost winded him, and struggled weakly back to the ladder.

And *then* he should have quit. But Robert and the rest of the line were inching slowly up the twenty-foot board, and Ed felt that all eyes were upon him. It was his last chance to drop out, but he could not.

The climb up the ladder was a timeless struggle of mounting, visceral terror. Ed could still remember asking for divine help as he neared the top. The boy in front of him turned.

"You going to go, Eddie?"

Ed remembered answering as if from another planet. "Course. How about you?"

Stoutly: "Course."

And finally, after an eternity not long enough, he stood at the top, hands sweaty on the rails, and watched the boy before him, half-sobbing, lope down the board and disappear into infinite space.

Ed hazarded a look. The pool was a million miles straight down. It was like looking through field glasses held backward. It took physical effort to loosen his hands from the rails. Then, his knees buckling, he began a half-trot down the board.

He did not know whether he would have dived or not, because halfway down the board a screaming police whistle had pierced him in his tracks.

The cubmaster had discovered the game.

"Hey! Hey, Eddie!"

Ed tried to answer, but his voice was lost. He felt that if he did not sit down he would fall. He smiled inquiringly and no doubt stupidly at the tiny figure of the cubmaster.

"Game's over, Eddie. That's too high for you guys anyway. You climb down, you hear?"

And somehow he had made his way back to the ladder without stumbling, and with even a show of disappointment.

He had had dreams of that trot down the board for years. Now, at Joey Lafitte's awakening, he felt the same sort of languid, weak-kneed relief that he had known when the cubmaster's whistle split the noisy air.

This, he told himself, was ridiculous. If he didn't get it over with, the strain would disintegrate him where he sat. His mind darted crazily for an out.

Would it, could it be possible, to tell her on the drive back to La Jolla? Before she met the children?

No. His father would be meeting them at Los Angeles. Telling her in front of him would be unthinkable.

Suppose he waited a few weeks. No, that was unrealistic. She was already digging at the edges of his secret. And even if he kept it from her, when he finally had to tell her, in twelve, sixteen, eighteen months—what would she think of him for lying?

The stewardess passed and Pat ordered Joey a glass of milk. The girl looked carefully at Ed.

"Cup of coffee, Doctor?"

Was it possible that his face was reflecting his turmoil? Did she think that he needed special attention? Well, he did.

He nodded. Pat said, a little hurt, "Maybe this will perk you up."

"Sure it will, Pat. I . . . I was just thinking of what a backlog there'd be at the office."

Already, for a few minutes' delay, he was telling her lies. What soaring wall of deceit would be built between them if he delayed for a week or a month?

How would it be to hear her plan things that you knew she could never do? How would it be, a year from now, to hear her say, "I can hardly wait to take Nita to kindergarten the first day. I can still remember my mother taking me." Or, "We ordered Killer's uniforms today. He's going to look so *manly*, like a junior-grade general."

Or, worst of all—so bad that he had not been able to use it even in his argument with Kronk—the sickening, impossible moments in the den when, if she didn't know, she would lay out her Atlas, and travel books, and itinerary, searching for little eddies in the stream of tourism where they might drop off to spend weeks or months.

That, he knew, would be more than he could bear. He must tell her. And he must tell her before she spoke one more word about the Trip.

His embezzled relief fled. He wished that the child beside her would sleep.

Flight Seven was intermittently in the clear, and Mike Ruble could look out the window and see, ten thousand feet above, starlit wisps of cirrus on the velvet canvas of the sky, as if some celestial artist had been testing his brushes.

Below, and sometimes around them, boiled alto-cumulus and strato-cumulus, presaging, perhaps, the weak Amarillo low they expected, or laggards of a front which had already passed.

When they were in the clear, it was smooth; when they entered clouds, it became softly, not unpleasantly, bumpy.

The engines were rumbling smoothly, kept perfectly in synchronization by Capelli now that their flight level was reached. No wonder, out of Washington, he had chided Mike for interfering—he tended them as carefully, now that they were cruising, as a conductor playing a symphony in Carnegie Hall. Mike looked at the starboard propellers, hazily green from the running light. There was no strobe effect—they were in perfect step.

Capelli shot him a twisted grin.

"They sound all right to you, Orville?"

Mike laughed. "Yes, Wilbur. You're doing a magnificent job. Now if we could only figure out how to land it . . ."

He lapsed into silence. There was something he wanted to speak to Capelli about . . . Oh, yeah. The beach. Well, did he really want the whole Capelli family cluttering up a Saturday afternoon?

Quickly, before he changed his mind, he invited him.

Capelli glanced at him quizzically as if he thought he was kidding. Then he smiled.

"Well . . . Geez, thanks. . . . I'll see what the Old Lady has planned next week. Thanks."

Kitty Foster returned for their coffee cups. She stood by his seat for a moment, gazing past him and into the darkness at the starlit scud.

The lights of a little town, some suburb of Tulsa, twinkled through a hole in the overcast.

"I like to see a town at night, through the clouds," she murmured to Mike. "It makes it feel not so lonely up here."

Mike looked at her in surprise. "Do you feel lonely up here, Kitty?"

"Sometimes," she admitted. "When the passengers are asleep and I'm sitting by the window . . . I just feel all alone. That's all. . . ."

Mike felt very close to her. "I feel the same way, sometimes. When you see a town, the lighted windows, and the drive-in movies, and the cars—it kind of reminds you that you're not the last soul on earth."

"That's right."

"We'll be in at eleven, it looks like. Unless we have to hold at L.A."

"Good."

"Can I drive you home?"

It was a normal question, but Mike found that he was awaiting the answer with anxiety. This was the girl he had been so impatient with—*now* who was making a production of it? Kitty looked a little surprised.

"Why, yes, Mike. If it's not too far out of your way."

"I live in Hermosa Beach," he pointed out. "It's not."

Impulsively she squeezed his arm and left.

When they landed, he'd ask her about dropping by the Snake Pit for a drink. Even if she wouldn't, the knowledge that he'd

not have to leave her at the terminal building, not face the ride
to the ocean alone, lent him warmth.

They broke into momentarily clear skies over Tulsa. The city
glittered with light, and the Arkansas River reflected it in a
shiny point that traveled upstream with them as they passed
over.

It was as close as they would come to Dallas, thirty minutes
south on Victor One-Six-One. A half hour south was his mother,
presumably reading or watching TV in her tasteful apartment
—lonely, perhaps, unless Tom and his wife were visiting her.

He had flown over Tulsa or Dallas a hundred times in the
last eight years, and always before he had felt closer to his
mother and Tom, and even Sam Ruble. But tonight he felt cut
off, not so much by twenty thousand feet of altitude as by the
passage of time.

With the feeling came one of freedom.

He knew all at once that he would quit the airline. Sometime
soon. Not this week perhaps or not this month . . . Perhaps not
even this year.

But much as he liked to fly, this life was not for him. . . .

Dick Barnett made the Tulsa position report himself. Ordinarily he welcomed Tulsa on the westbound flight as the halfway point on the trip back to Linda. But since he had first
thought of it, the gloomy suspicion that Linda was indeed behind Massey's offer had hardened in his mind to proven fact.
It was one thing to have them offer you a better job for merit,
and he knew that he could hold it down, but it was another thing
to have your wife pulling strings behind your back.

Well, she would be at the terminal with the car. He'd have
a chance to get it off his chest right away, but the obligation
to be gruff with her chilled some of his anticipation.

And if his copilot didn't quit worrying about a few feet of
altitude, he was going to give him the yoke and let him fly all
the way to L.A. Manually . . .

When he made his report, it was so swift and brittle that St.

Louis Center had to ask for a repeat. He repeated with elaborate clarity.

If they were going to try to run the skies, why didn't they hire people who could hear straight?

four:

NAVY JET 3325
SAYRE, OKLAHOMA

Dale Heath made a decision. He had throttled back to one-eighty knots to save fuel and begun holding over Amarillo omni the moment he passed it, orbiting at his cruising altitude of twenty-three thousand. He flew a standard race-track pattern, two minutes on the straightaways paralleling Victor One-Five-One-Eight, one-minute turns that swept him five miles from the airway and then back to it.

He had called Amarillo Center twice again, heard them answer once more, and again cut out before he could catch the new clearance. Now he made up his mind to flick his I.F.F. to "emergency." At least if radar was holding him at all he would attract attention on the scopes below.

He glanced from the cockpit. He was whistling through canyons and peaks of clouds, only dimly lit by moonglow filtered through a layer of cirrus above. The faint light was blotted out as he bored into a cliff of cumulus and shifted his attention back to his artificial horizon.

He had conquered the moment of panic he had known as he approached Amarillo. His mind focused now on his only three alternatives.

If he received no clearance and had, after the fuel-consuming low-level flight from Albuquerque, sufficient range to make

Memphis, he must continue to Memphis at his last assigned altitude. Since he had never rogered for a new altitude, twenty-three thousand would be protected for him by A.T.C.

If he could *make* Memphis at twenty-three thousand . . .

If not, he would simply have to broadcast his intention blind, hope that A.T.C. was receiving him, and make a standard instrument penetration to land at a closer airport. Clark-Chennault Air Force Base perhaps, only a hundred miles up Victor One-Five-One-Eight.

He shuddered a little at the thought of an unauthorized letdown. The tension began to build again and he thought of the third alternative.

It was one of blind desperation. He could turn off the airways and eject, leaving the jet to glide unguided through the crowded sky, to crash, perhaps, on some lonely farmhouse or in a desert town. No, that was unthinkable. . . .

Don't panic, he told himself. *They'll get your clearance through.* . . .

To give A.T.C. time to try to contact him, or at least to clear twenty-three thousand, he decided to hold for three more minutes. Then he would check his fuel again and if necessary make his decision.

But they'd contact him. . . . They'd contact him with a clearance to thirty-seven thousand feet, perhaps, or at least thirty-three. An hour and a half to Memphis, with a visual letdown if the weather prognosis was correct; there to ask for a new U.H.F. set; if none was immediately available, to desert the plane and ask Memphis to fly him early in the morning to the Washington conference. . . .

Pick up the plane next week on the way west. He might still lunch with Jeanie. . . .

They would dine at O'Donnell's. It was her favorite spot. They would have, perhaps, a martini, and lobster Louis, and speak of the things they had done for the last month—had it been a month?

And the time that they were together would collapse, as it had then.

He knew that within moments they would be in immediate communication—as if they had never been apart.

With how many people did you ever communicate, really? Out of the hundreds, the thousands, you spoke to in a lifetime, how many did you touch?

There were brief moments of understanding, of course, even with passing strangers. There had been a frightened plane handler in predawn flight-deck confusion off the Marianas, caught with Dale in the prop-blast of an eager Corsair. Together they had slid helplessly aft along the slippery deck toward the fantail and oblivion, hugging each other in a flail of thrashing hands and legs, silent with terror. And then the quick cessation of the blast, and a glance into the handler's eyes.

"Thanks, buddy," Dale had said gratefully, thinking that the man had tackled him.

The handler had stared. "Christ, Lieutenant, I thought *you* grabbed *me!*"

And for a brief second there had been communication between them.

Sal Porter and he had sometimes touched minds, and there had been moments of empathy with his mother, and an Academy instructor who had shown him something of the universal rightness of calculus and then sat back smiling as the unity of all mathematics began to dawn for the first time on Dale.

And with Anne, of course, there had been instant, complete, and joyous communication from the time she could toddle.

Between most people there was always a barrier. Between Dale and Cheryl, in their wildest passion, there had been no meeting at all. Between Jean and him a crowded Navy cocktail party or an evening at bridge was enough; if both were there, they were aware of it from beginning to end if they spoke not ten words to each other.

How much time had he spent with Jean? Over the years, two weeks, perhaps. An hour in silent communion, possibly, while she washed Cheryl's dishes and Cheryl dressed for a movie, an hour of awareness of her presence at a class reunion, a whole day spent with Anne and her sailing at Norfolk because Sal and Cheryl were too hung-over to go.

There had been the glorious times with Anne, like this afternoon at the zoo—and how much time had he spent alone with her? Three months, maybe, in his whole life.

His throat tightened. Two weeks with a woman who understood and loved you, three months with a child whose mind and body seemed a part of your own, seemed little to show for the last fifteen years.

If fifteen years before he had taken another path . . .

And yet, if he had not married Cheryl, there would not have been the days with Anne. You did what you were motivated to do, and if the total chunk of pure happiness you had reached one month, or two, or three in a lifetime; if you touched a dozen people, you could probably count yourself lucky.

You did what you were motivated to do, not because fate willed it, perhaps, but because your fiber demanded it. When the pressure got too great, you made a move, if only to save your sanity.

Well, the pressure had become too great. He had known it a month before, perhaps he should have chosen then. Would Jean have let him?

They had sat after lunch, long after he should have returned to the Navy Department, in the booth at O'Donnell's. He had told her about Cheryl, wryly, now, as much without bitterness as he could.

And she had not given *him* sympathy; only Anne. (For she must have known that essentially he couldn't be hurt by Cheryl.) "Oh, that poor child!"

"God knows how long it's been going on." With an attempt at levity, "Ain't that something?"

"Cheryl's an off-beat, fascinating person," Jean said. "But why did she have to do that to Anne?"

Dale smiled grimly. "Jean, she's a bitch. You knew it from the first. You knew it from that day I met you sitting at the piano at Mrs. Z's. Didn't you?"

Jean's eyes filled with tears. "No. I like her."

"I can't quite hate her myself," Dale admitted. "But to do that to Anne . . . Suppose I hadn't found out? Suppose I'd been killed off Quemoy last year? What a life for a little girl!"

And then the glimmer of inspiration had come. "Jean, if I could fix it up—if anything happened to me, would you take care of Anne? If I could arrange it?"

She slapped her hand on the table. "Don't say that!"

"All right, but if it did?"

"Of course I would!"

They sipped their coffee, waiting for the check. Dale was watching Jean, lost in the cool depths of her eyes, when the elation began to rise in him. This, he knew suddenly, was the girl. . . .

There was nothing physical. He wanted her, all of her, not only her body. And standing outside the door to her little apartment near the hospital, he had told her:

"Jean, I love you. I don't know how long I've known it. An hour, maybe, or maybe for years."

Her wonderful eyes had filled again with tears. "I've been thinking how I'd answer you. But I can't lie about it. I love you too. And I don't know how long it's been either."

He had kissed her, and her lips were cool and soft and her cheeks were wet. They had stood for another moment.

"I'm going back to get Anne. I'm going to move her out, or move Cheryl out, and then I want you to join us."

She shook her head. "No. It isn't fair. You do what you have to do, what you and Anne decide to do. Try to leave me out, until you've made up your mind."

"I've made it up."

But she had only shaken her head.

And when he returned, when he flew back to California, he had been duped like a choir boy at a Havana blackjack table.

Well, you did what you were motivated to do, and this would turn out all right. At least, he had tried everything. . . .

He would marry Jean, he knew, and with the knowledge he was suddenly lightheaded with joy. He relaxed and looked at his clock.

The three minutes was up. He tried again to contact Amarillo control for his further clearance. He could hear nothing.

He looked at his "fuel remaining" gauge. Four-twenty gallons. Quickly he worked his "R.E.S.T." computer. From Amarillo to Memphis at twenty-three thousand would take . . .

He groaned into his mask. Four-eighty gallons. If he had left Amarillo without holding, he could still not safely have made it at twenty-three thousand. Did they think he was flying a tanker?

But it was not their fault. It was his radio's. . . . And now he must act.

He pressed the mike button and broadcast blind: "Amarillo Center, this is Navy Jet One-One-Three-Two-Five-Five. I have been unable to read your further clearance. I have less than eighty minutes' fuel remaining. I intend to make a standard jet penetration to Clark-Chennault Air Force Base. . . ." He heard his voice rising and forced himself to relax. "Descending to two-zero-thousand feet west of Sayre omni, crossing the Sayre omni at five-five, two-zero-thousand. I am departing Amarillo at two-three-thousand, I.F.R. to Clark-Chennault. Do you read? Over."

He clapped his hand to his ear and listened. He heard nothing.

He would maintain his protected altitude until the last moment, but the knowledge hung heavy on his stomach that within fifteen minutes, unless Amarillo Center contacted him, he must descend unheralded to an altitude of opposite flow.

He steadied himself on Victor One-Five-One-Eight.

At 10:30, Norm Coster had finally talked to Dr. Hudspeth on the phone.

"How is she, Doctor?"

"Fine, Mr. Coster. Not a thing to worry about."

"How long do I have?"

"You mean—"

"How long do I have to get down to see her?"

"Well, if you want to see her, I think you better trot right over. It really isn't necessary, though."

The idea of not seeing Sally before she entered her ordeal was so fantastic that Norm rejected it.

"Oh, I'll be there. You tell her I'll be there, all right. You say I ought to leave now?"

"If you want to get in under the wire. Once she's started, I can't let you in. Hospital rule."

"Yes sir. I understand. . . ."

Norm hung up and turned to Mel. "Well, Mel, that's it. I have to go."

Mel nodded resignedly. Together they walked to the board. Rocky stepped to the coffee machine, and Norm gave Mel the traffic situation. He hesitated when he got to the silent Navy jet.

"This is that Navy Jet Three-Two-Five-Five, Mel. He's apparently still holding; we haven't been able to give him his further clearance. He's transmitting kind of sporadic, and I guess he's receiving that way too. I've protected twenty-three thousand for forty minutes ahead of him, just to be sure. Guess he'll give up and go on any minute now."

He turned to the scope. Yes, the Navy jet had already given up to proceed. His pip, showing emergency I.F.F., was crawling east now along Victor One-Five-One-Eight. They would have to change his estimate at Memphis.

I wonder, thought Norm suddenly, *how his fuel state is?*

Then he put the matter from his mind. It was really none of the Center's business—presumably the pilot had worked out his reserves.

But all the way to Memphis in a jet at twenty-three thousand feet?

Norm pointed to another pip on the scope. "This is Pacific Central Flight Seven, estimating Sayre at zero-two-five-five. Twenty thousand feet."

Mel winced perceptibly. He had never accustomed himself to the volume of traffic, and to Norm's certain knowledge hated to see aircraft pass head on regardless of altitude separation.

"I hope that Navy guy's holding his altitude," Mel said.

"Why wouldn't he be?"

Mel shrugged and Norm started to move away. It was not his

responsibility to try to outguess a pilot. The rules were clear—the pilot would continue to his destination at his last assigned altitude. And in a few minutes he would be out of the Amarillo control area. And damn it, why not leave it to Mel, anyway? He was certainly cautious enough.

Suddenly he sat down on the chair, preoccupied and studying the vertical columns of strips before him. The Navy jet was at twenty-three thousand. Suppose he was low on fuel. Where would he land? At Clark-Chennault, crossing Sayre at twenty thousand in a standard instrument penetration. A wild assumption? Maybe, but eighteen thousand feet, a westbound altitude, was clear. Why not descend Flight Seven to eighteen thousand feet before they passed? It would be a safety factor. . . .

He picked up the microphone.

Mike Ruble watched his altimeter. They were still almost two hundred feet high; he still wanted very strongly to ask Barnett to stick to their altitude, but the captain's mood seemed suddenly to have changed from good-natured tolerance to a sort of peevish crankiness.

Into the sporadic flow of transmissions issuing from the speaker behind his head, he heard a call garbled by static, understandable more from the rhythm of the words than from their content. A less experienced copilot might have missed it completely. But Mike Ruble heard, "Pacific Central Seven, Amarillo Center. Over . . ."

He looked at Barnett. Barnett had apparently missed it.

"Captain? You hear them call us?"

Barnett shook his head. "No. I didn't hear anything."

Mike nodded thoughtfully. *Maybe I was wrong,* he decided. Nervousness, perhaps, or the vague unease that had plagued him throughout the trip.

But then he heard it again, distinctly. And although he could not have repeated it—it was too faint for that—he thought he heard instructions to descend. And he caught a swift glance from Barnett that meant he too had heard the transmission.

"What did he say?" Mike asked him.

"I didn't get it," Barnett said. "Let it go. If it was Amarillo Center they'll get us at Sayre."

But Mike was dissatisfied. Perhaps it was his imagination, but he thought he had detected in the voice of the ground controller a note of restrained urgency.

Communications problems in the air were not always radio ones; pilots had honestly missed instructions simply because psychologically they didn't want to hear them, or because the orders deviated from normal procedures and they didn't believe what they heard.

Ignoring Barnett, he picked up the microphone.

"Station calling Pacific Central Seven, say again?"

This time it was loud and clear.

"Flight Seven, this is Amarillo Center. . . ." There was a pause. "Will you accept eighteen thousand feet?"

Dick Barnett winced. He said to Mike, "The hell with that. It's more turbulent down there. We're in the clear here, and this is our altitude. Let 'em clear somebody else out. It's probably some S.A.C. bomber thinks he owns the airways. Ask 'em to leave us."

Mike shrugged, reluctantly. There was a legitimate way to influence them on the ground, if the situation was not serious and if they were not too rushed to be generous.

"Amarillo Center, this is Pacific Central Seven. Request we be allowed to maintain two-zero-thousand for passenger comfort. Over . . ."

There was a pause, and then: "This is Amarillo Center. Roger. Wait . . ."

Mike Ruble felt sorry for the man in the Center. He could easily *order* them to eighteen thousand, but was obviously thinking of another solution, would probably find one. It must be hell to have a decision questioned by the very people you were trying to help. . . .

Dale Heath watched the needle of his receiver stiffen as Sayre omni flew toward him under the murk below. His muscles tensed as he neared the point of his final, irrevocable decision. He glanced swiftly from the cockpit.

Still I.F.R., with a floor of solid cloud and even at his present altitude only spotty visibility of a mile or two, suddenly blotted to within twenty feet when he slammed into cumulus. Still I.F.R., with Victor One-Five-One-Eight doubtless swarming with craft.

He took a deep breath, shifted to "guard" on his U.H.F., and pressed his mike button. "Amarillo Center, Amarillo Center . . . This is Navy Jet Three-Two-Five-Five. Two minutes west of Sayre omni at five-three. Leaving two-three-thousand immediately to commence descent to cross Sayre at two-zero-thousand. Intend standard instrument penetration and landing at Clark-Chennault. Estimate Sayre five-five. Do you read?"

Desperately he strained for an answer. He found that his eyes were squeezed shut, his breath held in anticipation. But over the chaotic airwaves came nothing but static.

He sat back. There was nothing he could do. He cut back on his power, popped his dive brakes, and dropped into the soup.

Norm Coster listened to Flight Seven's request to stay at twenty thousand and ground out his cigarette angrily. Moving another airliner arbitrarily, with no more to back him up than a vague suspicion that a Navy plane *might* descend to its altitude, did not appeal to him. Especially not over the airliner's protest, however mild . . .

And he had already been questioned for the Tri-State hassle. Maybe he was simply nervous. It had been a rough night; perhaps he was jumpy over Sally. . . .

He had decided to leave Flight Seven at twenty thousand when he heard it, a jumbled transmission understood only because its rhythm carried over its omissions.

"Amarillo . . . Navy Jet Three-Two-Five-Five. Leaving two-three-thousand . . . descent to cross Sayre . . . two-zero-thousand . . . standard instrument penetration . . . landing Clark-Chennault . . ."

Mel Carnegie gasped suddenly. Norm found himself leaping

for the handset, his pulse pounding, but his voice was calm and clear in his ears.

"Navy Jet Three-Two-Five-Five, Amarillo Center. Do not descend! There's westbound traffic at two-zero-thousand. I say again, there is westbound traffic at two-zero-thousand. Climb immediately to two-three-thousand. Acknowledge. Over."

He waited only a moment for an answer he knew he'd not get, then flicked to V.H.F. "Pacific Central Flight Seven, this is Amarillo Center. Descend immediately to one-eight-thousand. I say again, descend immediately to eighteen thousand feet. Report leaving two-zero-thousand. There is jet traffic letting down to your altitude!"

He hardly waited for the roger before he switched back to emergency, fear tearing through him. He broadcast blindly again to the Navy jet, then swung around to the scope, bumping Mel.

The two pips were inching ominously closer. The Center was suddenly still.

Dry-lipped and shaking, Norm stared at the radar and waited.

Mike Ruble turned to Barnett. He was angry.

"You hear *that*, Captain? You hear that all right?"

Barnett nodded. "I hear 'em. The stupid bastards . . ."

Gradually he eased the yoke forward. "They want us to toss passengers all over the cabin?"

Mike did not answer. He watched the altimeter. They were starting almost three hundred feet high. As the yoke eased slowly forward, the altimeter wavered, then began to unwind almost imperceptibly. He fought an impulse to shove on the yoke himself.

Come on, you idiot, he moaned inwardly. *Let's get this thing down. . . .*

But Barnett was the captain. Mike could only sit and sweat.

Dale Heath glanced at his altimeter. He was at twenty-one thousand, descending at four thousand feet per minute; in fifteen seconds he would be through the critical oncoming altitude of twenty thousand, making his penetration in the relatively safe Clark-Chennault pattern.

He was beginning to reach for his checkoff list when he heard it, a tantalizing, elusive voice on his radio, vibrant with urgency.

". . . Jet Three-Two-Five-Five . . . Do not descend. . . . Westbound traffic at two-zero-thousand . . ."

Dale's heart stopped. His altimeter still showed seven hundred feet above twenty thousand, but altimeters lagged; he was probably lower. And it took time to stop a descent and begin a climb. . . .

"Dear God," he murmured, horsing back on the stick. "Climb, baby, climb. . . ."

He tore his eyes from the instruments as the altimeter needle touched twenty thousand two hundred, wavered, and began to inch upward.

He was in a cloud, a black, turbulent mass that fogged his running lights.

Then, all at once, he was in the clear, and he saw it. . . .

It was head on, dead in his path, dead on his level, the red and green wing-tip lights blinking as if in surprise, perhaps a thousand yards away. He knew instantly that a collision was unavoidable, that to turn would be useless.

His first impulse was to climb, to protect his body—to put the belly of his plane between himself and what was surely an airliner pregnant with life. His instinct screamed to climb, to protect his canopy, to leave himself free to eject.

In a flash he remembered Stub Baker telling the story in the bar: "It was me or them. Somebody had to get his cockpit clobbered. So I climbed. . . ."

In the last, irrevocable second, he knew what he must do. He had a vivid impression of Anne, laughing up at him, and of Jeanie, staring deep into his eyes, and then, using all of the strength in his soul, he jammed the stick forward and dived.

In the ultimate moment, with his body weightless and tugging at his belt, with the monstrous sky creature spreading its wings to clasp him like an animate beast, he knew that the few months of happiness he had lived, *really* lived, were enough.

And after the grinding crash and the slithering instant along the belly of the liner there was mercifully nothing. . . .

Norm Coster watched the blips. Surely now, surely now that the airliner was diving, there would be clearance. Surely the two spots of light would meet and pass, merge and split, continue their separate ways. . . .

He heard someone breathing over his shoulder. He spared a glance, thinking that it was Mel. But Mel was standing stiffly at the board, as if studying the strips could change the progress of the planes themselves. It was Rocky Fontaine, a cup of coffee in his hand, staring at the pips.

"If you didn't know there was three thousand feet between those planes," Rocky murmured, "this sort of thing could scare the hell out of you."

We don't know, thought Norm. *We don't know.* . . .

He turned back to the scope. The blips were almost on each other now, and they merged, and before his very eyes they grew and grew and grew. . . .

And they did not split. . . .

He heard a sob above him.

"Oh God . . ." Rocky Fontaine groaned. "Oh my God!"

five:

MAYDAY AT TWENTY THOUSAND

Mike Ruble was the only one who saw it. They were still two hundred feet above their altitude, Barnett was descending, his eyes on the instruments, and Capelli was entering fuel quantities on his log.

Mike saw it because he happened to be looking ahead. He saw its running lights burst from a wall of clouds, a hair to his side of their path, the red light to his right, the green to his left. He shouted and grabbed uselessly for the yoke.

He instantly recognized the plane as a jet, from the span between its swiftly spreading wing-tip lights, knew instinctively that the crash was inevitable, that there was less than a second for the jet pilot to act; that when he acted he would try to climb and would slam into their cockpit with celestial force. He knew only sorrow and loss, a sense of having missed too much. His body shrank from the blow, but in a flash his mind accepted it.

This was how it would end, the dream of warm days on the beach and cool mornings at an easel, of quiet communion with a girl like . . . Kitty. It would end before the things were said that should have been said, before the great adventure had even started.

With the lightning spatial judgment of a fighter pilot, he knew in that second that the jet would strike his side of the cockpit. He tensed, and then his eyes widened.

The jet dropped. The movement was so unexpected that Mike blinked. He had *dived!*

He caught a flash of a light-colored object to his right and below, and then it hit, with an impact that hurled him against his seat belt, slamming him double against the unyielding yoke.

For a moment he was unconscious. When he came to, he found that he was sitting erect, his hands on the yoke as if he were flying the plane. His ears were splitting with sound and pressure. Beside him, Capelli was spread grotesquely over the pedestal between pilot and copilot, hurled face down over the controls. Barnett was sitting dazedly, rubbing his forehead.

The aircraft was vibrating violently, shrieking with sound. He smelled smoke, knew vaguely that there was an electrical fire. A cherry glow on the starboard wing showed him that there was an engine fire, too. And his ears were killing him. He tried to clear his tubes, opening his mouth and yelling. It brought him some relief, but explosive depressurization from a hole somewhere in the skin of the plane was not to be handled so easily.

The fire must be fought, circuit breakers must be pulled, the very weight of things to do pressed on his temples. But first they must lose altitude before their ears split. . . . He shoved forward on the yoke, half expecting to find it listless in his hands, nerves of cable severed in the crash.

But it was solid, and the nose dropped. It was then that he began to hope. . . .

Joey Laffite, asleep again, stirred and snuggled close to Pat Benedict. She was sleepy herself, had decided that whatever Ed was trying to tell was going to have to wait, and was drowsily imagining that Joey was Killer, snuggling close to her as they watched TV at night.

It had been years. . . . Killer at eight would have died before he'd have shown her the affection he had at six. . . . But it was nice to imagine that the child beside her was her own.

She was slipping into slumber when she awakened screaming. She had been thrown forward heavily against her seat belt, and the man behind her, apparently not belted, had been hurled against the back of her seat, jamming it upright.

Pat had scraped her chin, but it was the unbearable, knifing pain in her ears that tortured her.

She straightened, pressing her palms to her head. Her first thought was of the child. He was staring at her, moaning in terror.

She turned to Ed. The lights in the cabin flickered and came on again. Ed was holding his hands to his temples.

"God," he shouted. "What happened?"

She was speechless. Joey began to bounce in his seat in agony. "My ears . . . My ears . . ."

The cabin was a shambles. The stewardess was picking herself up from the aisle forward, holding her ears. Somewhere in the rear a baby began to scream, and a woman's voice joined it in short animal yells of pain.

It was very cold. Pat stared outside. Incredulously, she saw a streamer of fire flutter from an engine, longer and longer, as if it were being unfurled from an endless roll of confetti.

This, then, was how it was to be: they would fall in flames, as the men did in the movies she had seen of World War I, trapped and screaming. It would happen like this, and all the things they had wanted to do would go undone.

And she would never see Nita or Killer again. . . .

Joey was whimpering in terror. Instinctively she hugged him close to her.

"Don't cry, Joey. Don't cry, honey. Please."

"My ears," he whined. "My ears hurt. . . ."

And pressing him close, she touched her lips to his cold forehead. She was tired, all at once, unbearably tired, but somehow as she hugged him, the pain in her ears became more endurable.

"Don't cry," she said again. "It will stop. . . ."

She turned to Ed. He was looking at her with such tenderness that her heart lurched.

"Ed," she piped, above the howling cacophony, "what happened?"

"We hit something, Pat." And in his voice was a note almost of elation. "Darling, I think we've had it. . . ."

She stared at him. The bond between them was suddenly whole again, but why the note of joy?

"No," she said, rejecting it, though she felt that he was right. They could hope! "No, no, *no* . . ."

Mike Ruble wondered where the fuselage was ruptured. The cabin had been pressurized to seven thousand feet, its living cargo riding in an artificial environment rather than the true one of twenty thousand feet. When the skin had been punctured the cabin pressure was suddenly the true one. It was as if nature was paying them back for cheating, as if they had all been shot the remaining thirteen thousand feet into the air with no time for their ears to adjust. Ears, or blood . . . He had a sharp pain in his knee as a nitrogen bubble tried to ride an artery too small for it.

And without oxygen the human being does not live long at twenty thousand feet. Already his vision was blurring. *Smoke mask,* he thought wildly, jamming the black rubber device over his face. Oxygen . . .

His vision returned. They were in a dive, losing three thousand feet per minute. At twelve thousand feet, their passengers could survive; he was already down to eighteen thousand. He had two minutes to go. . . .

Through the glass plate of his mask he stared at Barnett. The captain's eyelids were dropping. He leaned across, shook him, and pointed to his mask. Barnett nodded lethargically, struggled with his own, almost gave up, and with a supreme effort adjusted it.

Mike put on his earphones and saw Barnett follow suit. "You read me, Captain?"

"Yeah. Christ, what happened? What happened?" His voice was thin.

"Mid-air collision." He glanced at the tachometers. Number three was pushing the upper limit. "And we must have thrown number three prop. . . ."

"Feather the son-of-a-bitch," said the captain. "I mean cut it." Then he moved toward number four throttle.

"*Three*," yelled Mike. "Christ. Let's get organized. . . ."

The captain nodded and cut number three engine. He stared at Capelli. "What happened to him?"

"Clobbered," Mike said. "We got a fire in number three, too."

The captain turned on the engine fire extinguisher. Mike craned backward, watching the glowing engine. Please, God, let it work. . . . Please.

A cloud of white vapor shone in the light from the fuselage. The engine still glowed, might burst into flames again, but the flaming orange banner they had been towing left them as if it had been a target sleeve cut loose from a towplane.

He turned back to the cockpit. What was next? They were at fourteen thousand now, in murky darkness. What was next?

The passengers? Uselessly, knowing that the lines were surely cut, he tried to call Kitty on the interphone. There was no answer. Someone would have to go back, but not now. . . .

"You call Mayday yet?" asked Barnett.

Thank God, thought Mike, shifting frequencies to "emergency." *He's getting hold of himself.*

"Negative."

He heard Barnett's voice on the radio. "Mayday, Mayday, Mayday. Pacific Central Flight Seven, on Victor One-Five-One-Eight . . ."

The answer came back immediately. "Flight Seven, Sayre Radio. What's your position? What's your trouble?"

Barnett flicked to intercom. "Where were we on One-Five-One-Eight?"

"Just past Sayre."

"Sayre Radio, Flight Seven. We're west of your station, descending, depressurized. Mid-air collision. We lost number three engine. . . ."

"What are your intentions?"

A sharp controller, thought Mike. The voice was brisk and unexcited. Of course, *he* was on the ground. . . .

"You heading for Amarillo?" Barnett asked suddenly.

"I guess. . . . How long's their runway? Where's the chart?"

"Six thousand feet, hard-surfaced, high-intensity runway lights," Barnett said immediately without looking.

And Mike knew that he was right.

They were at twelve thousand now. Mike hoped that the passengers who lived had survived the descent.

Barnett still made no attempt to take the controls. Dazed, or scared? In clammy, opaque darkness Mike began a one-eighty-degree turn. He chilled. His omni-receiver swung listlessly. So did the low-frequency A.D.F. bird-dogs, both of them. He tried to remember where their sensing antennas were. The canopy of the jet had apparently carried them away.

"We got G.C.A. at Amarillo?" he asked suddenly.

"No."

"How the hell we going to land in that stuff?"

"Clark-Chennault!" Barnett said suddenly.

"What?"

Barnett seemed suddenly to come to life, taking the yoke. Mike sat back.

"Clark-Chennault Air Force Base," chanted Barnett from memory, "east of Sayre. G.C.A., Tacan, a thirteen-thousand-foot runway, high-intensity lights, the works!"

Mike had never heard of the place. *By God,* he thought, *this guy might be the sloppiest instrument pilot in the sky, but he sure is the local authority on Victor One-Five-One-Eight. . . .*

Mike called Abilene. "Sayre Radio, Flight Seven. We'll try to land at Clark-Chennault. Can you give us a G.C.A. channel?"

"This is Sayre Radio. Roger. Contact Clark-Chennault G.C.A. on 121.5. Over . . ."

Quickly Mike shifted frequencies. "Clark-Chennault G.C.A. Pacific Central Seven. West of Sayre. Twelve thousand feet. On fire. Request G.C.A. descent to your field. . . ."

There was an interminable wait, and then a crackling Brooklyn accent: "Flight Seven, this is Clark-Chennault G.C.A. Roger. Commence a ninety-degree right turn for identification. . . ."

Immediately Barnett banked to the right. Mike prayed that

they were close enough for Clark-Chennault to pick them up on radar. The smoke was worse. . . . Someone had to do something about the fire. Capelli had slid off the pedestal, moved restlessly. Mike saw with pity that his face was a pulp. Capelli could be eliminated.

"Captain, I better pull the circuit breakers. . . ."

Barnett hesitated. Reluctantly he nodded. "Go ahead."

Mike unbuckled himself, swung Capelli's chair out of the way, and gently laid the flight engineer prone and stepped over him. Then he saw it. . . .

When number three prop had carried away, it had ripped out of the belly a jagged hole at least five feet in diameter. Its edges burst outward, like the exit hole of a gigantic projectile, from the blast of the decompression. All of the loose gear and books in the radio compartment had been whisked away. It was a wonder that it had not sucked Capelli into the void. As he neared it, groping for the circuit-breaker panel, he felt the suction of air whistling past the puncture grasp him in a giant grip. He clutched at his armrest, dropping into a squat.

The history of aviation was salted with stories of navigators hurled into space when their navigational domes had popped off during a starsight; of passengers ripped from their seats into eternity when a window had blown; of gunners yanked into the night when a Plexiglass bubble had failed.

And the circuit-breaker panels were close to the hole; too close. But the smoke in the radio compartment was thickening. . . .

Mike Ruble weighed close to two hundred pounds, but he knew that the law of decreasing pressure of air rushing past an opening—Bernoulli's principle—the same law that kept them aloft—could whisk him from the plane as if he were a ten-pound baby.

He began to inch toward the rupture.

Ed Benedict, who had sworn he would never pray again, thanked God that he had not told Pat before. The plane was rocketing earthward now, his Eustachian tubes and maxillary sinuses were intermittently jabbing with pain, he knew that in moments they would be hurled into jagged nothingness, but at least he had not told her. Her last few hours had been free of the shadow of doom.

Even the thought that he would never again see Killer or his own tiny Nita could not mar that fact—Pat's last hours had been happy ones.

Thank God, he thought, *for that.* . . .

He was suddenly pressed into his seat. The lurching, screaming dive had come to an end. He braced himself, awaiting the impact, squeezing Pat's hand.

It did not come. Had the pilot regained control? As the moments passed, it seemed that he had. They were no longer diving —it was cold, and the wind shrieked as loudly as before, but they were no longer diving. . . .

Would he have to tell her after all?

But now a bone-weary lassitude began to enfold him.

That he could take up later, now he was tired. . . . Very, very tired.

And he knew what it was, and he almost welcomed it because it untied the knots in his body. Anoxia? How high had they been flying? He could hardly remember. He looked at the back of his hands in the dim light. Anoxia, sure enough—

His fingernails were blue.

Blue . . . blue? What about the woman in the seat ahead? The one with the bluish lips?

He struggled to his feet and peered at the woman.

She was unconscious. Her lips were as blue as ever, and she was unconscious.

He looked for the stewardess and saw her kneeling by a passenger in the aisle. He beckoned her, and she came to him.

"Yes, Doctor?" she cried above the noise.

"Can you get me some oxygen? This woman's had a heart attack."

Panting herself, the stewardess went aft and returned with a portable tank and mask. "I don't know what happened, Doctor. . . ."

He shook his head. "It doesn't matter. . . ."

He covered the purple features with the mask, turning on the valve. The woman's eyes flickered immediately.

"You're all right," Ed said.

The stewardess pulled at his sleeve. "Doctor, this man up here was unstrapped. When you're finished, would you take a look?"

He glanced back at Pat questioningly. She nodded.

When the woman could handle the oxygen bottle, Ed went forward.

Mike Ruble clung to a frame, fighting the suction, and tugged at the tiny circuit breakers. It was freezing cold, and he had to force himself to work methodically, when his impulse was to yank them all and get away from the gaping hole. He had to leave the essential circuits operative; if one of them was causing the electrical fire, it was just too bad; if he pulled the V.H.F. breaker, for instance, he would kill them by cutting the artery of their communication with the ground as surely as would a surgeon whose knife slips to his patient's jugular. His knees began to wobble from the cold and the strain. He took a last look at the panels and dropped to the deck to crawl back.

Some change in the pressure tearing at his clothes made him look aft. He saw Kitty's face appear in the dark passageway, oddly near the floor. She was on her hands and knees, fighting the blast. Her nose was bleeding, her short hair streamed forward, but she seemed unaware of her danger, her brow furrowed in concentration.

He attracted her attention, waved her back. For a strange moment the two stared at each other over the hole, down the length of the compartment. She beckoned to him, pointed aft to the cabin. He nodded, held up a finger to wait, again waved her back. She nodded and retreated, closing the door.

Mike lurched back to his seat. They were at eight thousand, descending fast, and as he plugged into the radio he heard the voice of a G.C.A. final controller, a little garbled, but gloriously readable and strong.

"Pacific Central Seven, I have you at eight thousand feet, five

242 • *THE CROWDED SKY*

miles north of Sayre. Turn right to a course of one-eight-zero
degrees."

"Understand one-eight-zero degrees," answered Barnett,
banking to the right. "Steady on one-eight-zero . . ."

Mike said, "Captain, somebody's got to go aft. The stewardess came up. . . ."

"Look, Ruble, our nose wheel's jammed. Where you been?"

"Yanking the circuit breakers, like I said." Mike looked at the
landing-gear indicator. Barnett was right. . . . Two green lights
showed the main gear down, thank God, but a red light showed
the nose wheel "up." Its doors must have been jammed on the
impact. Well, it could be done, had been done before. A careful,
soft landing, holding the tail close to the runway until the
weight of the engines teetered the plane to its nose as the speed
dropped off. Then a skidding, scraping run to a stop. There was
fire danger, of course, from the sparks they'd make, for there'd
be no time to ask for foam on the runway; there was the problem
of getting passengers out of a cabin door which would end up
thirty, forty feet above the ground, but it could be done. . . .
Somebody had to get aft. . . .

He thought of Kitty struggling in a blazing cabin, trying to
calm a hundred fear-crazed passengers.

"I got to go back, Captain."

Barnett shook his head. "I need you up here."

"*You* go back, then. I'll land the damn thing. But somebody's
got to help the stewardess."

For a long moment Barnett stared at him. "*I* land this airplane, Mister. Don't forget it!" He thought for a moment. "O.K.
Go aft and help her."

Then Mike stepped over Capelli and dropped to his belly to
snake around the yawning hole.

Norm Coster shrugged Rocky Fontaine's agonized hand
from his shoulder, staring at the scope. The two blips had
merged and grown for an instant, and then, after an eternity,
finally split like a living cell in a biology movie. One pip remained where it was, grotesquely still in a fluorescent sea that

never supported unmoving objects. The other crawled slowly toward the north.

"They hit," Rocky murmured uncomprehendingly. "They hit!"

Norm shook his head impatiently, watching the pip which had stopped moving. In a few seconds, as he had known it must, it sank into the tiny ocean before him, leaving only a trace of luminescence as the sweep rotated, searching for more animate targets.

Faint words knifed through the Center, words calm and businesslike, but hated and sickening to the men at the boards.

"Mayday, Mayday, Mayday! Pacific Central Flight Seven . . ."

Norm whirled back to the control board. He already knew what had happened, there was no time to waste. But he could not ignore the quiet voice.

"Mid-air collision. We lost number three engine. . . . Descending . . ."

"God," breathed Norm, his mind racing. "Let's go!" He looked at the narrow slips. He would have to take over, clear the airways, but first he had to think.

There were four eastbound aircraft in the vicinity; at five, seven, nine, and eleven thousand. There was an Air Force MATS carrier making a low-frequency approach to Amarillo; Amarillo approach control would handle him. There were five westbounds; at six, eight, twelve, fourteen, and sixteen thousand. Presumably he could forget the one at sixteen thousand; it was simply too late, surely Flight Seven had dropped through that altitude already. And the Navy jet? Where was it? It had probably spun crazily through the crowded airway already. . . .

He took a deep breath and picked up his microphone. "TWA Flight Three-Five-Four, this is Amarillo Center. Climb immediately to one-eight-thousand. Maintain one-eight-thousand." He took a deep breath. The board, with its vertically stacked slips, seemed slowly to enlarge.

"American Flight Four-Two-Three, there is traffic at your altitude on Victor One-Five-One-Eight. Hold southeast Finley

Intersection at one-four-thousand until further advised. . . ."

The board became his whole world; Sally faded from his thoughts. The board encompassed the room, the town, the living ocean of air above him. . . .

Mike Ruble crawled through the cabin door into a shambles of food trays and magazines. He shut it and stood up. Kitty and a passenger were kneeling by a man amidships, lying in the aisle.

Mike looked down the lines of faces, some resigned, some white with fear, some dabbing at bloody noses. A man spoke to him.

"We going to make it, Mister?"

Mike nodded with an assurance he did not feel. "Of course."

He lurched up the aisle to Kitty. The howl of the wind over the rupture died behind him, but he still had to speak loudly. "What's wrong?"

She looked up. "He wasn't strapped in. He's got a concussion, the doctor says. And we have a heart case in 13C, but the doctor gave her oxygen and she seems to be O.K."

Mike, with the help of the doctor, lifted the man to his place and strapped him in tightly. The doctor left for his seat. "Nose wheel's jammed," Mike murmured to Kitty. "We'll go through the crash-landing procedure. I'll do the talking."

"I have the checkoff list, Mike. Do you want it?"

Reading from a checkoff list might indicate a lack of assurance, but he didn't want to forget anything. "You follow me, and tell me if I forget anything."

He returned to the front of the cabin. How much should he tell them? Everything, he decided. He talked as loudly as he could without seeming excited.

"Ladies and gentlemen—I'll repeat this aft, so don't worry if you don't hear me—Ladies and gentlemen, we had a collision with another aircraft. From our standpoint, it's a minor one. We're in contact with ground radar, and we'll land in a couple of minutes at a large Air Force base. There will be all the equipment necessary to get us out, should anything happen when we land, which is doubtful. It'll be an ordinary landing until we slow down, when the nose will drop, not too hard. We'll skid to a stop. There'll be very little impact. Landings like this have been made safely many times before."

He took a breath. "Just the same, I'll ask you to do a few things to protect yourselves. And we'll have to do some of them quickly, now. First, fasten your safety belts tightly." He waited until the forward passengers had done so and Kitty had checked them. "Now, push your seat buttons and raise your seats upright. O.K. . . . Now anybody with false teeth, please take them out and put them in your purses or pockets." He essayed a grin. "We won't tell anybody."

They were suddenly smiling, and a woman tittered a little, her voice high with release.

I'll be damned, thought Mike. *They're not as scared as I am. . . .*

"O.K. Take all the sharp objects from your pockets, pens and keys, and jam them between your cushions. Take your pillows and put them by your feet. Then when I give the word, lean forward, grab your ankles. Not now . . . Just when I tell you to lean forward." He hesitated. "Any questions?"

No one spoke.

"No one is to move before the plane is well at rest. Then you'll go aft to the back of the plane. It'll be a slight uphill climb, because the nose will be down. There you'll slide to the ground on a canvas chute we'll have rigged. Someone will catch you at the bottom. Please don't crowd."

He paused. He had to tell them now; it might save all their lives.

"There's of course a slight possibility of fire. The same thing goes; don't crowd. There'll be time to get out no matter what happens. . . ."

If, he thought, *the captain doesn't screw up the landing. . . .*

He repeated the instructions farther aft. He turned to Kitty. "Did I forget anything?"

"Not a thing. You were great, Mike."

"Let's turn on all the emergency flashlights," he said. He

picked two of the solidest looking men and seated them aft, instructing them on how to slide down the emergency line to the ground and hold the canvas chute. Then he returned to seat 11C, next to Kitty, belted himself tightly. Suddenly he took her hand and she squeezed his. "Fingers crossed?" she murmured. He nodded, staring out the window. The plane banked left. Were they turning to the base leg, or the final? Four minutes, or one to go? Instinctively he knew that it was final.

He felt sudden communion with Barnett. Ultimately the show was his, sweating alone in the cockpit, with the final controller's voice in his ears: "On glide-path . . . going below glide-path, fifty feet below, sixty feet below glide-path . . . fifty . . . coming up on glide-path . . . come right three degrees to two-two-zero. . . ."

He remembered sweating the late and incompetent Colonel Neilson into the fatal landing at Seoul. No one had liked the colonel by then; his flying had scared them all again and again, yet dully dangerous as he was, he had been of the brotherhood. The group of hardened jet pilots crowded around the radio in the comm-shack had been with him every foot of the way, until he had creamed himself in a thudding boom a mile from the field. Then, when the shock passed, they had turned away, a little ashamed of their grief. "That stupid son-of-a-bitch had no right in the air. . . ."

And it was so now with Barnett. He was a pilot, and in trouble, and the fact that it might be partly his fault that they were all in trouble with him made no difference.

He pressed his nose against the glass of the window, watching, watching, waiting. . . . And suddenly he saw them through thin scud. . . . The lights of some lonely farmhouse, five hundred feet below. They were almost down!

"Everybody bend forward," he yelled. "Everybody bend forward!"

He sensed the movement, and across the aisle someone began to pray, loudly and clearly: "Our Father which art in heaven . . ."

Ed Benedict reached across Pat and checked Joey Lafitte's safety belt. Then he checked hers for tightness, and cinched his own up another half inch.

"Ed?" Pat said.

"Yes, darling?"

"Ed, I think we're going to make it."

They would make it, Ed thought. They would make it, and forever he would call back the experience, for all the time that Pat lived, to remind him how tissue-thin was the wall between those whose death was predictable and those whose death was not. A great weight had lifted from his shoulders.

He was sure that they would make it. And he had a surprise for Pat, once he thought up an excuse. Once he thought up an excuse, they were going on the Big Trip, and she was going in happy ignorance. They were going not next year, not even next month. They were going within weeks. . . .

He looked into her eyes, and for the first time since he had known, there was nothing veiling his love.

"I think we're going to make it, too."

When their wheels touched, it was with a gentle "awk, awk . . ." of rubber. Mike waited for a bounce, and there was none. *He's done it;* he thought, *if he didn't overshoot, or if he doesn't slam the nose down, he's done it. . . .*

Despite himself, he had to look. He raised his head. Out the window he caught a flash of garishly lighted hangars, bombers inside. A last emergency vehicle was chasing down an adjoining runway, red light flashing. Interminably the runout continued —to brake would slap the nose down and probably break it off. Finally, gently, it fell, bounced in a grinding series of bumps. Sparks showered the runway. *Oh, God,* Mike breathed. *No fire . . . No fire . . .*

"But deliver us from evil: For thine is the kingdom, and the power . . ."

The plane stopped long after it seemed to have lost motion, with a lurching heave that slung him against his belt, and he was suddenly on his feet, racing to help the men at the door. When they had slid into the darkness, he turned.

Incredibly the passengers were standing at their seats and in the aisle, facing him. They were attentive, but no one made a move. A great, leaping pride in these strangers clutched at his throat. He could only take the arm of an old lady nearest him and lead her to the door.

"O.K.," he said hoarsely, close to tears. "One by one, down the chute . . ."

Then he lifted the woman effortlessly, placed her on the chute, lowered her as far as he could, and let go.

A voice from the darkness below shouted, "Got her. Next!"

Within moments the plane was surrounded with fire trucks and ambulances. In thirty seconds there were two ladders at the door, and the chute was forgotten.

There was no fire, but in two minutes there was not a soul in the plane.

Mike sat on the running board of a fire truck and quaked.

Captain Barnett stood in the center of a group of Air Force officers. Mike, off to the side, watched a bird colonel shake his hand, squeeze his shoulder, and indicate the Operations Building. The passengers and Kitty were already inside, with the flight surgeons. Capelli and two passengers were in the base hospital. Barnett spotted Mike and they walked together toward the office.

"Nice landing, Captain," Mike said simply. A realization that he was facing a decision, one of the hardest he had ever met, had sobered his elation at their deliverance. That, and the thought of the trapped jet pilot, diving into eternity . . .

"Thanks, Ruble," said Barnett. He was sober. "They want a preliminary report."

"Yes."

"What was that stupid bastard doing at our altitude?" Barnett demanded suddenly.

"We'll find out. And that stupid bastard saved our lives, Captain. Let's not forget that."

"Saved our lives? What are you talking about?"

"I saw him just before we hit. He dived."

"So what?"

"So he wouldn't cream our cockpit."

"Bull! He probably never saw us."

"He saw us all right. He dived." Mike shook his head. "I'd have climbed, Captain. Any fighter pilot would."

"What difference did it make?"

"He just jammed his cockpit canopy, that's all. If it didn't kill him on contact, it sure as hell trapped him."

"That's your theory. What was he doing at our altitude?"

This was it, then. He was sounding him out, trying to find what he'd say.

Because Mike Ruble knew that his own character was painted in soft hues, he knew why a part of him longed to soften the truth to save a man who, after all, when the chips were down had come through. But mixed into his fiber on the palette of war in the air had been harsher tones, too. The sky was a place of no delicate half-colors. If you tried to tint truth with pastels, you killed, eventually, or injured. The sky was an element of stark blacks and whites.

"I'm sorry, Captain. We weren't on our altitude. You know that, don't you?"

Barnett's eyes glinted. "What are you trying to say?"

"We were two hundred feet high."

"I was letting down."

"We were still two hundred feet high."

"And he was eight hundred low. Why?"

"We'll find out pretty soon, I guess."

Barnett stopped, facing him. "You going to *tell* them we were two hundred feet high?"

Mike faced him sadly. "Yes sir."

Barnett's face collapsed. "Listen . . . Listen, Ruble . . . This thing wasn't our fault. Why confuse the thing?"

"I'm not. I'm going to clarify it."

"We weren't that far off!"

"Yes sir. Two hundred feet. I'd just looked."

"Look, Ruble, why are you going to tell them that? What about your company loyalty? And the F.A.A. could ground me for that. Why do you want to do that?"

"Captain, I think they ought to know. You saved our tails twice; you know this airway like you built it; you landed that thing like it was full of eggs. But I don't think you're safe, sir. I'm sorry, but I don't. And I'll have to tell them the facts."

Mike tensed for the explosion. The captain looked back at the silver plane. It knelt on the runway, still graceful in its nakedness under the glaring lights.

"Suppose I tell them, myself?"

Mike's heart leaped. "If you do that, I'd appreciate it, sir. More than I can say. I really would. . . ."

Barnett moved toward the building. "I'll tell them," he said. "I'll tell them. . . ."

Mike watched the captain move toward the lighted building. He was no longer dapper, not so fresh and handsome looking. But there was pride in the set of his shoulders. Some of the sour taste left Mike's mouth.

He went to look for Kitty. . . .

The hot-line from Abilene croaked and Norm Coster picked it up wearily. He listened to the voice and turned to the men of the watch just going off duty.

"The Navy jet crashed and burned on a farm five miles east of Elk City. Pilot never got out. Flight Seven landed at Clark-Chennault. No crash. Couple of minor injuries."

Mel Carnegie stood behind him. "The hospital called, Norm. Your wife's doctor."

Norm's heart stopped.

"Sally had a boy," said Mel.

"Is she O.K.?" Norm blurted.

"She's O.K., Norm. He said she was O.K."

"Oh, God," Norm said brokenly. "Oh, God . . ."

Carnegie seemed subtly changed, now that the worst had befallen. He squeezed Norm's shoulder and walked to the door with him. The storm had passed and a few golden stars glittered through lonely cirrus.

"Rough night," said Mel, and it did not somehow sound inane.

"Yes."

"You did everything you could, Norm."

"I think of that poor bastard alone in the jet, and wanting to hear us, cut off, like we weren't even here—"

"You did everything you could," Mel said again. "Believe me, you did."

Norm nodded. He walked slowly across the parking lot under the immense sky. He had talked to a man a few minutes before, and now the man was dead, and if the man had heard, he had been the last human being to reach him.

If he had heard . . .

A man had died, and a little boy had been born.

He headed toward town to meet his son.

glossary

aerology: Meteorology.

air evac: An air evacuation ambulance plane.

airspeed: Speed through the air in knots.

airway: A wide aerial highway along which are placed navigational aids and along which passes the preponderance of cross-country aerial traffic.

A.L.P.A.: Air Line Pilots Association. Not conceded to be a union, but at times bears a striking resemblance to one.

altimeter setting: A setting given a pilot by radio so that he can set his altimeter to the local pressure to read correct altitudes.

anoxia: Lack of oxygen in the blood.

artificial horizon: The basic cockpit instrument showing an aircraft's attitude.

A.T.C.: Air Traffic Control. A function of the Federal Aviation Agency.

ball-bank: A cockpit instrument showing the rate of turn.

to bilge: Naval Academy language for failing.

bird-dog: The needle of a low-frequency radio compass, which ceaselessly sniffs out the radio station to which it is set.

blip: A radar target on a scope.

C.A.A.: Civil Aeronautics Administration. Superseded in 1959 by the Federal Aviation Agency.

cat shot: Catapult shot from a carrier's bow. A "cold" cat shot is one in which the catapult fails, usually dribbling the plane off the bow.

Center: In Air Traffic Control, the Center is a central control and communication station which handles traffic over a large area in the U.S. There are 26 Centers.

clearance: A routing given an aircraft by Air Traffic Control. A "short" clearance is one to a point short of a pilot's destination at which he will radio for further clearance.

clobbered: "Socked-in," "zero-zero."

controlled traffic: Traffic under the control of Air Traffic Control as opposed to V.F.R. aircraft on their own.

controller: The man in a control center responsible for the separation of aircraft within a given sector or above a certain altitude.

to copy: To write down a radio transmission, such as a clearance.

cross section: In weather, the picture of a vertical slice of air, cut along a projected route, showing the pilot what clouds and frontal activity he must expect to encounter.

cruise and maintain: In a clearance, an instruction to "cruise and maintain five thousand" means that five thousand feet is the basic cruising altitude for the plane cleared. Redundant, and usually now shortened to "maintain."

deadhead: A pilot or copilot riding as a passenger.

departure control: The Air Traffic Control man responsible for aircraft departing from an area of high traffic density.

direct: Used in an A.T.C. clearance, denotes a direct route cross-country between two radio fixes, rather than a route along a given airway.

to eject: To bail out of a jet.

explosive decompression: The effect occurring when a pressurized cabin at high altitude suddenly fails structurally, exploding all of its pressure through the failed member.

F.A.A.: The Federal Aviation Agency, responsible for administration of the airways and of all civil and military aircraft flying them.

F.E.I.A.: Flight Engineers International Association. A union.

to file: To turn in a request for clearance along a certain proposed route for a cross-country flight. The pilot "files," Air Traffic Control "clears."

final controller: The Ground Control Approach operator who takes over to guide an aircraft in the last few moments of its G.C.A.

five by five: Radio parlance for perfect reception, loud and clear.

flight level: Above twenty-four thousand feet, "flight levels" are assigned rather than altitudes. Thus "flight level two-nine-zero" means twenty-nine thousand feet.

flight strips: Narrow strips of stiff paper on which air traffic controllers write estimates of the times aircraft will reach various en-route points in their sectors.

flow control: In Air Traffic Control, the regulation of traffic flowing from one sector or zone to another.

G.C.A.: Ground Control Approach. A system of guiding a plane to a landing by using radar and talking him down.

G.C.I.: Ground Control Intercept. A G.C.I. site controls interceptors sent to check on unidentified aircraft by the Air Defense Command. Primarily military, these stations, through civil liaison men, utilize their more accurate radar to aid Air Traffic Control centers in the control of civil traffic when necessary.

graveyard spiral: The descending turn a pilot slips into when vertigo panics him into believing his own senses rather than his instruments.

gripe sheet: The form on which a pilot lists defects in an aircraft he has just flown.

Ground Control: The tower operator at an airport charged with communicating with aircraft on the ground or taxiing.

ground speed: Speed in knots over the ground, aided or retarded by winds.

gyro-compass: A sensitive gyro-controlled compass in the cockpit.

to hold: To fly in an oval pattern until cleared to proceed on one's flight.

I.F.F.: A device to "identify friend from foe." Triggered by search radar, it responds with a code visible on the scope of the man on the ground.

I.F.R.: Instrument Flight Rules. Briefly, rules a pilot *must* follow when visibility is such that he must depend on Air Traffic Control to separate him from other aircraft because he cannot see. And rules he often follows anyway.

illegal: Flight personnel are "illegal" when they have exceeded the eighty-five hours maximum flight time permitted them by the Federal Aviation Agency.

instrument letdown: The procedure for letting down from cruising altitude to an airport, using a radio aid to navigation.

intercom: The system that allows communication between pilot and passengers.

Intersection: On the airways an intersection is a point where two beams from a radio range intersect or where two radials from an omni-range intersect.

jet stream: An eastbound river of wind of phenomenal speed crossing the U.S. at thirty thousand feet or above.

Link trainer: An indoor instrument trainer simulating a real aircraft.

low: In weather, a low-pressure area, often the center of a storm.

Mayday: International distress call.

omni-needle: The needle of an omni-receiver, sensitive to an omni-range.

omni-range: A very high frequency range emitting a signal that activates a needle in a cockpit instrument. The basic navigational aid in commercial flying.

penetration: In jet flying, descent during a letdown.

pip: A radar target. Synonymous with "blip."

posit: Short for position.

position report: A report by a pilot to a ground station giving his position, his altitude, and usually his next estimate. Given as he passes over navigational fixes.

radio beacon: A beacon emitting low-frequency signals in all directions which can be sensed by a radio direction-finding needle in the cockpit.

radio facilities chart: A map or series of maps on which are shown the airways and their navigational aids.

rate-of-climb: A cockpit instrument showing the rate of climb or descent.

R and R: Rest and recreation in Japan from Korea.

to read: In communication parlance, "to hear."

read back: "Repeat your clearance to me."

Red Mike: A Naval Academy midshipman who doesn't date girls.

scramble: To take off after an unknown target.

Selcal radio: A radio in an airliner on which its private company communication stations can call the pilot direct.

side numbers: Large numbers painted on military aircraft to identify them.

strobe effect: The effect on the eye of two propellers of a multi-engine plane not in perfect synchronization.

surveillance radar: Radar being installed in Air Traffic Control Centers which shows the position but not the altitude of traffic.

tail-pipe temperature: A gauge in the cockpit showing the heat at a jet's tail pipe.

tin can: A destroyer.

TV-2:   The basic two-seater Navy instrument jet trainer. Pilot sits in front and passenger or student in rear.

U.H.F.:   Ultra-high-frequency radios. Common to military aircraft.

V.F.R.:   Visual Flight Rules. Briefly, the rules a pilot can follow when visibility is good enough so that he can "see and be seen." If he uses these rules he does not need clearance from Air Traffic Control, but is responsible for staying clear of other aircraft himself. Keeping him clear is not the responsibility of A.T.C.

V.H.F.:   Very High Frequency radios. Common to civil aircraft.

via flight plan route: In a clearance, denotes approval of the route the pilot has requested. Obviates necessity for controller to repeat entire clearance.

victor: The letter "V" in the phonetic alphabet—the prefix for airways using omni-ranges as opposed to the "colored" airways such as Green Five or Amber Three, using low-frequency ranges.

winds aloft chart: A chart with symbols showing the direction and velocity of winds at a given altitude.

yoke: The control wheel in an airliner.

Bed & Breakfast Homes Directory

Homes Away From Home

West Coast

Bed & Breakfast Homes Directory

Homes Away From Home

West Coast

by
Diane Knight

Graphic Artist, Sondra Prull
Contributing Writer, Patricia Carr
Editor, Suzy Blackaby

Library of Congress Catalog Card Number: 84-080032

ISBN 0-942902-02-5

Typography by Jean Graphics, San Jose, California

Printed in the United States of America by
Delta Lithograph Company, Van Nuys, California

KNIGHTIME PUBLICATIONS
P.O. Box 591
Cupertino, CA 95014

CONTENTS

INTRODUCTION vii

ABOUT BED & BREAKFAST IN PRIVATE HOMES viii

HOW TO USE THIS DIRECTORY viii

HOW TO ARRANGE A B&B VISIT x

B&B HOME LISTINGS BY REGION

  CALIFORNIA

    North Coast 11

    Central Coast 23

    San Francisco & the Bay Area 41

    Wine Country 81

    Central Valley to Mount Shasta 103

    Gold Country & the Sierra 115

    Southern California 133

  OREGON 163

  WASHINGTON 183

APPENDIX 196

INDEX OF CITIES & TOWNS 201

ORDERING THE 1985 SUPPLEMENT 205

How each friend represents a world in us, a world possibly not born until they arrive, and it is only by this meeting that a new world is born.

—Anaïs Nin

The only things I own which are still worth what they have cost me are my travel memories, the mind-pictures of places which I have been hoarding like a happy miser for more than half a century.

—Burton Holmes

INTRODUCTION

With this new West Coast Edition of *BED & BREAKFAST HOMES DIRECTORY*, the network of private home B&Bs is expanded to reach into the Pacific Northwest, as well as adding new host homes in Northern and Southern California. Although the number of homes in Washington and Oregon is limited at this time, the 1985 Supplement (see page 205) will further expand the listings. Take it from one who knows, it is now possible to travel the entire West Coast—from San Diego, California, to Anacortes, Washington— staying exclusively in homes listed in *BED & BREAKFAST HOMES DIRECTORY*. That trip, or any portion thereof, makes a vacation worth writing home about!

The aim of this book continues to be making travelers aware of the private home B&B alternative. It appeals to the adventurer, the romantic, the foreign visitor, or anyone seeking more personal and less expensive accommodations than are commonly available through travel agents or other guidebooks.

While country inns and small hotels offering bed and breakfast proliferate on the West Coast, many are quite luxurious and are priced beyond the means of many travelers. In selecting homes for this directory, I am mindful of the British tradition upon which "B&B" is based—clean, friendly homes where the owners welcome the passing traveler and furnish lodging and breakfast for a modest price. Although rates in *BED & BREAKFAST HOMES DIRECTORY* vary greatly, I have attempted to keep a balance between the inexpensive ($20 - $35) and the expensive ($60 - $75), with most falling somewhere in the medium range ($36 - $59). All homes listed are judged to represent good value for your travel dollar.

I would like for *BED & BREAKFAST HOMES DIRECTORY* to inspire you to consider a new destination for your next trip. There are marvelous discoveries of people and places to be made, even in the most unlikely spots (how many of you have ever heard of Yorkville or Elmira?). Keep your spirit of adventure alive, and do let me know about *your* discoveries.

May this book open many doors for you,

Diane Knight

ABOUT BED & BREAKFAST IN PRIVATE HOMES

The B&B homes in this directory, in most cases, are strictly private homes, not commercial establishments. As a guest, remember to act with the same courtesy and consideration that you would expect of a guest in your own home.

B&B hosts aren't innkeepers. They're not in business full time; there may be occasions when hosts can't accommodate you because they'll be on vacation, or because Great-Aunt Martha from Omaha will be using the guest room.

For the most part, there is no daily maid service or room service. Thus, guests should make their own beds and get their own ice (after asking, of course).

With some exceptions, B&B hosts will accept only cash or traveler's checks as payment for accommodations. Be sure to establish the method of payment with your host *before* your visit.

When reserving accommodations in B&B homes, it is very important to agree upon your time of arrival with the host. This is only courteous when you consider that hosts have their own private lives and family obligations. They would like to know when to be at home to greet you. Of course, there's always some flexibility, but arrival time should be discussed. If it appears you will be later than planned, a phone call would be appreciated.

Room rates include at least a Continental breakfast. In some cases, the rate includes a full breakfast; in others, there may be an extra charge if you wish a full breakfast. This is considered a complimentary meal.

Many hosts look forward to having guests join them for a family-style breakfast. In certain situations, if the guest unit is totally separate and has cooking facilities, the host will simply leave the ingredients for breakfast so that guests can prepare it for themselves. There are hosts who will be glad to serve you breakfast in your room, or even in bed. As in many phases of B&B travel, the accent is on *variety*.

HOW TO USE THIS DIRECTORY

For each listing:

The first line tells either the name of the host or the name given to the B&B home and the phone number to call for reservations.

The second line gives the mailing address of the home to use if you're writing for reservations.

The third line, in parentheses, indicates the general location of the home. You should get specific directions from your host.

Next you'll find a descriptive paragraph about the B&B home. It often tells something about the unique qualities of the home itself, the setting, the host, points of interest in the area.

The second paragraph indicates whether there are indoor pets and gives the host's preferences, such as "no smoking" or "children welcome." These appear in a consistent sequence in each listing. They are given only if the host has indicated a specific policy on the subject. The paragraph also lists facilities or features available to guests, such as "laundry" or "hot tub."

Available transportation is sometimes indicated, as well as the host's willingness to pick up guests at a nearby airport (mainly for the benefit of private pilots).

The code which follows refers to the heading at the top of each listing page:

ROOM — Refers to guest unit. The unit may be a room in the host's home, an adjoining apartment or a separate cottage near the home. Each letter (*A, B,* . . .) designates one guest unit, whether it has one, two, or more rooms.

BED — Number and type(s) of bed(s) given for each guest unit. This means total beds per unit.
T = twin, **D** = double, **Q** = queen, **K** = king.

BATH — **Shd** means you'll share a bath with the host. **Shd** means the bath is shared by other guests, if present. (Chances are you may have it all to yourself.) **Pvt** means the bath goes with the guest unit and is not shared by the host. It may be down the hall, but it is all yours.

ENTRANCE — **Main** indicates you'll use the main entrance of the home. **Sep** means there's a separate entrance for guests.

FLOOR — Floor of each guest room is indicated by number in most cases. **LL** indicates lower level, with steps down. **1G** means a ground level room.

DAILY RATES — **S** refers to a single (one person); **D** refers to a double (two persons); **EP** refers to the rate charged for each extra person (above two) traveling with your party. **Some of the rates quoted include a local tax; others do not.**

Example:

ROOM	BED	BATH	ENTRANCE	FLOOR	DAILY RATES S - D (EP)
A	1K	Pvt	Main	2	$30 - $36 ($6)

Room (or unit) A has one king-sized bed, a private bath, uses the main entrance to the home, is on the second floor. One person will pay $30; two persons will pay $36; each extra person will pay $6.

In the San Francisco Bay Area, **BART** refers to **B**ay **A**rea **R**apid **T**ransit.

HOW TO ARRANGE A B&B VISIT

1. Try to plan your visit as far ahead as possible. This helps to ensure you'll get to stay in the B&B home of your choice. Notify your host immediately of any change in plans.
2. Call your host for reservations before 9 p.m. Be sure to allow for the time difference if you're not on Pacific Time.
3. Carefully check details about the listing you're considering before calling or writing. Confirm with your host anything that's not clear to you. Ask pertinent questions!
4. Check what form(s) of payment your host will accept. Ask if a deposit is required.
5. Agree on time of arrival.

Hosts listed in *BED & BREAKFAST HOMES DIRECTORY* have agreed to honor rates stated in the directory until April 1985. Any changes in rates will be stated in the supplement, scheduled for publication by May 1, 1985.

The information contained in these listings has been prepared with great care, but we cannot guarantee that it is complete or in all cases correct. It is the user's responsibility to verify important information when making arrangements.

North Coast

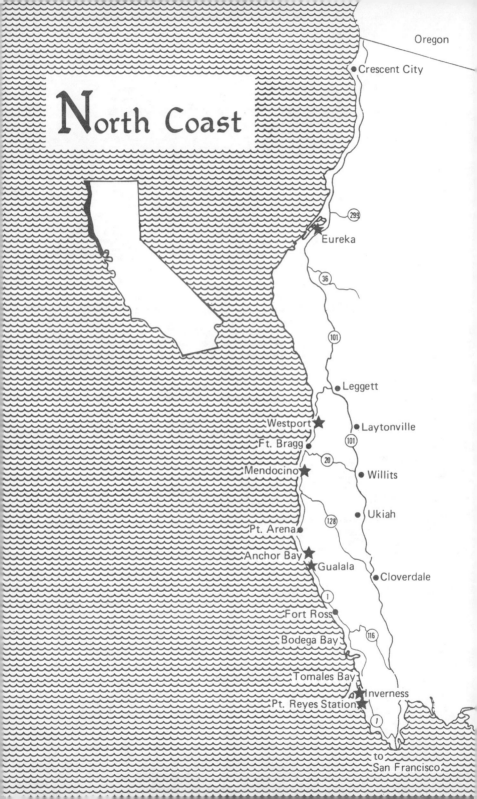

Waves, woodlands, and wind-wafted fog work to enchant the traveler to the North Coast—the spell of nature is irresistible. From the surf-swept shores of the Sonoma and Mendocino coastlines to the towering trees of the Redwood Highway, the scenery is a frontier for the exploring imagination.

The contrast of wood and wave is perhaps nowhere more dramatic than at Point Reyes National Seashore. The steep cliffs, sighted four hundred years ago by Sir Francis Drake, guard a peninsula of dense forest, fern-filled canyons, and open pasture land. Beach aficionados can choose between expansive sandy strands and futuristic convolutions of rock. Tule elk, deer, sea lions, huge jack rabbits, and three hundred sixty-one species of birds share the space with you; migrating whales cruise by each winter.

From Bodega Bay north to Gualala, rolling hills spill into the sea, where white foam swirls around imposing sea stacks. Here too, Fort Ross—historic survivor of the nineteenth-century Russian presence in California—sits high and dry on an isolated bluff. You can climb the stairs of the restored stockade to watch the waves of the past wash up below.

"Talk to me of Mendocino" sings the song, and indeed, nostalgia has been known to overtake even the least sentimental in this transposed bit of old New England. The town itself has sunk its sturdy roots into a precarious-looking headland jutting into the sea and studiously ignores the insistent pounding of the surf at its door. The nucleus of a coastal community of artists and artisans, Mendocino offers an abundance of galleries and shops housed in nineteenth-century buildings.

Seasoned wave-watchers recommend Mendocino Headlands State Park for a show-stopping performance of water in motion, while from Fort Bragg, wilderness devotees ride the "Skunks" (railway cars originally named for their pungent gas engines) through forty miles of redwood groves inaccessible by car.

A compelling symbol of California, the legendary redwoods rise in original splendor along the Redwood Highway that stretches from Leggett to Crescent City. It is hard not to think of these trees as the stuff of myth. The hushed messages of their branches tell a story of enduring grandeur. They are a discovery that never ages, and travelers reaching the town of Eureka—meaning "I found it!"—can only add, "You can't miss it."

ANCHOR BAY

Ed & Arlene Aaron **(707) 884-3790**
P.O. Box 130, Gualala, CA 95445
(35001 Woodside Court in Anchor Bay)

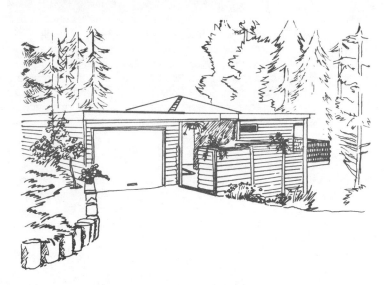

   The Aarons' home is designed to harmonize with its setting of trees and great ocean views. The living area has a fireplace, comfortable seating, and interesting work by local artists; it's a perfect place for conversation with the Aarons, who really enjoy having visitors. Ed, a retired veterinarian, will be glad to show you the exotic plants he raises. Arlene is especially interested in Oriental cooking, tennis, fishing, and her pets. The guest suite has its own bath, deck, and view of the Pacific.
   Dog and two cats in residence; no guests' pets; no children preferred; full breakfast; TV; deck; soaking tub; good hiking nearby; some French spoken; airport pickup (Ocean Ridge).

ROOM	BED	BATH	ENTRANCE	FLOOR	DAILY RATES
A	2T	Pvt	Main	1	$35 - 40

EUREKA   S - D (EP)

The Carter House   **(707) 445-1390**
1033 Third Street, Eureka, CA 95501
(Third at L; north end of Old Town district)

The Carter House looks as if it's had a long and illustrious past. Though it is a new structure, it does, in a manner of speaking, have quite an interesting history. Mark Carter, a native Eurekan, constructed the mammoth three-story home according to plans prepared in 1884 by San Francisco architects Samuel and Joseph Newsome (designers of the nearby Carson Mansion). The original home built from the plans was the Murphy House of San Francisco that was destroyed in the 1906 Earthquake. Mark recreated the home in its present location "as a modern tribute to the splendor and intricate beauty of Victorian architecture." In keeping with the original, Mark used clear heart redwood for the exterior and finished the interior in polished redwood and oak. The main floor serves as an antique and art gallery. The second floor is the private residence of Mark, Christi, and Joseph Carter. Bed and breakfast accommodations are on the third floor. All antiques and original works of art throughout the house are for sale. I'll let you be surprised by the wonderful culinary offerings to be experienced in this gracious and hospitable setting. People interested in history, architecture, art, antiques, and extraordinary cuisine will be satisfied beyond their wildest expectations.

No pets; full breakfast; first floor open to guests; Bentley limousine service by arrangement; bus transportation; airport pickup (Eureka-Arcata). Room B: $10 extra charge for a fourth person only. Brochure available.

A	1D	Pvt	Main	3	$65
B	2D	Shd*	Main	3	$65
C	1D	Shd*	Main	3	$55

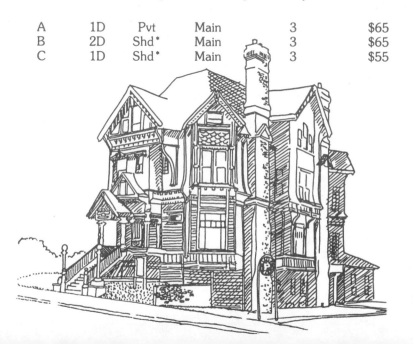

EUREKA

Old Town Bed & Breakfast   **(707) 445-3951**
1521 Third Street, Eureka, CA 95501
(Third near P; north end of Old Town district)

   This historic home was built in 1871, and was bought by lumber
magnate William Carson in 1872. He lived in it until 1915, when it was
sold and moved to its present location. More recently, Bob and Agnes
Sobrito have taken it over; they've refurbished the whole house and have
decorated each room with care, allowing guests a nostalgic glimpse into
Eureka's past. Lovely antiques fill rooms that have intriguing names:
Tulips & Evergreen, Raspberry Parfait, Blue Calico, and Samoa. William
Carson's celebrated Victorian mansion is located one and one-half blocks
away; you may choose to walk or bicycle by it on your way to explore Old
Town's architecture, fine shops, and superb restaurants. At the end of the
day, Bob and Agnes invite you to relax and unwind with wine and hors
d'oeuvres in the Raspberry Parlor. They want to make your stay in Eureka
a warm and memorable experience.
   No guests' pets; full breakfast; TV; bicycles; bus transportation; airport
pickup (Eureka-Arcata).

A	2T	Pvt	Main	2	$55
B	1Q	Shd*	Main	2	$50
C	1Q	Shd*	Main	2	$50
D	1D	Pvt	Main	2	$45

GUALALA

S - D (EP)

Gail York Rodgers   **(707) 785-2141**
P.O. Box 164, Gualala, CA 95445
(The Sea Ranch, northern Sonoma County coast)

If you sometimes yearn, as I do, for a place with ocean views, a blazing hearth, and lots of privacy, then this guest house will be a fantasy-come-true. Like all structures at Sea Ranch, it blends with the natural environment. Gail's residence, sculpture studio, and guest house open onto a sunny garden courtyard with a large, inviting deck. The gentle coastal landscape can be seen from all the rooms in the guest house, and there's a spacious window seat in the living room for stretching out and watching the surf, the migrating whales, or the wildlife in the surrounding meadows. A sleeping loft above the living room holds a double bed. A solarium and dining area, a kitchenette, a large bathroom, and a separate bedroom complete the unit. There are several beaches nearby for walking, picnicking, exploring tidepools, and diving for abalone. Other outdoor pleasures include fishing in the ocean or nearby Gualala River and hiking along cliff tops, across fields of wildflowers, or through fern-filled redwood forests. All in all, this is a fantastically romantic place.

Living room with loft, window seat (extra sleeping space), fireplace, TV, stereo; kitchenette; deck; complimentary wine and cheese; Sea Ranch tennis courts, pools, saunas, restaurant, and bar available to guests; airport pickup (Sea Ranch). Two-night minimum stay.

ROOM	BED	BATH	ENTRANCE	FLOOR	DAILY RATES
A	1D & 2T	Pvt	Sep	1	$75 ($10)

INVERNESS

MacLean House **(415) 669-7392**
P.O. Box 651, Inverness, CA 94937 **or 837-4434**
(One block above the town of Inverness and Tomales Bay)

What could be a more perfect setting than Inverness for the perfect Scottish guest house? Among trees overlooking Tomales Bay, the redwood-shingled home of Ginny and Bob Cuenin has been renovated and furnished with great attention to detail, carrying out the Scottish theme through the main quarters and the guest rooms below. The clan MacLean tartan provides the color scheme, looking crisp and clean against the white walls of each spacious room. Lovely antiques and brass accents complete the picture, adding up to the utmost in quality lodgings. Flowers and birds abound in this quiet, secluded, often sunny location. Point Reyes National Seashore and some excellent local restaurants have always been good reasons to visit the area; now the Cuenins and MacLean House are also high on *my* list.

No pets; smoking in bedrooms not encouraged; no RV parking; private patio.

| A | 1T & 1D | Pvt | Sep | 1 | $50 | ($5) |
| B | 2D | Pvt | Sep | 1 | $50 | ($5) |

MENDOCINO

Marge & Dick Dickson   **(707) 937-0098**
P.O. Box 347, Little River, CA 95456
(On Mendocino coast)

   Perched on the headlands overlooking the Navarro River's union with
the Pacific Ocean—and beyond—the Dicksons' home offers perhaps the
most striking of all views along the Mendocino coast. Can you imagine lying in bed watching whales cruise by? Wide, spectacular vistas are yours
from every room and from the two decks. Weathered wooden walls,
plenty of glass, wood-burning stoves, handmade quilts, country furnishings, and a player piano (requests, anyone?) create an atmosphere so
heartwarming that it's very hard to leave. Even with the attractions of Mendocino awaiting, don't be surprised if all you want to do is stoke up the fire,
snuggle deeper under the covers, and stare out to sea. You'll find whale-
watching at its best and lots, lots more at the Dicksons'.
   Three dogs in residence (one indoor, two outdoor); extra beds available
for larger parties; decks; barbecue; extra meals available; some French and
Spanish spoken; airport pickup (Little River). A deluxe breakfast for two is
$8 extra.

ROOM	BED	BATH	ENTRANCE	FLOOR	DAILY RATES S - D (EP)
A	1D	Pvt	Sep	1	$50 ($15)

POINT REYES STATION

Thirty-nine Cypress   **(415) 663-1709**
P.O. Box 176, Point Reyes Station, CA 94956
(Near Point Reyes National Seashore)

Julia Bartlett and her family feel a special connection to the Point Reyes area and, in particular, to the land on which they've made their home. One easily understands this feeling after being their guest. The house is nestled into a hillside and faces a pastoral vista where cattle graze and all seems right with the world. Inside, there's a strong sense of "home"—a cozy fireplace, floors covered with aging Oriental rugs, warm quilts to sleep under. The house is natural and rustic with an ambiance of warmth and comfort. Throughout the house, many interesting original works of art catch the eye. There are skylights in every room, and from your bed at night, you may see stars and hear the hooting of owls; in the morning you might awaken to the sound of Julia's gentle, free-roaming horses munching on the greenery outside the sliding glass door. Julia is happy to share her extensive knowledge of the Point Reyes-Inverness area with her guests.

Two cats in residence; guests' pets negotiable; TV; patio.

ROOM	BED	BATH	ENTRANCE	FLOOR	DAILY RATES
A	1D	Shd	Main	1G	$45 - $50
B	1D	Shd	Main	1G	$45 - $50
C	1T	Shd	Main	1G	$45

WESTPORT

S - D (EP)

Howard Creek Ranch
P.O. Box 121, Westport, CA 95488
(Three miles north of Westport on Highway 1)

(707) 964-6725
(Keep trying!)

Sally and Sunny invite you to retreat to the romance of yesteryear at Howard Creek Ranch. Their ranchhouse was built in 1872 by Alfred Howard, newly arrived from the coast of Maine. At one time a stagecoach stop, it is now a quaint and cozy home filled with collectibles and antiques. The guest suites allow privacy, and the old fireplace inspires conversation and fun. The house is set in a wide, secluded valley at the mouth of Howard Creek. It faces the ocean and a wide sandy beach where you can walk for miles at low tide. At this bed and breakfast resort, you can find your own pace and tune in to the natural beauty all around you.

Dog and two cats in residence; kitchen privileges by arrangement; extra beds available; decks; barbecue; swimming pool; hot tub; sauna. All guest rooms have sinks; Room A has a balcony; Rooms A and B have kitchenettes; Room C has a loft and a skylight. Unit D is a boathouse; Unit E is a cabin; both have woodstoves and electricity. Full ranch breakfasts are featured. Lower rates off-season and midweek.

A	1D & 1Q	Shd	Sep	2	$45	($10)
B	1D & 1Q	Shd	Sep	1	$45	($10)
C	1T & 1D	Shd	Sep	2	$45	($10)
D	1D	Shd	Sep	1	$45	
E	1D	Shd	Sep	1	$30	

21

Wise, cultivated, genial conversation is the last flower of civilization . . . .
Conversation is our account of ourselves.

—Ralph Waldo Emerson

Do you know that conversation is one of the greatest pleasures in life? But it wants leisure.

—W. Somerset Maugham

Central Coast

Central Coast

San Francisco ●

Half Moon Bay ●
Pescadero ★

Año Nuevo State Reserve ←

(17)

★ Davenport

Santa Cruz ←

(1)

● Watsonville

Pacific Grove ★
Pebble Beach ★
Carmel ★

★ Monterey
● Salinas

● Big Sur

● San Simeon

(1)
★ Cambria
(101)

Morro Bay ★

San Luis Obispo ●

Pismo Beach ★

"The Coastside," as the area surrounding Half Moon Bay is known, remains a part of the Pacific's edge where travelers can still make their own discoveries. A favorite country café tucked back in the farmlands, a pebble beach where you can still find jade, a redwood grove that stands as a memorial to the dedicated environmentalists who fought for it (the lumber company slashes still visible on the venerable giants marked for cutting) are some of the little-known treasures of the area. The Año Nuevo State Reserve, the James Fitzgerald Marine Reserve, and the Pescadero Wildlife Refuge provide sanctuary for the abundance of coastal wildlife that is yours for the watching, while several state and county parks offer hideaways in the redwoods. A respite from bustling tourism, this stretch of coast allows time and tide their ebb and flow.

Monterey Bay, with its crescent of sandy beaches from Santa Cruz to Carmel, is the heartland of the Central Coast. Here beach-lovers sun, surf, and even swim in the quieter waters of the bay. On the northern shore of the bay, Santa Cruz enjoys a unique ambiance, a mixture of the spontaneous street fun concocted by musicians, dancers, and impromptu actors along the Pacific Garden Mall, the lazy sea lions snoozing beneath the feet of anglers on the municipal pier, and the staid Victorians that keep an eye on the goings-on.

Monterey, on the southern shore, offers a different mood entirely, one steeped in California history and natural beauty. The adobe buildings on the city's Path of History mark its nineteenth-century prominence, while Cannery Row, no longer Steinbeck's turbulent cauldron of the sardine industry, survives as a complex of shops and restaurants. The adjoining town of Pacific Grove has many visitors, some of whom fly in on velvet orange-and-black wings. The Monarch butterflies hang out in select groves of pines from October to March. Carmel-by-the-Sea, a few miles south, is still trying to be a quaint little village in the forest, but its bumper crop of shops, galleries, and restaurants gives it an air of sophistication.

For some people, the poetry of the Monterey Peninsula is to be found at Point Lobos State Reserve. The wind-twisted Monterey cypress, the soft sighs of pine, the azure water foaming milky white around dark rocks that host the miniature worlds of the tidepools—all say Monterey.

Farther south, travelers experience an exquisite fragility riding the thin ribbon of Highway 1 through Big Sur country, under the imposing brow of the Santa Lucia Mountains and along the precipitous cliffs overlooking the Pacific. Gradually, the landscape softens into something less wild, more idyllic. Just when you're thinking it's the perfect place for a fairy-tale castle—Shazam! There it is! San Simeon, William Randolph Hearst's fantasy made real. A concourse of gardens, classic pools, and mansions displaying a dazzling collection of art make San Simeon the wonder of the Central Coast. Nearby Cambria, a tiny coastal town in the pines, is a delightful country contrast.

Dune buggies wheel up and down the dramatic sand dunes of Pismo Beach, where those little bubbles in the sand may mean you're onto something big. A Pismo clam can be the size of a fist. Take a Clam Taxi to the prime spots and go for your limit.

San Luis Obispo's history tour is a surprise, covering nearly every period and contributing culture of California history. Architecture ranges from adobe to Frank Lloyd Wright. To the east, rolling countryside provides pastoral scenes to inspire an old-fashioned Sunday drive, even on Mondays.

NOTICE TO CENTRAL COAST TRAVELERS:

Although Scenic Highway 1 between San Simeon and Big Sur is often closed due to slides, Hearst Castle and Cambria are always accessible via U.S. 101 and Highway 46. They are well worth the detour when necessary.

CAMBRIA

Duane & Miriam Benell   **(805) 927-3112**
340 Weymouth, Cambria, CA 93428
(Just east of Highway 1)

The Benells look forward to spending the summers in their lovely Cambria home, and it's no wonder. They're seven miles south of Hearst Castle, two blocks from the beach, and within walking distance of quaint Cambria Village. The guest room is on the ground level of the house; the living-dining area is on the upper level and has a good view of the ocean. Having greatly enjoyed B&Bs abroad, the Benells are especially interested in extending hospitality to foreign visitors traveling in California.

No pets; no smoking; small RV parking only; full breakfast; TV. OPEN JUNE 15-SEPTEMBER 10, 1984, *EXCEPT* JULY 27-AUGUST 11. (Dates for 1985 will be published in the 1985 Supplement.) Reservations possible with advance notice September through June; the Benells can be reached at 12002 Beverly Drive, Whittier, CA 90601, (213) 695-5431.

ROOM	BED	BATH	ENTRANCE	FLOOR	DAILY RATES
A	2T or 1K	Pvt	Main	1	$25 - $35

CAMBRIA

Don & Desi D'Urbano   **(805) 927-8145**
910 Northampton Road, Cambria, CA 93428
(Overlooking West Cambria Village and Pacific Coast)

It's hard to imagine a *friendlier* overnight stop along the Central Coast. Guest books filled with the names of international travelers attest to this. Don and Desi give new meaning to the term Western Hospitality. Great personal warmth combined with decor reminiscent of the real American West are the key elements. Travelers from afar have found themselves enjoying a barbecue or playing tennis with their hosts. (Don is a tennis instructor.) The D'Urbanos characterize their style as "country living by the sea"—and they like helping others discover the treasures that make Cambria a great place to consider "home," however briefly.

Two cats in residence; no guests' pets; no smoking; full breakfast; TV; kitchen privileges; patio; barbecue; some Spanish spoken; airport pickup, $12 roundtrip (San Luis Obispo). Shuttle bus between San Luis Obispo, Morro Bay, and Cambria—75¢ one way. Rate is $25 in winter.

A   2T or 1K   Pvt   Main   1G $25 - $35   ($5)

ROOM	BED	BATH	ENTRANCE	FLOOR	DAILY RATES
					S - D (EP)

CAMBRIA

John & Barbara Hoyt   **(805) 927-3340**
1891 Ogden Drive, Cambria, CA 93428
(Two miles west of Highway 1, off Ardath)

   The Hoyts are fond of long freighter voyages around the world—ask to see the map outlining the trips they've taken. Until wanderlust strikes again, they're enjoying entertaining guests in their magnificent Cambria home. It is set on a hillside and takes full advantage of the expansive, uninterrupted ocean view. From every room one gets the feeling of being in constant touch with the outdoors—sky, trees, and ocean—while at the same time feeling the warmth of hearth and home. The Hoyts know Cambria well and will be glad to share their knowledge of this charming seaside community with you.

   Dog in residence; no small children; no smoking; full breakfast; TV; extra beds.

ROOM	BED	BATH	ENTRANCE	FLOOR	DAILY RATES	
A	1Q	Pvt	Main	LL	$35 - $40	($15)
B	2T	Pvt	Main	1	$35 - $45	

CARMEL-BY-THE-SEA

House of England   **(408) 624-3004**
25020 Valley Way, Carmel, CA 93923
(At Third Avenue and the Coast Highway)

Guests at House of England consider it a real "find"—which is why they keep coming back. Sharing details of perfect days in Carmel makes for lively conversation as people gather to partake of delicious morning treats. The house is a two-story, Mediterranean stucco with old-world charm. Mature shade trees grace the ample yard, which has a hot tub/Jacuzzi—another popular gathering spot. Accommodations are spacious, comfortable, and attractive. A room with a private half-bath is on the first floor, and three rooms sharing two baths are on the second. Your host, Dr. Gene England, has traveled widely and values the people-connections he has made. He certainly does his share in enabling other travelers to do likewise.

Two dogs in residence; no guests' pets; smoking outdoors only; TV in Rooms A and D; hot tub/Jacuzzi; wheelchair access; bus transportation; airport limo from Monterey. Two-night minimum stay on weekends. Rates are $10 less on weekdays, off-season.

A	1T & 1K	½ Pvt	Main	1G	$50	($5)
B	1Q	Shd*	Main	2	$40	
C	1Q	Shd*	Main	2	$40	
D	1T & 1Q	Shd*	Main	2	$40	($5)

CARMEL-BY-THE-SEA

S - D (EP)

Stone Charm
(408) 625-4293
24640 Lower Trail, Carmel, CA 93923
(One block off Coast Highway)

   Stone Charm is the place to stay if you want to experience the *real* Carmel—the Carmel of narrow streets and storybook houses hiding in the hills among Monterey pines. Appropriately named, the home has a fireplace made of stones unique to the area. The flavor of old Carmel abounds here, and your hosts, Will and Phyllis Sherburne, can help make your experience complete by sharing their vast knowledge of this very special town with you. A walk to the heart of things proves invigorating as well as scenic. After a day of enjoying Carmel in your own way, it's nice to return to the Sherburnes' for a glass of wine on their sunporch and an idyllic view of the bay through the pines.

   No pets; no children under eight; smoking outside only; no large RV parking; TV; extra bed on sunporch; patios and covered porch; bus lines nearby; airport pickup (Monterey). Two-night minimum stay; 10% discount after second night. Call for reservations *at least* a week in advance.

A   2T   Pvt   Main   1 $45   ($10)

CARMEL-BY-THE-SEA

S - D (EP)

Villa Serena

(408) 624-1188

P.O. Box 113, Carmel, CA 93921
(Walking distance to Carmel Mission and beach)

Villa Serena couldn't be more aptly named. It has the feel of a villa on the Italian Riviera. The true romantic will find its still, quiet beauty irresistible. Each guest accommodation is totally private and unique. There's a storybook cottage with a fireplace (A), an upstairs suite with a view out to Point Lobos (B), and a lovely room with oak furnishings (C). It's the kind of place where it's perfectly fine to keep to yourself, or you're welcome to enjoy the patio and deck areas. The back yard is graced by a huge shade tree and lush flowering plants. Full breakfasts are prepared by host Gabriel, a former restauranteur; they may be served on the deck or in your own quarters, according to the weather or your mood. When a romantic splurge is in order, Villa Serena is a place to make some special memories.

No pets; no children; full breakfast; color TV in all units; pantry with refrigerator in A and B; deck; daily maid service; beach and tennis courts nearby; Italian and French spoken; airport pickup (Monterey).

A	1Q	Pvt	Sep	1G	$75
B	1Q	Pvt	Sep	2	$75
C	1D	Pvt	Sep	1G	$65

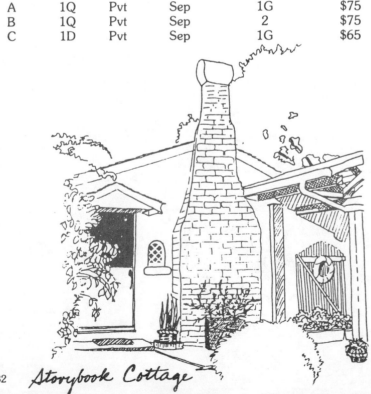

Storybook Cottage

DAVENPORT

S - D (EP)

New Davenport Bed & Breakfast
Davenport, CA 95017
(Nine miles north of Santa Cruz)

(408) 425-1818
or 426-4122

The New Davenport Bed & Breakfast is located in one of Davenport's original old buildings just across Highway 1 from the ocean. Four bright, comfortable rooms, furnished with antique beds and oak dressers, are available to B&B travelers. Delicious breakfasts and lunches are served next door at the McDougals' New Davenport Cash Store. This landmark also houses a pottery, gift, and craft gallery. Dinner is served on Friday, Saturday, and Sunday nights. Weekend festivities often include live music and a lively crowd. The New Davenport is an ideal getaway from the Bay Area. Though the trip is short, there's a wonderfully remote feeling about the place. And when you don't have to spend hours driving, there's much more time for fun.

No pets; no children under twelve; no smoking in rooms; bus service from Santa Cruz. Additional rooms are now available in the main (Cash Store) building. Some are quite large and have ocean views. Two rooms will have fireplaces (Summer, 1984) and one, a kitchen. Rates range from $55-$75 for two.

A	1D	Pvt	Main	1G	$45
B	1D	Pvt	Main	1G	$45
C	1Q	Pvt	Main	1G	$50
D	1D	Pvt	Main	1G	$45

ROOM	BED	BATH	ENTRANCE	FLOOR	DAILY RATES
					S - D (EP)

MONTEREY

Ed & Jean Mosieur   **(408) 646-8761**
700 Colton Street, Monterey, CA 93940
(Walking distance from downtown Monterey)

The Mosieurs' home epitomizes Old Monterey, its architecture and setting recalling a slower, more refined era of Monterey's history. Mature shade trees and many flowers abound on the lovely estate. The spacious two-story home has bedrooms that open onto the surrounding veranda, and each is elegantly yet comfortably furnished. The ocean can be seen through the trees from Rooms A and B. On the grounds is a carriage house where Jack London reputedly was a long-time resident. The Moseiurs provide relaxed, warm hospitality that makes their guests feel very much at home.

No pets; no children under forty-three (a bit of Jean's humor); no smoking preferred; no RV parking; Room A is a suite with a powder room.

Room	Bed	Bath	Entrance	Floor	Rate	(EP)
A	1K	Pvt	Main	2	$60	($10)
B	1K	Pvt	Main	2	$50	($10)

MORRO BAY

Bayview House   **(805) 528-3098**
1070 Santa Lucia Avenue, Baywood Park, CA 93402
(On Morro Bay)

You'd have to search a long time to find a spot more peaceful than Bayview House, home of Jack and Frieda Murphy. The waxing tide brings the sound of lapping waves, and birds abound with their varied calls (Audubon Winter Bird Count has sited over two hundred species)—other than that, it's profoundly quiet. A ground floor apartment offers absolute privacy. Unusually spacious and impeccably furnished, it consists of a living room, dining area, bedroom, bath, completely equipped kitchen, and a private deck that faces the bay. Deluxe breakfasts at Bayview House include such things as homemade sausages and bread. Frieda not only bakes the bread, but grinds the grain for it by hand. This is a place to savor some of life's simpler pleasures: gorgeous sunsets, miles of beaches and sand dunes, great birdwatching, hiking in state parks, and a quaint fishing village. It's the Central Coast at its most relaxing.

Dog in residence; no guests' pets; full breakfast; TV; living room with sofa bed; kitchen; deck; some Dutch and Indonesian spoken; bus transportation; airport pickup (San Luis Obispo County).

A	1D & 1Q	Pvt	Sep		1G	$35 - $45 ($10)

PACIFIC GROVE

Blue Horizons   **(408) 373-5285**
1232 Surf Avenue, Pacific Grove, CA 93950
(One block from ocean)

A panoramic bay view from the master bedroom delights Joanna's guests as they watch the moving landscape of otters, seals, whales, birds, boats, joggers, and divers. The entire upstairs of this split-level house can be used as a suite of rooms (A and B) for up to five guests. A breakfast of your choice is served at a table in the master bedroom (A)—you won't want to miss the view for a moment! Joanna has many interests, but particularly enjoys traveling, music, and folk dancing. Her easygoing manner and prize location make Blue Horizons a favorite stop for visitors to the Monterey Bay.

Three cats in residence; airport pickup (Monterey). Another bedroom may be available at times. Lower rates midweek.

ROOM	BED	BATH	ENTRANCE	FLOOR	DAILY RATES	
A	1T & 1K	Pvt	Main	2	$40 - $45	($10)
B	2T		Main	2		

PACIFIC GROVE

Joan Lascola   **(408) 373-6380**
P.O. Box 1106, Pacific Grove, CA 93950
(One half-block from ocean)

   The small-scale town of Pacific Grove is located at the southern tip of
Monterey Bay. The major avenues through town are crossed by numerous
narrow streets, dense with picturesque Victorians and bungalows. Joan
Lascola's house is on such a street, which ends up at the blue Pacific, only
a half-block away. Walk north to Cannery Row, or south through a
beautiful park that runs along the shoreline to Lover's Point, where rock
formations, crashing waves, and playful sea otters delight scores of visitors.
Below Lover's Point, walk or drive along what I think is one of the most
spectacular stretches of California's coastline. From Joan's house you can
also walk downtown, where you'll find shops, restaurants, a very good
museum—and study the interesting architecture all along the way. Accommodations at Joan's are comfortable, clean, and attractive. Colorful
original paintings enliven each room. It's a place to settle in, make yourself
at home, and get to know one of my favorite towns.
   No pets; TV; extra bed; airport pickup at extra charge or limousine service (Monterey). Entire home may be rented at times; inquiries welcome.

A	1Q	Pvt	Main	1	$30 - $35 ($10)

37

PEBBLE BEACH

Ocean Forest Hideaway   **(408) 372-7425**
P.O. Box 1193, Pebble Beach, CA 93953
(On Seventeen Mile Drive)

Follow the path that leads through fern-filled woods to a private, deluxe guest suite at Ocean Forest Hideaway. Staying here will make you feel like you're on your honeymoon even if you're not. A bedroom/sitting area has a queen-sized bed and a TV; the suite overlooks the woods and garden where deer, birds, and squirrels come to feed. Breakfast can be served in your own quarters or in the glass-walled dining room, where you can take in an enchanting forest view. The second room has a king-sized bed. It can adjoin the suite and share its bath, or be a separate accommodation sharing the main bath down the hall. A third room with a queen-sized bed shares the main bath. Luxurious carpeting, electric blankets, comforters, and myriad personal touches add to the appeal of each room. As a guest at Ocean Forest Hideaway, you will feel truly pampered.

No pets; children welcome; smoking outside only; TV and refrigerator in suite (A); deck on Room B; a few minutes to beaches and golf courses, equestrian, jogging, and hiking trails; airport pickup (Monterey). Special rates for groups and midweek stays of three days or longer. Three-day minimum stay on holiday weekends. A twin-bedded room is often available at $50.

A	1Q	Pvt	Sep	1	$55
B	1K	Shd	Sep	1	$50
C	1Q	Shd	Main	1	$45

                                                              S - D (EP)

PESCADERO

Bob & Jane Rynders' Bed & Breakfast Cabin
P.O. Box 478, Pescadero, CA 94060
(Near Butano State Park)

(415)
(408) 879-0319
Keep trying!

Nestled in the ferns and redwoods alongside picturesque Butano Creek, this woodland hideaway is a unique blend of comfort and charm. Relax in a cozy sitting room (which can double as a second bedroom), warmed by the pot-bellied stove and soothing color scheme. From the bedroom, enjoy the embrace of a huge redwood tree just outside the patio door. Browse the book nook, which has books for every taste—from Lady Murasaki to Ian Fleming. Feel like a hike? Then you'll want to take the trail leading from the cabin to a waterfall that any outdoor lover should not miss. Amateur botanists will marvel at the profusion of flora, and field guides have been thoughtfully provided. The primitive gravel road that winds its way through the forest to reach this sequestered retreat (you will need directions) is an appropriate prelude for the rest and relaxation you can expect at the hospitable hands of the Rynders.

No pets; children over ten welcome; no RV parking; full breakfast; kitchenette equipped with essentials for simple cooking; deck; barbecue; some knowledge of Japanese language and culture. Two-night minimum stay on holiday weekends. Lower off-season and single person rates. Let phone ring at least six times.

A   2T & 1Q   Pvt   Sep   1G $45   ($5)

SANTA CRUZ

S - D (EP)

Bruce & Susan Bangert   **(408) 476-1906**
2501 Paul Minnie Avenue, Santa Cruz, CA 95062
(One quarter-mile from Highway 1, Soquel Avenue Exit)

The Bangerts' inviting old farmhouse seems to welcome you as you draw near, and once inside, the feeling is complete. Carefully and lovingly restored over the last few years, the house now stands ready to delight any traveler lucky enough to discover it. The decor centers around the many works of art collected by the Bangerts. A dazzling array of ceramic pieces have been selected by Bruce, who's head of the Ceramics Department at UC Santa Cruz. Two artists-in-residence work in the studio behind the house, where visitors can look over their wares. The Bangerts have a baby grand piano, a warm patio, and a relaxing deck that they enjoy sharing. Two gable-roofed bedrooms with an adjoining half-bath are available to B&B guests. The uncommonly welcoming atmosphere, along with some nice surprises, have turned many guests into friends.

Dog in residence; TV; refrigerator and barbecue available; bus transportation.

A	1D	1½ Shd	Main	2	$35
B	1D	1½ Shd	Main	2	$35

San Francisco
& the Bay Area

San Francisco
and the
Bay Area

Vallejo

Novato ★

San Rafael ★

Mill Valley ★

Tiburon ★
Berkeley

Sausalito ●

San Francisco ★

Martinez ★
Pleasant Hill ★   Concord ★
Walnut Creek ★
Alamo ★

Moraga ★
Piedmont ★
Oakland ★
Alameda ★

Castro Valley ★

Hayward ●   Liverm[o]

Pleasanton ●

Pacifica ★
Burlingame ★
Hillsborough ●

Sunol ★

Fremont ★

San Mateo ★

Atherton ●
Menlo Park ●
Stanford ★   Los Altos ●
Palo Alto ●   Santa Clara ●

San Jose ★

Saratoga ●
Los Gatos ★

When you hear the clang of a cable car and the moan of a foghorn, you know where you are. San Francisco is like nowhere else, a city for all senses. Bounded on three sides by water, the feathery touch of sea mist is a pleasant certainty. Views from its famous hills—Telegraph, Russian, Nob, and Twin Peaks—are feasts for the eyes. Delicate, mysterious aromas arising from Chinatown contrast with the sharp sea smells of Fisherman's Wharf. Taste buds are tempted by over twenty-six hundred restaurants with an astounding choice of menus—Basque, Moroccan, Hungarian, Greek, Armenian, Swiss, Jewish, Indian, Chinese, Japanese, Filipino, Korean, Italian, Scandinavian, Mexican, Spanish. Truly, San Francisco is a city to savor.

The City is really several. One out of every seven San Franciscans is either foreign-born or a first-generation citizen. San Francisco streets belong to the neighborhoods, ethnic communities whose diverse customs and lifestyles make San Francisco more than the sum of its parts. Whether you are a resolute explorer or a dawdling gadabout, the streets of San Francisco are guaranteed to fascinate.

Crossing the Golden Gate Bridge, travelers are often surprised to find themselves in a spot of wilderness, the Marin headlands. Hiking the headlands is exhilarating. The intense blue of the bay, often dotted with sailboats, and hills that can be either spring green or summer gold have a lucid radiance.

Hiking the streets of Sausalito is equally heady, although in quite a different way. This Marin town is a favorite for window-shoppers and trend-spotters. Go with the flow, if only for an afternoon. Only slightly farther north, Mt. Tamalpais offers a more challenging hike as well as an unforgettable view. Muir Woods, at its foot, is a refuge of redwood and fern.

The Other Bridge (the Bay) takes you straight to Oakland, where the Oakland Museum answers more questions about California than you ever thought to ask. And Oakland must be one of the few cities in the country with a downtown saltwater lake, Lake Merritt.

Just south of the City is the Peninsula. The cities of Palo Alto and Menlo Park bustle at the base of oak-studded foothills. Stanford University hosts a distinguished art museum and many cultural events. Marine World/Africa U.S.A. in Redwood City and Marriott's Great America theme park in Santa Clara are two popular family entertainment attractions in this area.

Many people have found their way to San Jose, one of the nation's fastest-growing cities. But not everyone has found the way to the hidden wine country surrounding it. More than fifty small to medium-sized wineries flourish in the Santa Clara Valley. Tours and tastings are unhurried and homey. The pastoral atmosphere may seem a world away from cosmopolitan San Francisco, but it's a mere fifty miles or so. In the Bay Area you can enjoy both.

ROOM	BED	BATH	ENTRANCE	FLOOR	DAILY RATES
					S - D (EP)

ALAMEDA

Shelly Osborne   **(415) 521-5539**
3448 Dutchcap, Alameda, CA 94501
(Just west of Oakland in San Francisco Bay)

   Alameda offers a real change-of-pace location in the Bay Area. It's an island connected to the mainland by a bridge and a tunnel. The atmosphere has a nautical flavor, and there are many points of historical interest. On a walking tour or bike trip you can view a delightful array of Victoriana. Shelly's roomy townhouse is attractively decorated in shades of blue. The upstairs guest quarters include a bedroom, a bath, and a TV/sitting area. When she isn't teaching school, Shelly enjoys cooking hearty breakfasts and getting to know her guests.

   Dog in residence; no guests' pets; no smoking; TV; extra bed; hot tub; bike and jogging trails nearby; extra meals optional; bus and BART transportation; airport pickup (Oakland). WEEKEND AND SUMMER GUESTS ONLY.

A	1D	Pvt	Main	2	$25 - $30	($5)

ALAMO

Ruth Feldman   **(415) 837-9038**
22 Gary Way, Alamo, CA 94507
(Two miles north of Danville, off Freeway 680)

   Alamo sits almost at the foot of Mount Diablo, the highest peak and state park in the Bay Area. Nearby historic Danville is a remarkable restoration of a former stagecoach stop, now a jewel of a town for strolling around, shopping, and dining in the hotel known for its fine cuisine and early California memorabilia. At Ruth's you'll find an atmosphere of solitude and park-like serenity, both inside the house and on the grounds. There's a swimming pool, a garden, ponds with waterfalls, and an old-fashioned swing. The guest quarters are in a separate wing of the house, facing the back yard. The peaceful view, a brass bed, healthy plants, artwork, and a collection of exotic baskets make the bedroom a pure delight. Ruth's breakfast specialties include homemade preserves from Oregon blackberries and backyard strawberries. Anyone seeking respite here is sure to be pleased beyond expectation.

   Cat in residence; no dogs; no smoking preferred; TV; swimming pool; some German and Spanish spoken; good connections by BART to airports, San Francisco, Berkeley, and elsewhere. Ruth is happy to recommend (and get advance tickets for) local specialties, such as the elephant seals at Año Nuevo State Reserve.

ROOM	BED	BATH	ENTRANCE	FLOOR	DAILY RATES
A	1D	Pvt	Main	1G	$30 - $35 ($5)

BERKELEY

Marvin & Donis Shapiro   **(415) 524-6523**
1840 Sonoma Avenue, Berkeley, CA 94707
(North Berkeley, Albany Exit from Highway 17)

The Shapiros live in a bungalow-style home typical of many that were built in Berkeley in the 1920's. The neighborhood has matured beautifully, and this home has grown in character over the years. The entire yard is lush with foliage and shade trees. In back, there's a large deck that overlooks a flowing creek and a bridge that leads to a small sitting area. Private guest quarters occupy the upper floor of the house. The lovely blue bedroom has a sloped ceiling, beds that are extra comfy, and windows with a view of backyard greenery. The bathroom skylight allows you to relax in the tub while sunshine filters in on you through the trees. Marvin and Donis are very personable hosts with a variety of interests. In the Berkeley area, they particularly enjoy the Pacific Film Archive, live theater, hiking in nearby parks, and finding interesting new restaurants (many of their discoveries are within easy walking distance). The Shapiros can help you make the most of the fascinating blend that is Berkeley.

No pets; no smoking preferred; no RV parking; full breakfast, if desired; extra bed; deck; buses and BART nearby; extra meals optional; Spanish spoken; airport pickup if convenient (Oakland) or connections (San Francisco). Rates for one-night stays are $30 single and $40 double. A small, two-room apartment nearby is available for extended stays; rates negotiable.

ROOM	BED	BATH	ENTRANCE	FLOOR	DAILY RATES
A	2T	Pvt	Main	2	$25 - $32 ($10)

BERKELEY

Ann Tondu   **(415) 845-2767**
2917 Ashby Avenue, Berkeley, CA 94705
(Almost three miles east of Highway 17, Ashby Exit)

Ann's large, comfortable home is on a main street within walking distance of the university, some of Berkeley's best shops and restaurants, and excellent transportation (local and to San Francisco). There are two bedrooms and a large suite with a sunporch (C) available to B&B guests. Lovely woodwork and antiques make each room special, and the sunny dining area on the main floor is a pleasant place to enjoy a morning meal. There's a fine deck in the back yard for breakfasting, relaxing, and sunbathing when the weather allows. Ann says of her B&B, "My standards are high and my guests satisfied." I can certainly understand why.

No pets; children by special arrangement; deck; good airport connections.

A	1D	Shd*	Main	2	$25 - $35
B	1D	Shd*	Main	2	$25 - $35
C	1T & 1Q	Shd*	Main	2	$45 ($5)

BERKELEY

Ward Street House   **(415) 843-4188**
2201 Ward Street, Berkeley, CA 94705
(Above Shattuck Avenue, near Telegraph)

At a glance you can tell you'll be comfortable and secure in the welcoming atmosphere of Sue Huestis's home on Ward Street. It's a large brown-shingled house on a quiet tree-lined street in the South Campus area of Berkeley. Three upstairs bedrooms with a shared bath (separate toilet and bathroom) are available to guests. Breakfast is served in a charming, sun-filled dining area where international visitors enjoy sharing experiences over perfectly brewed "Berkeley-style" coffee and croissants. Fresh seasonal fruit completes the meal. Guests like the relaxed atmosphere and the convenience of Ward Street House. Nearby are the UC campus, famous Telegraph Avenue, and excellent BART and bus service. Altogether, it's a combination that's hard to beat.

No pets; no children; TV; good airport connections. Room A has a sink; Room C has a sitting room with twin beds. Brochure available.

A	1D	Shd	Main	2	$25 - $35	
B	1T & 1D	Shd	Main	2	$25 - $35	($10)
C	2T & 1D	Shd	Main	2	$30 - $40	($10)

ROOM	BED	BATH	ENTRANCE	FLOOR	DAILY RATES

S - D (EP)

BURLINGAME

Joe & Elnora Fernandez   **(415) 344-5815**
1021 Balboa Avenue, Burlingame, CA 94010
(Six blocks west of U.S. 101, Broadway Exit)

    The Fernandez home is in a pleasantly quiet neighborhood only blocks from shops, restaurants, and public transportation. The City and many spots on the Peninsula are only minutes away by bus or train. Besides convenience, this home offers the privacy of upstairs guest quarters with a rear view of the creek and surrounding native flora. There's a large bedroom with a sloped ceiling, a bath, and a sitting area where breakfast is sometimes served—all very clean and cheerful. Having traveled extensively abroad, Joe and Elnora appreciate meeting culturally diverse people. Joe can converse in Spanish and has some knowledge of other languages, making this a perfect stop for foreign visitors.

    No pets; smoking outside only; TV; extra bed; barbecue; picnic area; Spanish, some Italian, and some French spoken; airport pickup at a small charge (San Francisco).

A	1K	Pvt	Main	2	$30 - $40	($5)

CASTRO VALLEY

S - D (EP)

Lore Bergman   **(415) 881-1533**
P.O. Box 2802, Castro Valley, CA 94546
(Thirty minutes from San Francisco via Freeway 580 or BART)

   While visiting the Bay Area, experience the European ambiance of Lore's home and her talent for seeing to the needs of travelers. She's a veritable potpourri of inside information about this exciting area, and sharing it with guests is her forte. If you wish, she can design personalized tours (and even conduct them—in English, German, or French!), making all the necessary arrangements—a truly hassle-free way to go. Home-cooked meals are available on request, the specialty of the house being expertly prepared German cuisine. While at Lore's, you'll feel free to relax in any room or in the magnificent garden (which is more like a park). "I open my entire house to guests," Lore explains, and that's exactly what she does.
   No pets; full breakfast; TV; kitchen privileges by arrangement at nominal charge; garden; transportation to and from BART station; personalized tours; extra meals optional; German and French spoken; airport pickup at extra charge (Oakland, San Francisco). Rooms A and B are generally used by a family or two parties traveling together.

A	1K	Pvt	Main	1	$45
B	1D		Main	1	$40

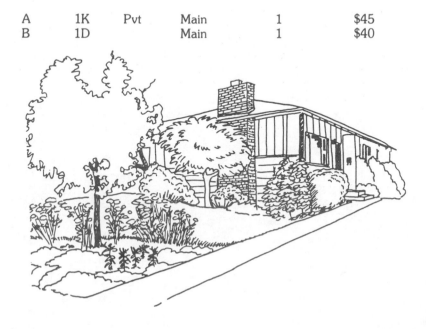

CONCORD

S - D (EP)

Buchanan House   **(415) 672-7190**
5484 Los Gatos Court, Concord, CA 94521
(At the foot of Mount Diablo, North)

There are a number of reasons to bed and breakfast in Concord. The most immediate are Mount Diablo's recreational opportunities and the top-name entertainment featured at the Concord Pavilion. An award-winning shopping center in the area attracts shoppers from all over. Day trips to the Wine Country, Old Sacramento, Oakland, and San Francisco are easily managed. Buchanan House supplies just the extra incentive for a stop in Concord. The ground floor guest suite is quite large, and upstairs there's a smaller bedroom for guests. A lounging area can be all yours during your stay. On nice days you're likely to be drawn to the beautiful patio-garden area in back. As for breakfast, your host helps teach pastry and bread baking at a nearby community college—enough said? Donald and Elizabeth Anderson invite you to experience gracious lodging in the Scottish tradition at Buchanan House.

No pets; smoking outside only; full breakfast; TV; AC; lounging area; crib in Room B; patio; bus and BART transportation; airport pickup (Buchanan).

ROOM	BED	BATH	ENTRANCE	FLOOR	DAILY RATES
A	1D	Pvt	Main	1G	$25 - $30
B	1D	Shd	Main	2	$20 - $25

FREMONT

S - D (EP)

Margot's Continental Lodging   **(415) 657-8862**
41600 Vargas Road, Fremont, CA 94539
(One-half mile west of Highway 680)

Margot & Nick Kover bid you to "enjoy the sweet life" at their home in the foothills of Mission San Jose. The inside is reminiscent of old-world grace. Each guest room is distinctively fashioned and appropriately named: Suite d'elégánce (A), Chantilly (B), and Capistrano (C). The grounds that surround the house are like a park. Views of rolling hills, lovely garden paths, a Jacuzzi to relax in under an open sky—all beckon you to unwind and fully enjoy your stay. Margot surprises guests with many complimentary extras, and I won't give them away. I'll just say that her disposition and her hospitality have a way of making you feel very specially cared for.

Dogs, cats, ducks, chickens, and peacock live on the grounds; no guests' pets; no children; no smoking in bedrooms; TV; AC; Jacuzzi; the Mission San Jose, Weibel Winery, wildlife refuge, Coyote Hills Regional Park, and Sunol Golf Course located nearby; transportation to and from BART station by arrangement; garden accommodations for small wedding receptions and parties; German spoken; airport pickup (Oakland, San Jose). Brochure and gift certificates available. **KNIGHTTIME PUBLICATIONS SPECIAL RATE: 10% discount with this book.

A	1K	Pvt	Main	1	$59**
B	1Q	Shd*	Main	1	$49**
C	1D	Shd*	Main	1	$49**

LOS GATOS

Frank & Geri deMoss   **(408) 354-6067**
18710 Bear Creek Road, Los Gatos, CA 95030
(Five minutes from downtown Los Gatos)

As you head for the Santa Cruz Mountains from Los Gatos, you soon come to Bear Creek Road. It's a winding country road with scenery of woods and vineyards. The deMoss house is half-hidden, like a tree house. A fascinating collection of sculptures along some inviting paths blend in quite agreeably with the natural state of the grounds. Frank and Geri offer guests the top floor of their home, consisting of a bedroom, bath, and TV/sitting room. Wood paneling, exposed beams, lots of windows, intriguing art objects gathered over years of travels, a wood-burning stove, and a profound peacefulness—all convey a warm, country feeling. It's hard to believe that bustling Los Gatos is only five minutes away, giving you the option of having lots of things to do. Or nothing to do. The choice is yours.

No pets; older children OK; TV; sitting room; kitchen privileges; extra bed; pool; sauna. RV camping overnight (no hookups) is $10. Alternate phone number: (408) 395-5050 (Frank).

A	1Q	Pvt	Main	2	$30 - $40 ($10)

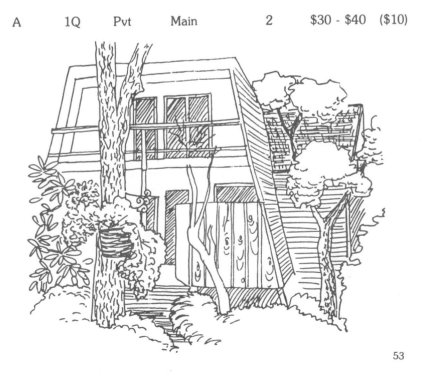

S - D (EP)

MARTINEZ

Home Acre   **(415) 228-0227**
2 Wanda Way, Martinez, CA 94553
(One and one-half miles south of Highway 4, Martinez Exit)

   Jim and Meg Thomas's acre is part of the original ranch of John Muir, whose nearby home and grave are major attractions in the area. Sharing the acre with the Thomases' comfortable ranch-style home are fruit trees, flower and vegetable gardens, and a swimming pool. Their yard backs up to Alhambra Creek. The Redwood Regional Park system in the surrounding hills offers extensive hiking trails, many with exceptional views. Within one-half hour are the Napa Valley, Mount Diablo, and San Francisco (by BART). History buffs will appreciate the stories Meg tells of the Bolbones Indians, John Muir, and other past inhabitants of this intriguing area. As a guest, you'll sample a taste of history when you're served a breakfast such as the Muir family might have enjoyed a hundred years ago.

   Dog and cat in residence; smoking outside only; full breakfast; TV; kitchen privileges by arrangement; swimming pool; living room with fireplace for guests; extra bed; some Spanish spoken; airport pickup at extra charge (Buchanan, Oakland, San Francisco).

A	1D	Shd*	Main	1G	$25 - $30	($5)
B	1Q	Shd*	Main	1G	$25 - $30	($5)

MILL VALLEY

Cecile Cutter   **(415) 388-5475**
220 Del Casa Drive, Mill Valley, CA 94941
(Twenty minutes north of San Francisco)

As you wind your way up and around a verdant hill in Marin County, you begin to suspect that you're in for a lovely experience. When you arrive at Cecile's home, there isn't any doubt about it. The garden setting is lush and peaceful, the home rambling and unusually comfortable. Though the greenery is thick, it's often sunny here, and the views are wonderful. Guests are offered a large bedroom, beautifully furnished in antiques, with enough windows to keep you in touch with Mother Nature's handiwork. There's extra sleeping space on the lanai. Cecile is a casual person who wants guests to use her home as their own, and her attitude makes that an easy thing to do.

Cat in residence; TV; kitchen and laundry privileges; sleeping bag accommodations by arrangement; deck; swimming pool; good hiking nearby; guided tours possible by arrangement; some Spanish and some French spoken; good airport connections.

ROOM	BED	BATH	ENTRANCE	FLOOR	DAILY RATES S - D (EP)	
A	2T	Pvt	Main	1	$40	($ 5)

MILL VALLEY

S - D (EP)

Jane Duncombe   **(415) 388-7932**
239 Princeton Avenue, Mill Valley, CA 94941
(One mile west of U.S. 101)

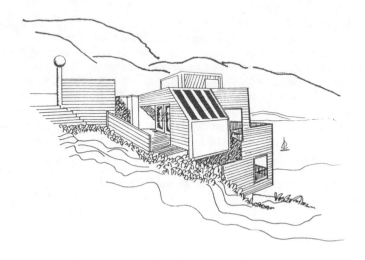

Architect Jane Duncombe designed her home which is set in the tree-studded hills overlooking San Francisco Bay. The recently finished guest area is a studio apartment on the lower level of the house affording complete privacy. There's a kitchen and dining area, sitting room, sleeping area, bathroom, and a sunny deck with an unforgettable view of the bay. Sausalito, Angel Island, Alcatraz, and the Bay Bridge are all visible from this idyllic spot.

Dog and two cats in residence; no RV parking; TV; kitchen; deck; bus transportation. Two-night minimum stay. Early morning or evening calls, please.

A	2T	Pvt	Sep	LL	$40 - $45	($5)

MORAGA

S - D (EP)

Frank & Virginia Hallman   **(415) 376-4318**
309 Constance Place, Moraga, CA 94556
(Five miles from Orinda BART station and Freeway 24)

At the Hallmans' Moraga home, you can have the best of both worlds while visiting the Bay Area. You can take off to "do" San Francisco in the best (carless) fashion, then scoot back across the bay to the quiet luxury of this tastefully appointed home where the Hallmans will see that you have all the restorative comforts you need. There's a large pool and redwood hot tub in a private garden setting. Guest rooms are especially pleasant. Moraga is usually sunny and is centrally located to the many places of interest in the Bay Area. Your hosts will help you find your way to the City, Berkeley, Napa Valley, Muir Woods, and elsewhere.

Two cats in residence; no guests' pets; no young children; no smoking; full breakfast, if desired; color TV in Room B; swimming pool; hot tub; living room with fireplace for guests; bus and BART transportation; airport connections from San Francisco or Oakland. The Hallmans are close to St. Mary's College.

ROOM	BED	BATH	ENTRANCE	FLOOR	DAILY RATES	
A	1Q	Shd*	Main	1G	$30 - $35	($5)
B	1Q	Shd*	Main	1G	$30 - $35	($5)

ROOM	BED	BATH	ENTRANCE	FLOOR	DAILY RATES

NOVATO

S - D (EP)

Faye & Robert Abbey   **(415) 892-5478**
55 Grande Vista, Novato, CA 94947
(Twenty-eight miles north of Golden Gate Bridge)

Novato is the northernmost city in Marin County and best-known to some as the site of the annual Renaissance Pleasure Faire. Its location in the "Valley of Gentle Seasons" gives it a mild, healthful climate, and its proximity to San Francisco makes for a combination of country charm and metropolitan style. Faye and Robert Abbey live in an older, well-groomed neighborhood. The Abbeys' huge back yard is a beautiful landscape of flowers, ferns, and trees, with sitting areas for enjoying the park-like environment. Two bedrooms on the main floor and a master suite to the upper rear of the house comprise the B&B accommodations. A front bedroom (A) is cheerfully decorated in red and white, and the room across the hall (B) is done in ivory lace and ruffles; both are absolutely lovely. The large master suite (C) offers complete privacy and a balcony with a view of the gardens. The Abbeys' home is an appealing place to stay, and its Novato location poises the traveler for a foray into the Sonoma Wine Country, San Francisco, or Marin County's unique towns, parks, and coastline.

No pets; no children; smoking outside only; TV; AC; deck; barbecue; hot tub; extra meals optional; bus transportation with pickup. The suite (C) has a king-sized waterbed. A fully equipped kitchen adjoins Room B and can be used by guests at an extra charge.

ROOM	BED	BATH	ENTRANCE	FLOOR	DAILY RATES	
A	2T	Shd*	Main	1	$25 - $35	($8)
B	2T	Shd*	Sep	1	$25 - $35	($8)
C	1K	Pvt	Sep	2	$45	($8)

OAKLAND

Jessie & Pete Taylor   **(415) 531-2345**
59 Chelton Lane, Oakland, CA 94611
(Oakland Hills)

The Taylors love sharing their home, which is set on a quiet lane in the Oakland Hills. Here you'll be assured of a gracious welcome and a good night's sleep—but that's only the beginning. For these generous-spirited hosts, taking special care of guests is of prime importance. You may have breakfast on the front deck enclosed by a Japanese garden, or on the rear deck facing San Francisco Bay. View jewel-like San Francisco by night from the rear deck, living room, or either guest room. Three islands (Yerba Buena, Angel, and Alcatraz) and two bridges (Golden Gate and Bay) are visible by day. Need I say more?

No RV parking; full breakfast; TV; decks.

ROOM	BED	BATH	ENTRANCE	FLOOR	DAILY RATES	
A	2T	Pvt	Main	LL	$25 - $35	($10)
B	1D	Pvt	Main	LL	$25 - $35	($10)

S - D (EP)

PACIFICA

Janet Spinosa   (415) 359-7020
309 Genevieve Avenue, Pacifica, CA 94044
(Less than a mile from Pacific Coast Highway)

Just a twenty-minute drive from San Francisco, Pacifica is a suburban coastal community. Janet Spinosa's home is in the Vallemar area, a verdant canyon with a flowing creek, huge old trees, and scenic views of the hills. It's a wonderful area for walking, either along the creek, in the hills, or to the ocean (twenty minutes). Janet owns a vintage clothing store in North Beach—she'll be happy to take guests to and from the City on her daily trips (in at 11:30, back at 7:30). Staying at Janet's affords a nice contrast between the excitement of San Francisco and the quiet seclusion of this wooded coastal site.

No pets; no children; full breakfast; TV; kitchen privileges; walking trails; beaches; airport pickup (San Francisco).

ROOM	BED	BATH	ENTRANCE	FLOOR	DAILY RATES
A	1D	Pvt	Main	1	$25 - $30

PIEDMONT

S - D (EP)

Martha & James MacIlvaine　　　　　　　　**(415) 655-5894**
252 Ramona Avenue, Piedmont, CA 94611
(Incorporated city within Oakland; Berkeley to north)

Piedmont is a lovely little surprise of a city that's surrounded by the city of Oakland. It has quiet, safe, tree-lined streets, well-tended yards and houses, and a friendly countenance. The MacIlvaines' home typifies the pleasant atmosphere of Piedmont, and its location offers quick access to San Francisco and East Bay cities. Guest quarters on the main floor include a corner bedroom with extra-long twin beds, a private bath, and a sitting room. In good weather, you'll no doubt want to relax on the deck and enjoy its view of the Golden Gate Bridge. For accommodations that are tops in comfort, convenience, and hospitality, the MacIlvaines' home represents one of the best values in the Bay Area.

Dog and cat in residence; no guests' pets; no RV parking; full breakfast; TV; sitting room; kitchen and laundry privileges; deck; good bus transportation (twenty minutes to San Francisco); German spoken; airport pickup (Oakland).

ROOM	BED	BATH	ENTRANCE	FLOOR	DAILY RATES
A	2T	Pvt	Main	1	$25 - $30　($5)

PLEASANT HILL

S - D (EP)

Charles & Gayle Garrison   **(415) 798-7528**
2130 Orin Lane, Pleasant Hill, CA 94523
(Two miles from Freeway 680, Willow Pass Exit)

Originally North Carolinians, Charles and Gayle Garrison know a thing or two about that special kind of hospitality that puts you at ease immediately. Their home is your home, and you may come and go as you please. Pleasant Hill is ideally located for interesting day trips in every direction; many are convenient by BART. Your hosts can help you plan an itinerary that makes the best use of your time and budget—I suggest doing this on the patio, a glass of iced tea in hand. For breakfast, grits and ham are served to Southerners on request. (If you're not a Southerner, fake it.)

Two cats in residence; children over six welcome; smoking outside only; TV; kitchen and laundry privileges; extra bed; patio; bus and BART transportation; airport pickup (Oakland, San Francisco) or BART (Oakland).

A	1D	Shd	Main	2	$20 - $25	($10)

SAN FRANCISCO

Casa Arguello
225 Arguello Boulevard, San Francisco, CA 94118
(Presidio Heights, between California and Lake)

(415) 752-9482
or 386-9918

Mrs. Emma Baires makes her B&B guests feel right at home in Casa Arguello, a large two-floor flat with spacious, immaculate rooms. The view from each room is a constant reminder that you couldn't be anywhere *but* San Francisco. Presidio Heights is a safe residential area within easy walking distance of the shops of Sacramento Street, Laurel Village, and Clement Street. Excellent restaurants and public transportation are also close by. It's no wonder Mrs. Baires has a lot of return visitors; the cheerfulness of her home lingers long after you have left.

No pets; large living room with TV; TV in Room D; Spanish spoken; good airport connections (San Francisco). Two-night minimum stay; one-night stays, add $5. A two-room master suite is also available at $70.

A	1D	Shd*	Main	3	$30 - $35
B	1D	Shd*	Main	3	$30 - $35
C	2T	Shd*	Main	3	$30 - $35
D	1K	Pvt	Main	3	$40 - $45

SAN FRANCISCO

Dorothy Franzblau   **(415) 564-7686**
2331 Ninth Avenue, San Francisco, CA 94116
(Just south of Golden Gate Park and UC Medical Center)

Another of the City's interesting neighborhoods is Forest Hill, and Dorothy's home is located on its upper street. A few of the area's assets include wonderful views, good places for walking and running, and proximity to lively shops and restaurants near Ninth and Irving. Guests in Dorothy's home are treated with care. Breakfast is a potpourri of her special creations, and snacks await you in your private sitting room at night. The guest suite is a calm haven to return to after a busy day.

No pets; limited smoking; full breakfast; TV; sitting room; extra bed; good public transportation; limited German, Hungarian, and French spoken. Call for reservations before 9 a.m. or after 3:30 p.m.

ROOM	BED	BATH	ENTRANCE	FLOOR	DAILY RATES	
A	2T	Pvt	Main	2	$35 - $45	($15)

ROOM	BED	BATH	ENTRANCE	FLOOR	DAILY RATES

SAN FRANCISCO

S - D (EP)

Jackie's Bed & Breakfast   **(415) 474-1076**
3 McCormick Street, San Francisco, CA 94109
(Nob Hill area)

This deluxe garden apartment is tucked away on a quiet Nob Hill cul-de-sac. It's a tranquil oasis for the busy traveler to return to after sampling the best of San Francisco. From Jackie's, all the choice spots can be easily reached by cable car, bus, or on foot. Many excellent restaurants and specialty shops are within walking distance. Accommodations consist of a bedroom, dressing room, bath, kitchen, and living-dining area with sliding glass doors leading to a private garden. Your thoughtful host provides all the amenities you could want—and many you haven't thought of—to make your stay in San Francisco truly exceptional.

No pets; children over five welcome; full breakfast; TV; living-dining area; private garden with furniture; fully stocked kitchen; living room sofa converts into extra double bed; French spoken; good public transportation and airport connections. Weekly rates 10% less; small car parking $3 per day; one-night stays are $70 for two.

A	1D	Pvt	Sep	LL	$60	($10)

S - D (EP)

SAN FRANCISCO

Lyon Street Bed & Breakfast   **(415) 552-4773**
120 Lyon Street, San Francisco, CA 94117
(Next to the Panhandle of Golden Gate Park)

Ruth and Eric Johnson live on the first two floors of a lovely Queen Anne Victorian and have turned the third floor apartment into a B&B accommodation. The house has an interesting architectural history documented in several books on San Francisco Victorians. The Johnsons are carefully renovating the structure to its original concept. The apartment has a kitchen, a bath, two sitting rooms, and a bedroom; it could easily accommodate four people. The home is in a pleasant and convenient part of the City. There is good public transportation, and many interesting places can be reached on foot. Ruth will gladly serve a large farmhouse breakfast with advance notice at an additional charge.

Two cats in residence; no guests' pets; children welcome; no smoking preferred; TV; kitchen; bus and trolley transportation.

| A | 2Q | Pvt | Main | 3 | $60 - $65 | ($8) |

SAN FRANCISCO
S - D (EP)

John & Alice Micklewright
(415) 753-3574
1387 Sixth Avenue, San Francisco, CA 94122
(Two blocks from Golden Gate Park and UC Medical Center)

    The Micklewrights recently became the second owners of this 1910 Edwardian-style home. It is quite handsome in appearance, from the unusual sloped roof to the extensive interior woodwork, which is all original. There are two fireplaces, one in the living room and one in the dining room. Each is flanked by built-in bookcases and cabinets with leaded stained-glass doors. The feel of the house is rich, solid, and handcrafted. The upper floor is used exclusively for guests. It has been carpeted, painted, and furnished with obvious care. Room A is light and airy, with an adjoining kitchen and a small deck. Room B is painted a regal-looking blue and has a cheery, flower-filled window box. The front bedroom (C) is the most spacious; it's done in a dusty rose and has a large bay window. Guests share a split bath with a clawfoot tub and skylights. The accommodations seem tailor-made for a group of up to seven people, but unrelated parties also find the arrangement convenient. John is English; Alice has a strong background in French. Well-traveled hosts themselves, they very much enjoy the adventure of getting to know new people in their own home.

    Dog in residence; no guests' pets; kitchen with Room A; extra bed; good public transportation and airport connections; French spoken. Weekly and monthly rates.

ROOM	BED	BATH	ENTRANCE	FLOOR	DAILY RATES	
A	1D	Shd*	Main	2	$32 - $42	
B	1D	Shd*	Main	2	$32 - $42	
C	2T or 1K	Shd*	Main	2	$32 - $42	($10)

SAN FRANCISCO

S - D (EP)

Riley's Bed & Breakfast
(415) 731-0788

1322-24 Sixth Avenue, San Francisco, CA 94122
(Between Irving & Judah, near Golden Gate Park and UC Med Center)

    Riley's captures the spirit of a real home away from home in a 1908 antique-furnished Victorian. While neither grand nor luxurious, the refurbished guest rooms at Riley's have great appeal for their neat and tasteful simplicity. Host Sandy Riley's easygoing manner and concern for his guests add to the homey, comfortable feeling that is sometimes hard to find in an unfamiliar city. He can point out interesting neighborhood spots, or tell you about some wonderful walks in the vicinity. One of his favorites is the five blocks to Golden Gate Park where you can visit the Steinhart Aquarium, de Young Museum, Strybing Arboretum, and more. I found Riley's agreeable in every aspect, and I consider it quite a "find."

    No pets; families welcome; smoking outside only; shared cooking facilities; split bathroom; good public transportation; some Spanish and French spoken. B and C are connecting rooms. Weekly accommodations available on a separate floor. Brochure available.

A	1Q	Shd	Main	2	$30 - $35
B	1Q	Shd	Main	2	$30 - $35
C	2T or 1K	Shd	Main	2	$30 - $35

SAN FRANCISCO

S - D (EP)

A Room at the Inn   **(415) 821-4454**
1458 Kansas Street, San Francisco, CA 94107
(Potrero Hill)

Potrero Hill is one of the City's diverse, energetic neighborhoods, and A
Room at the Inn enriches it even further. It's a blue Victorian cottage with a
multifaceted personality. Hosts Sam and Carol have traveled extensively
and their home is generously endowed with art and antiques that spark
memories of faraway places. For your musical inclinations, there are two
pianos (one, a player); soft strains of recorded classical music are usually
heard wafting through the house. A guest room on the first floor has a cozy
European feeling. Upstairs, there are two adjoining bedrooms and a bath
(a large whirlpool tub is a special feature). In the afternoon, guests are offered tea, wine, or champagne. For gracious lodging that you'll warmly
remember, treat yourself to A Room at the Inn.

No pets; no smoking preferred; TV; kitchen privileges or specially prepared dinners by prior arrangement; French spoken; good public transportation and airport connections; airport pickup (San Francisco).

Room	Bed	Bath	Entrance	Floor	Daily Rates	
A	1D	Pvt	Main	1	$45	($10)
B	2D	Pvt	Main	2	$60	

SAN FRANCISCO

Elizabeth Shore-Wilson   **(415) 346-8468**
2212 Divisadero, San Francisco, CA 94115
(Pacific Heights)

For a slice of the elegant life of old San Francisco, this Pacific Heights Victorian would be hard to top. Just walking around in this neighborhood you can catch some heart-stopping views of the City, note examples of distinctive architecture, and dawdle in a plethora of small boutiques and restaurants. Elizabeth, a native of New Zealand, is building a career as a concert singer. She will share her grand piano with anyone who is musically inclined. A large, high-ceilinged guest room is quiet and private; a modernized private bathroom is just across the hall. The entire house is kept in first-rate condition and offers the traveler an atmosphere of refined comfort.

No pets; no children; full breakfast; TV; kitchen and laundry privileges by arrangement; good bus, taxi, and limousine service; German and French spoken.

| A | 1Q | Pvt | Main | 1 | $45 |

SAN FRANCISCO

S - D (EP)

Unicorn House   **(415) 753-5194**
156 Carl Street, San Francisco, CA 94117
(Upper Haight District, near Cole)

    Nowhere is the City's sense of vibrancy felt more keenly than in the Haight. Here the unexpected and offbeat find expression in a melange of quirky shops, small cafés, and people of all descriptions. Golden Gate Park, with its museums, aquarium, biking and walking paths, is within walking distance. Unicorn House is set amidst this festive neighborhood. Miriam Weber, a resident since 1956, fits right in. Her small Victorian home is a tribute to her interest in music, the arts, and, of course, Unicorns. (Ask to see the "Unicorner.") She occupies the top floor, and guests reside in a pleasant room on the main floor where a marvelous San Francisco quilt is on display. All in all, it's a setting guaranteed to warm the body and the soul.

    Cat in residence; no guests' pets; no children; no smoking; no RV parking; good public transportation. Add $3 to rate for one-night stays.

A	1D	Shd	Main	1	$25 - $35

ROOM	BED	BATH	ENTRANCE	FLOOR	DAILY RATES
					S - D (EP)

SAN JOSE

Liz Carney   **(408) 266-6070**
1557 Husted Avenue, San Jose, CA 95125
(Willow Glen area, near Los Gatos and Highway 17)

Willow Glen is one of San Jose's nicest older neighborhoods. Liz Carney's home is on a quiet street with lots of large trees and well-kept yards. The interior is tasteful and attractive with an emphasis on comfort. The guest bedroom is unusually spacious and has the added convenience of a desk with a telephone. A sliding glass door allows guests access to the shaded patio and lovely back yard. Liz can recommend some interesting diversions if you have the time. A few of her favorites include picnicking at a small winery just outside of town, dinner and a film in Los Gatos, or a day trip to Santa Cruz. Whether your visit to San Jose is for business, pleasure, or a bit of both, Liz's makes a good home base.

Cat in residence; no guests' pets; TV; laundry privileges; extra bed; patio; airport pickup if convenient (San Jose). Evening calls are best.

A	1D	Pvt	Sep	1G	$30 - $35	($5)

ROOM	BED	BATH	ENTRANCE	FLOOR	DAILY RATES

SAN JOSE

S - D (EP)

Barbara & George Kievlan

(408) 371-0593

14497 New Jersey Avenue, San Jose, CA 95124
(Junction of San Jose, Campbell, and Los Gatos)

Although you'd never guess it, this sprawling suburban home occupies part of the old Blossom Valley Ranch, and the Kievlans can point out the historical ranch house that still stands nearby. The first thing you notice upon entering the spacious living room is an oversized fireplace that dominates the room, offering its warm glow when the weather's chilly. In warmer weather, the large family room and adjacent patio with pool are the usual gathering places. The guest room is on one corner of the house and can be closed off and entered by its own door. Barbara and George are very accommodating people, and their home conveys the feeling that you can truly do as you please, whether your urge is to socialize, do some light cooking, or spend some time alone. As a guest here, you'll soon feel like just blending into this comfortable household.

Dog in residence; no guests' pets; smoking outside only; TV; AC; kitchen and laundry privileges; extra bed; patio; swimming pool; pool table; wheelchair access; airport pickup (San Jose).

A	1Q	Pvt	Sep	1G	$25 - $30	($5)

ROOM	BED	BATH	ENTRANCE	FLOOR	DAILY RATES

SAN MATEO

The Palm House　　　　　　　　　　　**(415) 573-PALM**
1216 Palm Avenue, San Mateo, CA 94402　　**(415) 573-7256**
(One block east of El Camino Real, between 12th and 13th Avenues)

Alan and Marian Brooks have enjoyed creating The Palm House. Built in 1907, it is a picture-book home in a quiet residential area of San Mateo. Inside, dark wooden panels and beams and multi-paned windows give it a warm European ambiance. You'll notice some stunning works of art on the walls; most were done by Alan, who's an accomplished and successful painter. The Palm House is located within walking distance of shops and restaurants; San Francisco International Airport is a short bus or taxi ride away. You can get to San Francisco, Stanford University, or the Pacific Ocean in less than thirty minutes, and all can be reached by public transportation. There are quite a few tourist attractions in the area, including Bay Meadows Racetrack. Alan and Marian are familiar with the British concept of bed and breakfast, and they wish to convey this ideal to their guests.

Children welcome (one or two).

A	1T & 1Q	Shd	Main	2	$35 - $40	($5)
B	1D	Shd	Main	2	$35 - $40	($5)

SAN RAFAEL

S - D (EP)

The Bed Post   **(415) 457-0740**
242 Locust Avenue, San Rafael, CA 94901
(One block from Dominican College)

   The Bed Post has a lot going for it: a convenient location, good weather, and its setting in a gracious residential area that's sunlit and wooded. The initial appeal heightens as you enter the house. The eclectic style inside is a pleasing mixture of art, antiques, and fun. The private guest suite has two bedrooms, each imaginatively furnished with a four-poster bed and other well-chosen pieces, a bath, a sitting room, and a patio. Your personable hosts, Gloria and Gordon, are ardent travelers who delight in providing guests with news of the Bay Area music, art, and drama scenes. They can also offer local maps and information on nearby places of interest, including San Francisco (twenty-five minutes away). A wholesome breakfast, provided in your sitting room, includes fresh fruit and home-baked bread. Staying at The Bed Post is definitely a treat.
   Cat (Stewart) in residence; no guests' pets; no children; smoking outside only; TV in sitting room; laundry privileges; patio; swimming pool; bus transportation. *Early* morning or evening calls preferred.

| A | 1D | Pvt | Sep | 1G | $35 - $40 |
| B | 1D | Pvt | Sep | 1G | $35 - $40 |

STANFORD

S - D (EP)

The Oasting House   **(415) 321-5195**
P.O. Box 4528, Stanford, CA 94305
(Between El Camino Real and Freeway 280)

Staying at The Oasting House is my idea of Going First Class. Picture a country estate with private, automatic gates in a park-like setting. It's peaceful, tree-studded, and has resident owls, quail, and mockingbirds. Difficult to imagine all this in proximity to major freeways, peninsula attractions, and San Francisco? Well, it's true. Wilheim Oasting, a German potato chip baron, built the Tyrolean house in the 1920's as his summer residence. He used to bring his entire family and staff of servants to the estate from San Francisco, their main residence, to escape the summer fog. Your host, Tricia, has succeeded in making her home tasteful and luxurious, yet extremely liveable. The amenities provided for guests are too numerous to mention. Let me put it this way: If you have a hard time giving way to indulgence, you'd better go someplace else.

Dog and a few pet fowl on premises; no guests' pets; one older child OK; no smoking preferred; color TV in each guest room; kitchen and laundry privileges by arrangement; heated swimming pool; patio and barbecue; sunken tub with Jacuzzi (B and C); refrigerator and dining area (Room A); bicycle trails nearby; bicycles available; German and some Spanish spoken; airport pickup at extra charge (Palo Alto, San Francisco, San Jose). Two-night minimum stay in summer, except by special arrangement. Additional bedroom can adjoin Room D and share its bath at $30.

A	1Q	Pvt	Sep	LL	$56	($15)
B	2T	Pvt	Main	2	$48	
C	1Q	Pvt	Main	2	$60	($15)
D	2T or 1K	Pvt	Sep	LL	$52	

ROOM	BED	BATH	ENTRANCE	FLOOR	DAILY RATES
					S - D (EP)

SUNOL

Don & Jan Scheer   **(415) 862-2046**
508 Kilkare Road, Sunol, CA 94586
(West of Freeway 680, off Route 84)

This is pure country living in the quaint East Bay town of Sunol, formerly a weekend retreat for city-weary San Franciscans. It once boasted four hotels and was the shooting site of many silent movies (starring such notables as Charlie Chaplin and Mary Pickford). The house of Phoebe Apperson Hearst is still standing just a few doors away from the Scheers. Kilkare Road was once the stagecoach road to Dublin and is now an idyllic country road to drive along. The Scheers live in an old house with new additions, sharing their two and one-half acres with a number of cats and dogs, and wild animals that roam the area. It's tree-shaded and very quiet, offering B&B travelers a relaxing place to pause. The guest suite consists of two bedrooms and a bath. For pleasures such as hiking, picnicking, boating, and camping, various recreational parks are within easy reach. Good restaurants can be found in Pleasanton, Fremont, and Sunol.

Hosts have many pets; no guests' pets; children welcome; prefer non-smokers and non-drinkers; airport pickup (Livermore, Oakland, San Francisco, San Jose). A 26-foot Dufour boat for charter, bareboat or skippered.

A	1D	Shd*	Main	1	$20 - $25	($5)
B	1D	Shd*	Main	1	$20 - $25	($5)

TIBURON

Sandy Paul   **(415) 435-0605**
27 Old Landing Road, Tiburon, CA 94920
(Marin County, on San Francisco Bay)

Sandy's ranch-style adobe home is set among trees and faces the bay. Deer roam freely in the yard. Inside, it's the essence of coziness and country charm. There's a small private beachfront across the street where some guests like to sip morning coffee while contemplating the day ahead. A "must" for many visitors is the ferry trip from Tiburon to Angel Island (ten minutes away), a good place for hiking, picnicking, and bicycling. With the variety of unique shops and restaurants in Tiburon and nearby Sausalito—not to mention the stunning view of the City from both spots—you don't really *need* to venture further to have a perfect holiday.

Cat in residence; no guests' pets; small beachfront; good airport connections from San Francisco International by Marin Airporter.

A   1D   Pvt   Main   1G $30 - $35

WALNUT CREEK S - D (EP)

Lois Martin **(415) 934-8119**
2113 Blackstone Drive, Walnut Creek, CA 94598
(Near north entrance to Mount Diablo State Park)

Mount Diablo looms in the background of Lois Martin's rambling California ranch home. She calls it "B&B *Gasthaus zum Bär*," which translates to "Guest House at the Sign of the Bear." The California bear was first drawn by German explorer-artist Ludwig Choris; hence the California-German theme, which is carried out in the decor and in Lois's breakfast specialties. The Martins have made their home in a number of other parts of the world. Art, artifacts, and furniture collected along the way add color and texture to the rooms—evidence of lives richly lived. The atmosphere at the *Gasthaus* is friendly and easygoing. A shaded patio, a swimming pool, and a separate Jacuzzi are most inviting. In winter, a two-sided fireplace provides constant warmth in much of the living area. When you venture out, it might be to Mount Diablo, Heather Farms Recreation Area (with abundant facilities), hiking or biking trails, an excellent golf course, or to the renowned Concord Pavilion (six miles away). Lois offers a special Pavilion Picnic (complete with silver goblets) to those attending an event. Her hospitality shows imagination and care—you'll count yourself fortunate to be touched by it.

Dog and two cats in residence; no guests' pets; families welcome; smoking outside only; full breakfast; TV available; kitchen privileges; extra beds; patio; barbecue; swimming pool; Jacuzzi; tennis rackets; bicycles; video games; extra meals optional; Pavilion (or tailgate) picnics at extra charge; Spanish, German, and Italian spoken; good public transportation; airport pickup (Buchanan, Oakland, San Francisco).

A	2T or 1K	Pvt	Main	1G	$30 - $35	($5)
B	1D	Shd	Main	1G	$25 - $30	($5)

If you reject the food, ignore the customs, fear the religion, and avoid the people, you might better stay home. You are like a pebble thrown into water; you become wet on the surface, but you are never a part of the water.

—James A. Michener

The use of travelling is to regulate imagination by reality, and instead of thinking how things may be, to see them as they are.

—Samuel Johnson

Wine Country

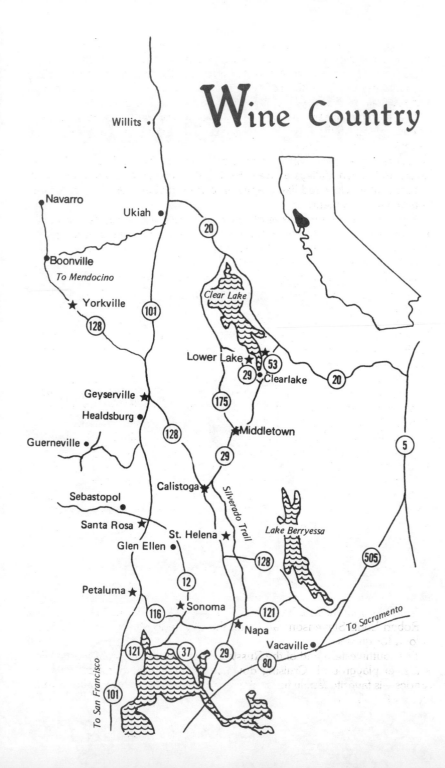

"How simple and frugal a thing is happiness: a glass of wine, a roast chestnut, a little brazier. . . ." Everyone probably has a taste of simple happiness they would add to Nikos Kazantzakis's list, but most of us would keep a glass of wine at the top. The varied character of wine, its surprises and revelations, transform a day in the country into a celebration.

The Wine Country is not a homogeneous plain of back-to-back vineyards, but rather several unique valleys separated by peaks and foothills. Napa and Sonoma are the best known valleys, but wine connoisseurs are eagerly following up new leads in the Anderson, Russian River, and Ukiah Valleys as well. Each valley has its own community of wineries, often clustered like grapes on a vine, making traveling from one to another convenient.

A picnic is *de rigeur*. A loaf of bread, a chunk of cheese, deli delights, and the season's fruit provide the makings of a main event. A good place to stock up is the Rouge et Noir Cheese Shop in Petaluma, where they have been making Camembert, Brie, Schloss, and their special breakfast cheese for over a century. Petaluma's Victorians and "Iron Front" buildings, with their factory-made fronts of cast or sheet iron, are well worth a walking tour.

Sonoma Valley has many excellent wineries and some equally excellent sun-dappled settings for picnics. These vary from open valley vistas to shaded crannies near elusive streams. The back roads are also famous for pick-your-own fruits and vegetables.

Sonoma itself is a reflection of the past. Somehow the early California ranchos are real again, the Bear Flag Rebellion might erupt at any moment, and wasn't it just yesterday that Kit Carson dropped by the Blue Wing Inn? Jack London's ranch near Glen Ellen looks down on his beloved Valley of the Moon, a name he borrowed from the Suisun Indians.

Napa Valley, with microclimatic conditions ideal for grape growing, has been called an agricultural preserve. Over twenty-two thousand acres are under cultivation here. Highway 29, running through Yountville, Oakville, Rutherford, and St. Helena, is the hotline of the Napa wineries. A parallel road, the Silverado Trail, is a more leisurely route, high enough for panoramic views of the vineyards. The two roads meet at various crossroads, so you can zigzag back and forth to visit the wineries of your choice.

Roving the Napa Valley turns up some interests extracurricular to enology. One of the world's three regularly erupting geysers, California's own Old Faithful, shows off every fifty minutes just north of Calistoga. The town itself is famous as a health resort of hot springs and mud baths. Fans of Robert Louis Stevenson can haunt the Silverado Mine near St. Helena to look for ghosts.

The southwestern end of the Russian River, especially near Guerneville, is a river playground. Cruising down the river—in inner tubes, rafts, or canoes—is favorite family fun in the summertime. In fall and winter it's the scene of serious fishing.

Northwest of Cloverdale, the Navarro River flows to the sea through the Anderson Valley, a fifteen-mile stretch where the wineries are within shouting distance of one another along Highway 128. The Anderson Valley is also known as apple country. One orchard alone produces thirty different varieties. Historical Boonville is a treat, whether or not you harp (speak) Boontling, the imaginative dialect spoken by the Boonters who live here.

At the quieter (northern) end of the Russian River is Lake Mendocino, near Ukiah. Fisherfolk go after bass, blue gill, and catfish here. Wineries in the Ukiah Valley have gained quite a reputation in recent years. Redwood and pine offer shelter for alfresco dining.

Many people think of boating, fishing, and water skiing when you mention Clear Lake, but wine lovers will be glad to know that a re-emergence of Lake County wineries is well under way. In the early 1900's, more than thirty Lake County wineries produced wine that won gold medals in American and European competitions. The difficulty of shipping wine over the rugged mountains that surround the county, and then Prohibition, caused most of the wineries to die on the vine. Today these are no longer problems, and several important wineries flourish here to tempt travelers. And of course, there still is the attraction of Clear Lake, the largest natural lake within California's borders (Lake Tahoe is bigger, but we share it with Nevada), the perfect place to picnic and dream up some additions to Kazantzakis's list.

CALISTOGA

Cedar Street Place
(707) 942-4817

1414 Cedar Street, Calistoga, CA 94515
(Just off Calistoga's main street, Lincoln Avenue)

It was lovely to find this 1904 summer-style Victorian B&B home just two blocks from the heart of Calistoga. Located in a quiet, shaded setting, Carole Lee Cole's Cedar Street Place is very large and very comfortable. Four generously proportioned guest rooms and two bathrooms occupy the top floor. The Yellow Room (D) can accommodate a small family, and children are welcome. Guests are invited to relax in the living room or on the front porch. Carole Lee's thoughtfulness is evident throughout the house. My favorite touch was the specially crafted, giant coffee mugs in each room. Imagine filling one of them first thing in the morning and then stealing back to bed for some leisurely waking up time—that's the idea, after all.

No pets; living room; porch; extra beds; spas and restaurants nearby; lower rates midweek.

ROOM	BED	BATH	ENTRANCE	FLOOR	DAILY RATES	
A	1D	Shd*	Main	2	$35 - $40	
B	1Q	Shd*	Main	2	$40 - $45	($10)
C	1Q	Shd*	Main	2	$40 - $45	($10)
D	2T & 1D	Shd*	Main	2	$55	($10)

85

S - D (EP)

CALISTOGA

Foothill House

(707) 942-6933

3037 Foothill Boulevard, Calistoga, CA 94515
(Western foothills just north of Calistoga)

Foothill House is definitely *special*. Gnarled old trees, abundant wildlife, and sweeping views across the valley characterize the setting. Formerly a simple farmhouse, the home has been remodeled in first-rate fashion. Guest rooms are spacious and individually decorated with country antiques. The color scheme in each room is derived from the handmade quilt that covers the queen-sized, four-poster bed. Hosts Michael and Susan Clow take pride in providing every amenity to pamper and please their guests. A wine-appreciation hour is held in the late afternoon, and a generous Continental breakfast is served in the morning. Each can be either a social or a very private occasion depending on where you choose to partake—the sunroom, the terrace, or your own room. Michael and Susan's concern for each guest is genuine, the quality of their lodgings superior. You don't have to wait for a special event to go to Foothill House—just being there is reason enough to celebrate.

No pets; no smoking; well-behaved child over twelve welcome (one per room in A and C). Each room has air conditioning, a ceiling fan, a woodstove, and a small refrigerator; Room A has a sleeper sofa; Room C has an alcove bed. Brochure available.

ROOM	BED	BATH	ENTRANCE	FLOOR	DAILY RATES	
A	1Q	Pvt	Sep	1	$70	($15)
B	1Q	Pvt	Sep	1	$65	
C	1T & 1Q	Pvt	Sep	1	$85	($15)

CLEARLAKE

S - D (EP)

Robert & Ingrid Hansen

(707) 994-7313

5128 Swedberg Road, Lower Lake, CA 95457
(Baylis Point)

    Robert Hansen built this utterly charming Bavarian Cottage—which manages to be quaint without being cute—some years ago, and it's a delight just to look at. There's moss growing on the roof, an ancient gnarled tree by the front door, stained-glass windows, and a quiet lakefront setting. Inside, lots of beautifully carved aged wood and a large stone fireplace create an impression of glowing warmth. Guests occupy the home's upper level, consisting of two bedrooms, a sitting area, and a bath. Guest rooms are small and immaculate, with comforters on the beds and a cozy appeal. Though most people visit during warm weather to enjoy the lake's activities, I think staying overnight at the Hansens' would be a joy any time of year.

    Cat in residence; no guests' pets; no children; no smoking in bedrooms; full breakfast; TV; AC; sitting area; kitchen privileges by arrangement; deck; barbecue; private beach; dock; seaplane landing; skiing; windsurfing; golf, tennis, horseback riding, and dining nearby; extra meals optional; German, Spanish, French, and Italian spoken; airport pickup (Pierce, Santa Rosa). Reduced rates for more than three days. Second bedroom is available only for two parties traveling together.

A	1D	Pvt	Main	2	$35 - $45
B	1D		Main	2	$35 - $45

ROOM	BED	BATH	ENTRANCE	FLOOR	DAILY RATES

CLEARLAKE

Muktip Manor **(707) 994-9571**
12540 Lakeshore Drive, Clearlake, CA 95422
(South shore of lake)

The home of Elisabeth St. Davids and Jerry Schiffman has a peculiar Early California charm of its own. The living area is all on the second floor with doors opening onto a wrap-around veranda. Located opposite the lake, it affords good views and a small private beach. A guest unit consists of a bedroom, living room, kitchen, and bath—while far from luxurious, the decor is delightfully eclectic. Elisabeth is primarily a journalist and Jerry, an actor. (Look for him on reruns of *Streets of San Francisco*—Elisabeth says, "He always played a cop or a corpse.") Both are presently working as real estate brokers. They enjoy sailing their catamaran most every evening. Whatever your particular pleasure might be, there's a host of activities to choose from: boating, swimming, canoeing, fishing, rock-hunting, and wine-tasting at Lake County wineries. The lifestyle here is casual, unpretentious, and laced with humor—a thoroughly engaging combination.

Two dogs and many cats in residence; no children under fourteen; full breakfast; TV; kitchen; large deck; sofa bed in living room; swimming beach; launch ramp and public fishing piers nearby; extra meals optional; good local transportation; French, German, Spanish spoken; airport pickup (Pierce). Animal lovers preferred.

A	1D	Pvt	Sep	2	$30 - $35	($10)

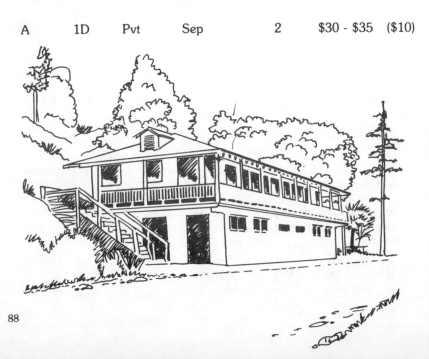

GEYSERVILLE

S - D (EP)

The Campbell Ranch   **(707) 857-3476**
1475 Canyon Road, Geyserville, CA 95441
(Two miles west of U.S. 101)

Mary Jane and Jerry Campbell's hillside home offers spectacular views of the rolling vineyards of Sonoma County. Guests may play tennis, horseshoes, or Ping-Pong and take hikes and swims without leaving the ranch. Close by are Sonoma County wineries, Warm Springs Dam and Lake Sonoma, a fish hatchery, geysers, a network of bike trails, and excellent restaurants. Mary Jane and Jerry provide a luxurious array of elegant touches to make your stay special: lavish breakfasts are served on the terrace; fresh flowers, fruit, and wine are in each room; lemonade and iced tea are served courtside and poolside; pie and coffee may be enjoyed before retiring. Bring your camera, your tennis racket, and an appetite for Mary Jane's delicious cooking.

No pets; no children (teenagers OK); no smoking inside; full breakfast; TV in Room A; AC; queen-sized hide-a-bed in Room C; patio; swimming pool, tennis court; airport pickup at extra charge (Sonoma County, Cloverdale, Healdsburg, Sonoma County). Room B is $65 if bath is shared.

A	1K	Pvt	Sep	1G	$75	
B	1K	Pvt	Main	2	$75	
C	1K	Shd*	Main	2	$65	($10)

MIDDLETOWN

Nethercott House   **(707) 987-3362**
P.O. Box 671, Middletown, CA 95461
(Four miles north of Middletown, off Highway 29 on Putah Lane)

Nethercott House is located in a country setting part way between Calistoga and Clearlake. The 1871 farmhouse is one of the oldest in Lake County, and hosts Ned and Ginny Nethercott are understandably proud of it. The furnishings are mainly Eastern antiques, some of which are for sale. Both guest rooms, one upstairs and one down, are cozy as can be. They have a shared bath and a common room where coffee can be ready as early as you like. Nethercott House is as comfortable and down-to-earth as a favorite old rocking chair—and just as hard to leave.

Smoking outside only; TV; common room; extra bed; golf, fishing, tennis, and horseback riding close by.

A	1D	Shd*	Main	1	$35	($5)
B	2T	Shd*	Main	2	$35	($5)

S - D (EP)

NAPA

Gallery Osgood   **(707) 224-0100**
2230 First Street, Napa, CA 94559
(Two blocks east of Highway 29)

Bed and breakfast in an art gallery? I liked the idea, but I didn't know how much until I toured this splendidly restored Queen Anne home. Professional artists Joan Osgood and Howard Moehrke live and work on the premises. This exceptional husband and wife team have between them all the talents necessary to make this unique concept work. Perhaps only artists can decorate with such a flourish, create such lavish breakfasts, and arrange the gallery space to such advantage. Their work, as well as that of other award-winning artists, is on display in the two main rooms; eleven-foot ceilings and bay windows give the gallery a light and airy look. B&B visitors stay in two elegant guest rooms with a shared bath. The comfortable living room is a fine place to relax, and the exquisitely landscaped yard invites a stroll. If I had to sum up this home in one word, I think I could—perfection.

Dog and cat in residence; no guests' pets; living room; gardens. For more details of the guest rooms, the decor, your hosts, and the gallery itself, write for a brochure.

A	1D	Shd*	Main	1	$60
B	1Q	Shd*	Main	1	$60

NAPA

Ronald D. Larson   **(707) 253-2106**
3530 White Cliff Circle, Napa, CA 94558
(Off Brown's Valley Road, three miles west of downtown)

Ron's comfortable, quiet suburban home is a pleasant headquarters for
people exploring the Napa Valley. Ron is an amicable host who enjoys
relaxed conversation with his guests. You'll feel free to stay around and
visit, or go on your way to take in the many surrounding wineries, shops,
restaurants, and historical points.

Three cats in residence; no guests' pets; TV; AC; sitting room; kitchen
and laundry privileges; barbecue; extra beds.

A	1Q	Pvt	Main	1G	$32 - $40	($5)
B	1D	Shd*	Main	1G	$22 - $28	($5)
C	1D	Shd*	Main	1G	$22 - $28	($5)

PETALUMA   S - D (EP)

Perkins House   **(707) 763-3560**
343 Keller Street, Petaluma, CA 94952
(Three blocks from historic downtown area)

For people who thrill at discovering interesting small towns, Perkins House is just the place to stay while getting to know Petaluma. It is a labor of love for Richard and Joleen Colombo to painstakingly bring Perkins House back to the elegance of its heyday. Built in 1892, it was the home of Dr. C.O. Perkins, a well-known Petaluma dentist who settled here after leaving his native Maine. Of the surprising number of Victorians that survived the 1906 Earthquake, it is truly an outstanding example of the Queen Anne style. Two guest rooms are charmingly furnished with period pieces and trimmed with careful attention to detail. Perkins House is convenient to many other historic sites that have been mapped out in a Walking Tour of Old Petaluma. Also easy to reach on foot are antique shops, boutiques, theaters, entertainment spots, and excellent restaurants. The Wine Country and the beautiful Sonoma coastline are but a short drive away. I think you'll find the Petaluma area, and especially Perkins House, well worth discovering.

Dog and cat in residence; no guests' pets; smoking downstairs only; TV; bus transportation (local and to San Francisco); airport pickup (Petaluma). Room B has a kitchenette.

ROOM	BED	BATH	ENTRANCE	FLOOR	DAILY RATES
A	1D	Shd	Main	2	$45
B	1D	Shd	Main	2	$45

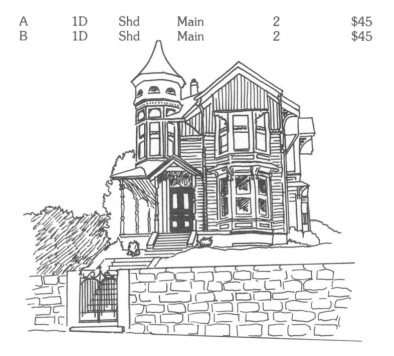

PETALUMA

Sonoma County Bed & Breakfast   **(707) 795-5328**
106 Wambold Lane, Petaluma, CA 94952
(Midway between Petaluma and Santa Rosa, off U.S. 101)

    William & Lisa Wambold offer B&B travelers a recently refurbished bedroom and private bath designed with the comfort and pleasure of guests in mind. The small bedroom, with its antique iron bed and soft, light print wallpaper, is made to look spacious by the use of French doors that lead to a solarium—a great place to relax and read, or perhaps have breakfast. An abundance of grass, flowers, and trees of all kinds are visible through the glass, giving one the feeling of being indoors and outdoors at the same time. The setting of rolling farmland and country quiet is just the right atmosphere for sampling Lisa's baking, fresh eggs, and homemade fruit jams. (Her breakfasts get rave reviews from guests.) The Wambolds welcome you to enjoy their entire home and acre of land, including the small ponds, outdoor barbecue, den, TV, and woodstoves. Sonoma County Bed & Breakfast is just the place for a quiet escape to the country that won't strain the family budget.
    Two dogs in residence; no guests' pets; no children; no smoking; full breakfast; TV; den; barbecue; German and Spanish spoken.

ROOM	BED	BATH	ENTRANCE	FLOOR	DAILY RATES
A	1Q	Pvt	Main	1	$20 - $25

ST. HELENA

Bell Creek Bed & Breakfast   **(707) 963-2383**
3220 Silverado Trail, St. Helena, CA 94574
(East side of Napa Valley, near Glass Mountain Road)

Bell Creek seems to be worlds away from the bustling tourism of the Napa Valley. Hidden from the sound and view of the highway, this home is tucked away in a walnut orchard and offers a pleasant, homelike atmosphere. Hosts Hermann and Jean Suter welcome families and try to adapt to their needs. The two upstairs bedrooms with a shared bath are clean and comfortable. A full country breakfast served in peaceful surroundings is sure to start the day off right, and a refreshing dip in the pool just might be a perfect way to end it.

Dogs, cats, and chickens on premises; children welcome; no smoking preferred; full breakfast; extra beds; crib; swimming pool; some French, German, and Spanish spoken.

A	3T	Shd*	Main	2	$35 - $45	($10)
B	1T & 1D	Shd*	Main	2	$35 - $45	($10)

ST. HELENA

Deer Run Bed & Breakfast   (707) 963-3794
3995 Spring Mountain Road, St. Helena, CA 94574
(Five miles west of Highway 29, above the Napa Valley)

As you wind along the road up Spring Mountain, glancing back occasionally for heady views of the valley below, a sense of anticipation begins to build. Once you reach Deer Run, you will be well rewarded. It's a rustic gem of a home on four acres belonging to Tom and Carol Wilson. There are two guest units, each with a private bath and entrance, one with a fireplace (B). The swimming pool looks inviting, and the deck is a fine place to relax among the trees. Chances are good that you'll really see deer: the property actually *is* a deer run. You can enjoy this private hideaway in its secluded, tranquil setting and still be only minutes from shops, restaurants, spas, and the wineries for which the valley is so famous. Spring Mountain itself (Tom's birthplace) boasts two wineries— Spring Mountain and Chateau Chevalier—that welcome Deer Run's guests for touring and tasting.

Dog and two cats in residence; no guests' pets; children by prior arrangement; no smoking preferred; TV in Room B; deck; swimming pool.

Room	Bed	Bath	Entrance	Floor	Daily Rates
A	1Q	Pvt	Sep	1	$55
B	1K	Pvt	Sep	1	$65

S - D (EP)

ST. HELENA

Judy's Bed & Breakfast   **(707) 963-3081**
2036 Madrona Avenue, St. Helena, CA 94574
(One-half mile west of Main Street—Highway 29)

You'll get a warm wine-country welcome at Judy's. Bob and Judy
Sculatti have lived on their nine-acre vineyard for many years. They've
turned a room in their home into a B&B accommodation of great charm
and comfort. It's a large room, furnished with lovely antiques, Oriental
rugs, and a brass bed. You'll find complimentary wine and cheese in your
room when you arrive. After a day of winery touring and tasting, or
perhaps a hot-air balloon ride, you can come back for a refreshing dip in
the pool. In the evening, you'll have your choice of many superb Napa
Valley restaurants.

No pets; no children; no smoking preferred; no RV parking; TV; AC;
swimming pool; barbecue; Italian spoken.

A	1Q	Pvt	Sep	1G	$50 - $65

SANTA ROSA

Gee-Gee's   **(707) 833-6667**
7810 Sonoma Highway, Santa Rosa, CA 95405
(On Highway 12 in the Valley of the Moon)

Offering quality lodgings to travelers isn't new to Gerda Heaton-Weisz; she's just doing it on a smaller scale now. Gee-Gee's of Quincy has moved from the Feather River Country to the Wine Country. (Three wineries are within a mile of Gee-Gee's.) Four pleasant guest rooms are available for bed and breakfast, two in the main house and two in a separate guest cottage. Gerda, who attended the Sorbonne and speaks fluent French, brings some of her European traditions to the hospitality she offers at Gee-Gee's. What she appreciates most about her present setting is the "view of mountains on three sides, cattle grazing across the road, and seemingly endless stretches of prune and walnut trees bordering my one acre...." As a guest, you'll be glad she decided to share it.

Dog and cat in residence; no guests' pets; no children; no smoking; sitting room with fireplace and TV; decks; swimming pool; two bicycles for guests staying more than one night; lawn games; French and German spoken; airport connections by arrangement (Santa Rosa). Rooms A and B share a bath; Rooms C and D share a bath.

A	1D	Shd*	Main	1G	$40 - $50	($20)
B	1D	Shd*	Main	1G	$40 - $50	($20)
C	1Q	Shd*	Sep	1G	$55	($20)
D	2T	Shd*	Sep	1G	$55	($20)

SANTA ROSA

Helga Poulsen   **(707) 578-1661**
P.O. Box 3211, Santa Rosa, CA 95403
(Northeastern Santa Rosa)

The Poulsens' striking new contemporary home is set high on a hill among large oak trees, commanding sweeping views of Santa Rosa and beautiful Wine Country scenery. It has high vaulted ceilings, stone fireplaces, and big round decks. There is a great feeling of spaciousness throughout the house, and you'll have a choice of places to relax. Although the Poulsens' home is only minutes from downtown, it has a sense of remoteness from the rest of the world. A native Britisher, Helga offers her guests the traditional hospitality of her homeland. She can recommend some worthwhile spots to visit in the Santa Rosa-Sonoma area. Helga also operates "Wine Country Bed & Breakfast," a referral service which lists a number of homes in addition to hers, all offering B&B lodging. Give her a call and let her help you find just the accommodations you're looking for.

No pets; no children; no smoking; full breakfast; sitting room with TV; decks; German and some French spoken.

A	2T	Shd*	Main	LL	$40 - $50

S - D (EP)

SONOMA

The Blue Goose   **(707) 996-7243**
1210 Castle Road, Sonoma, CA 95476
(One and one-half miles east of downtown historical plaza)

The Blue Goose offers visitors to the Sonoma Wine Country a unique experience in lodging. The charming rustic cottage is discreetly tucked behind the home of Patricia Jansen. It has a living room, a bedroom, a kitchen, and a bath. The ambiance inside is country French, and the goose motif is incorporated into the decor. You're sure to find The Blue Goose a delightful place to stay while sampling Sonoma's many wineries, historical points of interest, and fine restaurants.

No pets; no children; TV; kitchen; barbecue; picnic area; airport pickup (Sonoma Sky Park).

ROOM	BED	BATH	ENTRANCE	FLOOR	DAILY RATES
A	1Q	Pvt	Sep	1G	$65

SONOMA

Alene Maches   (707) 996-7178
18860 Melvin Avenue, Sonoma, CA 95476
(Off Highway 12 in the Valley of the Moon)

You'll be warmly received in Mrs. Maches's home, which is in a quiet, secure neighborhood on the northern edge of Sonoma. Two of her three tidy bedrooms are available for B&B guests. Breakfast is served in the large, sunny kitchen; from here you can view the well-cared-for yard where flowers and fruit trees display their seasonal bounty. At Mrs. Maches's home, you'll be located in proximity to a number of historical and enological attractions you won't want to miss.

Children welcome; TV; kitchen privileges; patio and garden; barbecue.

ROOM	BED	BATH	ENTRANCE	FLOOR	DAILY RATES
A	1D	Shd	Main	1G	$18 - $22 ($4)
B	1T	Shd	Main	1G	$18

YORKVILLE

S - D (EP)

Redwood House   (707) 895-3526
21340 Highway 128, Yorkville, CA 95494
(Twenty miles from Cloverdale and U.S. 101)

I call Redwood House a buried treasure—it's tucked way back in the woods in a part of the Wine Country that's well off the beaten track: a real "find." Leslie and Freda Hanelt's private, self-contained guest cottage is redwood and glass; visible only are trees, sky, and Rancheria Creek (which joins the Navarro River). There are wooded paths for walking and water for summer boating and swimming. The Hanelts take pleasure in sharing this bit of heaven with their guests, whose options include wine-tasting at the fine Anderson Valley wineries, side-tripping to the Mendocino coast (thirty-five miles away), or simply settling into the freedom and joy of country living. An added bonus: works of culinary genius are now being produced at the nearby New Boonville Hotel.

Children welcome; smoking outdoors preferred; kitchenette; wood-stove; sofa bed and crib available; two decks overlooking creek; sauna; tree house; small children's beach; sleeping loft; two-night minimum stay. German and Greek spoken.

ROOM	BED	BATH	ENTRANCE	FLOOR	DAILY RATES	
A	1T & 1D	Pvt	Sep	2	$30 - $35	($5)

Central Valley
to
Mount Shasta

Central Valley to Mount Shasta

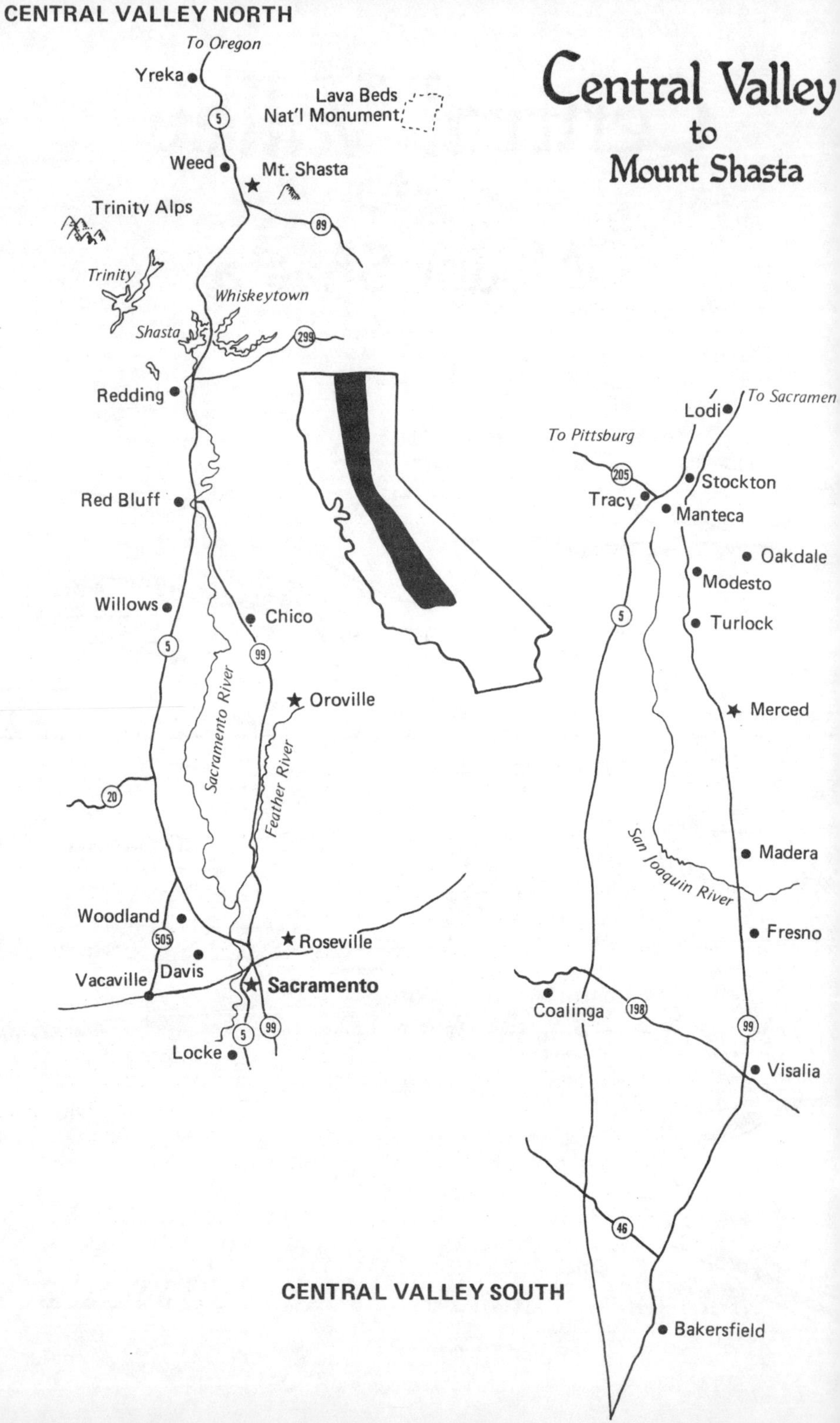

California's Central Valley is the richest, most varied agricultural area in the nation. Everything from fruit to nuts, literally, is grown here; two hundred forty different farm products are cultivated within these nineteen counties.

What this means for the traveler is that Highway 5 need not be boring. Although designed for people on their way to Somewhere Else, Highway 5 (and parallel 99) has many treats in store for the curious traveler, the kind of person who wants to know what a kiwi vine looks like. Many of the farms near the highways are open for tours and pick-it-yourself purists. Farmers' markets and stands do a brisk business. There are good picnic spots, too. For example, the area around Merced boasts three state parks, offering swimming and fishing, as well as cool oases to sample those melons you bought in Kings County and that dessert wine from Fresno.

The Central Valley is really two valleys. The southern valley is drained by the San Joaquin River, and the northern one is drained by the Sacramento. The two rivers meet in one of California's nicest surprises, the delightful Delta. The Delta is a rough, seven hundred forty thousand-acre triangle with Pittsburg at its western point, Sacramento its northern, and Tracy its southern. About eleven hundred miles of levees rim fifty-five islands reclaimed from marshland. Disappointment Slough, Bacon Island, Little Potato—the place names alone are worth the trip.

New visitors may be startled to see freighters sedately plowing through fields of waving grain. Actually, the ships in the water where they belong are hidden to the gunwales by the levees. You can drive along the levees, crossing from one bank to another on cantilevered drawbridges. Tiny Delta towns like Locke (an old Chinese community under consideration as an historical park) and Clarksburg date back to steamboat days. Boating (including houseboats) and fishing are big business here.

At the northern tip of the Delta is Sacramento. In 1849, Sacramento was the gateway to the Gold Rush, and a visit to restored "Old Sac" brings back the days of prospectors, plank sidewalks, and the Pony Express. A bronze rider is a monument to the boys who answered the following ad: *Wanted—Young, skinny, wiry fellows not over eighteen. Must be expert riders, willing to risk death daily. Orphans preferred.*

Sutter's Fort, which predates Sacramento by about ten years, and the State Indian Museum, which predates Sutter's Fort by many more, are other historical highlights, as is the Railroad Museum. The newly restored State Capitol building is a living work of art well worth a visit. So is the renovated Governor's Mansion, which today is free of the rats and bats that former residents complained of. A pleasant alternative to pounding the path of history is to bike along the American River Parkway, which has picnic tables, restrooms, and other facilities.

North of Sacramento lies the Feather River country with fern-filled canyons, pine-covered mountains, and chaparral slopes. The river was dubbed by Don Luis Arguello, who happned to be out exploring during a migration of band-tailed pigeons that filled the river with feathers.

Oroville, in the center of the Feather River region, is rich in history. California's largest Chinatown flourished here in the 1870's, and the four-structure Chinese Temple still stands. Another landmark is the Lott home, a gothic revival-style Victorian, surrounded by Sank Park. With a great deal of grace and charm, the park's regularity and symmetry were designed to express "the taste and affluence of the successful Victorian businessman."

Nearby is Lake Oroville, the site of the highest dam in the United States and a profusion of aquatic activity. A little farther east is Feather Falls, a picturesque cascade plunging six hundred forty feet. To the north is the famed Feather River Canyon, one of the most beautiful in California and a favorite for trout fishing.

In Red Bluff, more Victorian confections await the aficionado, while the William B. Ide Adobe, a monument to California's only president, provides a four-acre traveler's retreat. The Sacramento River, navigable by small boat all the way down to San Francisco Bay, is the scene for every imaginable small craft—canoes, rafts, paddleboats, inner tubes. At the Red Bluff Diversion Dam, you can watch migrating salmon on TV monitors as they pass through the fish ladders. Not too far away is Lassen Volcanic Park, where Mount Lassen (about a three-hour climb) overlooks a valley with bubbling hot springs, boiling mud, a mineralized river, and other evidence of the earth's fiery interior.

Redding marks the beginning of California's water wonderland. The Big Three—Whiskeytown, Shasta, and Trinity (Clair Engle) Lakes—make up a paradise for boaters, anglers, swimmers, water skiers, sailors, and windsurfers. To the east, Burney Falls drops a gossamer curtain of water at a rate of twenty-three hundred gallons per second. Fragrant cedar, fir, oak, willow, and cottonwood maintain the cool on even the hottest summer day.

Rivers, creeks, and streams abound throughout the area, and there are many smaller lakes as well. One stunner is Lake Siskiyou, a natural mirror for Mount Shasta's majestic profile. Nearby, glacier-polished Castle Crags rear up six thousand feet.

Just getting to the Shasta Caverns is an interesting trip. A catamaran cruise across an arm of Lake Shasta and a dizzying bus ride up a steep mountainside bring you to the cave entrance. Inside are magical limestone columns, draperies, and formations that look like soda straws or peanut brittle or spaghetti or . . . well, most visitors like to come up with their own comparisons.

The Mount Shasta area would be an idyllic destination for a highway, but Highway 5 does not stop here. It continues on into Oregon and beyond. But that, of course, is Somewhere Else.

S - D (EP)

MERCED

Scandrett House   **(209) 383-0387**
208 East 21st Street, Merced, CA 95340
(Central Merced)

Scandrett House is a large two-story home with French doors, stained-glass windows, hardwood floors, and lots of country comforts. It's located on one of those small-town, tree-lined streets where birds sing and the world seems peaceful and secure. The same feeling prevails inside. Carefully refurbished over several years, the house has an old-time atmosphere along with all the modern conveniences. Each room contains antiques and nostalgia pieces that hosts Dan and Leslie Stockton have "rescued" and turned into real treasures. The total effect is gracious, warm, and homey. Merced's proximity to Yosemite, the Gold Country, recreation lakes, and I-5 has long made it a popular stopover for travelers. But after stopping at Scandrett House for bed and breakfast, you may just decide to stay awhile.

Two dogs (Buckwheat & Rocky) in residence; no guests' pets; no children; smoking outside only; full breakfast; TV; AC; airport pickup (Merced).

A	1D	Pvt	Main	1	$30 - $35
B	1D	Pvt	Main	1	$30 - $35
C	1D	Shd	Main	1	$30 - $35

S - D (EP)

MOUNT SHASTA

Sisson 1904 Bed & Breakfast   **(916) 926-2913**
326 Chestnut Street, Mount Shasta, CA 96061   **or 926-3164**
(East of I-5 in the center of town)

Kay and Phil Mattos have a deep affection for their cheerful yellow Victorian, trimmed in brown with white gingerbread. It's located in the heart of the Alpine community now known as Mount Shasta. In 1904, when Kay's grandmother Katherine Kohn built the house, the town's name was Sisson. The enterprising Mrs. Kohn first built a livery stable and then decided to put a house next door to it. Rare photos in the family album document these events and more. Decades later, Kay and Phil began restoring the home. Today it glows with the love and endurance of the generations it represents. Early American furnishings blend amiably with period antiques, collectibles, and family mementoes. Upstairs, a carpeted two-room suite and half-bath offer space and privacy to B&B guests. On the main floor, a smaller guest room has its own nostalgic charm. The main bath in the house is quite large and features a roomy claw-foot tub that proves irresistible to many guests. I can't think of a more perfect ending to an active day than a long, hot bath followed by a glass of Kay's homemade raspberry cordial. You'll probably come away from Sisson 1904 as I did—holding the recipe for cordial and feeling like a member of the family.

Cat (Ginger) in residence; no guests' pets; one child over five welcome; no smoking preferred; living room with TV, stereo, and woodstove available to guests; airport pickup (Dunsmuir, Weed).

A	2D	½Pvt	Main	2	$30 - $35	($5)
B	1D	Shd	Main	1	$25 - $30	

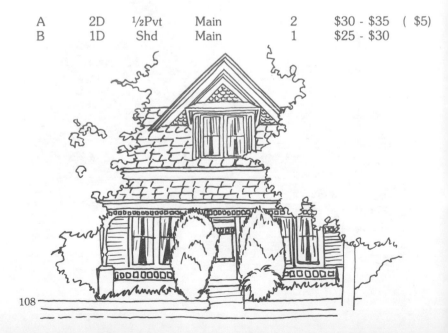

MOUNT SHASTA

S - D (EP)

Wards' "Big Foot" Ranch (916) 926-5170
P.O. Box 585, Mount Shasta, CA 96067
(1530 Hill Road; two miles northwest of I-5)

Barbara and Phil Ward, long-time educators from Saratoga, are now realizing their dream of returning to Phil's native Mount Shasta to appreciate it as fully as possible. Their rural ranch-style home is situated to allow for maximum views of the splendid mammoth mountain. The wrap-around deck and most of the rooms are excellent viewing spots. Inside and out, the home is well cared for and has the feeling of a luxury resort with homey touches. Guest rooms have special comfort and charm. The Wards are fond of entertaining and cooking for guests (a fortunate lot, to say the least). A small trout stream meanders through the property—you may want to try your luck. Nearby hiking trails offer fine mountain recreation. In winter, the woods are full of cross-country skiers; a downhill ski area will open in December 1984.

Hosts have an outdoor dog (Happy) and a toy-like burro (Jasper); no guests' pets (indoors); full breakfast; TV; private living room for guests; kitchen privileges by arrangement; huge deck; barbecue; tours by school bus (appropriately) possible. Room B has two extra-long twin beds that can be converted to a king. Pickup from bus/train stations or airport (Dunsmuir, Weed).

A	1D	Shd*	Main	1	$30 - $35	($5)
B	2T or 1K	Shd*	Main	1	$30 - $35	($5)

OROVILLE

Jean Pratt   **(916) 533-1413**
P.O. Box 2334, Oroville, CA 95965
(1124 Middlehoff Lane)

Jean Pratt's rustic home is set on the west bank of the Feather River. Lucky visitors enjoy idyllic views of the river and peaceful countryside, as well as easy access to boating, fishing, swimming, and gold panning. Although it's convenient to the freeway, shopping, and restaurants, Jean's acreage is so spacious and still that it's a haven for friendly wildlife. Your host, a seasoned traveler herself, knows of an amazing variety of places in the vicinity for visitors to explore—Feather Falls, Oroville Dam and Lake, Fish Hatchery, Table Mountain, Chinese Temple, Pioneer Museum, and historic cemeteries, to name but a few. It's an area rich with culture, history, recreation, and splendid scenery.

No pets indoors; children OK if supervised; TV; kitchen and laundry privileges at extra charge; barbecue; airport pickup (Oroville, or Chico at extra charge). Hunters' dogs with their own kennels welcome. Also available in this resort setting: a deluxe, furnished, two-bedroom apartment for visits of a week or more. Rate is $12.50 per person, per night (negotiable depending on number).

A	1T & 1D	Shd*	Sep	1G	$25 - $35	($10)
B	2T	Shd*	Sep	1G	$25 - $35	($10)
C	1D	Pvt	Sep	1G	$30 - $40	($10)
D	2T	Shd*	Sep	1G	$25 - $35	($10)

ROSEVILLE

S - D (EP)

Six Gables   **(916) 791-7574**
6627 Eureka Road, Roseville, CA 95678
(Just off Auburn-Folsom Road)

Imagine an 1870 farmhouse, small but proud, set in the bucolic country-side northeast of Sacramento. It is white with yellow trim and surrounded by lovely flowering trees and shrubs. A wooden front gate completes the picture. Six Gables could be straight out of a storybook. Two bedrooms, each single-sized and quite endearing, are available to B&B guests. Mimi Woodhouse has installed picture windows in her spacious kitchen and built a large back veranda so that the tranquil scenery is always in view. Close by, I recommend stops at the old towns of Folsom and Auburn. Just a bit further are Grass Valley and Nevada City. Other points in the Gold Coun-try, as well as Lake Tahoe, are less than two hours away.

Two dogs and several cats in residence; no guests' pets; no children under twelve; smoking outside only; full breakfast on request; TV; ver-anda; hot tub. Rate for use of *both* rooms is $45.

ROOM	BED	BATH	ENTRANCE	FLOOR	DAILY RATES
A	1T	Shd*	Main	1	$30
B	1T	Shd*	Main	1	$30

SACRAMENTO

The Iona   **(916) 441-1210**
2009 N Street, Sacramento, CA 95814
(Five blocks east of Capitol Park)

Situated within walking distance of the State Capitol, the Iona is ideally located for business or tourism. Public transportation is easily accessible, as are restaurants, shops, and coffeehouses. Your hosts, Kay Lynne Sherman and Dennis Evenson, are extended members of the Findhorn Community in Scotland. Excellent vegetarian cuisine is created by Kay Lynne, author of the internationally published *Findhorn Family Cookbook*. An entire upstairs flat is one of the bed and breakfast accommodations; a bedroom on the main floor is also available. The Iona, a turn-of-the-century charmer, is truly an island of peace in the midst of the bustling city.

No pets; smoking outside only; full breakfast at extra charge; kitchen in Unit A; kitchen privileges by arrangement for B; good public transportation; Spanish spoken; airport pickup at extra charge (Metropolitan).

A	1K	Pvt	Sep	2	$30 - $35	($5)
B	2T	Shd	Main	1	$30 - $35	($5)

SACRAMENTO

Vera J. Wallner   **(916) 455-1392**
4308 G Street, Sacramento, CA 95819
(East Sacramento)

The private guest cottage behind Mrs. Wallner's home overlooks a patio garden scene that could be a *Sunset* photo. The enchanting beauty of this spot alone is well worth a visit. However, the cottage itself is also quite pleasant, and it's complete enough to suit most travelers' needs. Mrs. Wallner has been known to serve her guests tea from a musical teapot, one of the products of her china-painting artistry.

No pets, children, smoking, or drinking; full breakfast; TV; kitchenette; bus transportation; airport pickup (Executive, or Metropolitan for $5).

A   2T or 1D   Pvt   Sep   1G $25 - $30

What is pleasanter than the tie of host and guest?

—Aeschylus

A guest never forgets the host who has treated him kindly.

—Homer

Gold Country
& the Sierra

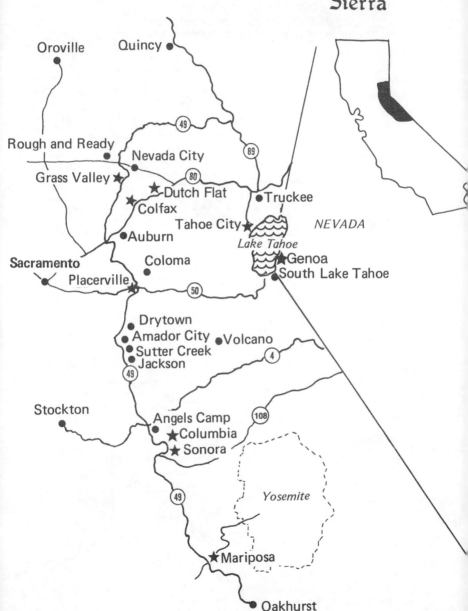

Gold Country
and the Sierra

Oroville

Quincy

Rough and Ready

Nevada City

(49)

(89)

Grass Valley

(80)

Dutch Flat

Colfax

Truckee

NEVADA

Tahoe City

Lake Tahoe

Auburn

Sacramento

Coloma

Genoa

South Lake Tahoe

Placerville

(50)

Drytown

Amador City

Volcano

Sutter Creek

Jackson

(4)

(49)

Stockton

Angels Camp

(108)

Columbia

Sonora

Yosemite

(49)

Mariposa

Oakhurst

Gold dust still seems to shimmer in the air of the Gold Country, as folded foothills and mahogany manzanita bask in the sun. Imagine: the whoops and hollers of a crowd gathered around the assayer's office as a nugget weighs in at one hundred ninety-five pounds. Imagine: banditos cresting one of these basking hills to descend on a passing stagecoach, their own version of the Gold Rush. Imagine: Mark Twain writing in a one-room cabin about a major sporting event he's just witnessed, a frog-jumping contest.

The northern gold mines centered around Nevada City and Grass Valley. Walking tours of these and nearby towns unearth some interesting stories about such characters as Lola Montez and Snowshoe Thompson and the secession of Rough and Ready from the Union in the 1850's. It joined up again in 1948, so you won't need a visa. In Grass Valley, the North Star Powerhouse Mine Museum has been called the best mining museum in the Gold Country.

At the eastern end of Nevada County, Truckee marks the gateway to Lake Tahoe. Writing postcards from here is a challenge. What more can be said of this pine-fringed blue eye of the high Sierra?

The seventy-one-mile drive around Lake Tahoe includes coves and casinos, mountains and marinas. Travelers can take their pick. Most people, however, would pick Emerald Bay. Scooped out by a massive glacier, it glitters brightly in its granite setting. At its southern tip is a replica of a Viking castle, authentic from its stone foundation to its sod roof. In winter, Lake Tahoe bundles up in snow and plays ski resort. Downhillers take to the steep slopes, while Nordic skiers make their way along the silent snow of the cross-country trails.

History buffs will strike it rich along the Gold Mine Trail, with towns like Sutter Creek, Jackson, Volcano, Amador City, and Drytown. (Dry as in Dry Creek; Drytown had twenty-six saloons in its heyday.) In Jackson, some travelers recommend a stop at St. Sava's Serbian Church and cemetery. The modest clapboard church is the mother church of the entire Western Hemisphere. What it lacks in size it makes up in dignity. An equally eloquent spirit resides at Indian Grinding Rock State Park, where descendants of California's original residents hold annual powwows in the fall.

Visitors to this area have a pleasant surprise in store for them if they have not heard of the rapidly growing wine industry here. The more than twenty wineries are often small, family-run establishments, making tastings a friendly and congenial experience.

The Gold Rush may be over, but Sonora, former hub of the southern mining district, has never taken a breather. Its hustling heritage blends well with its current role as county seat and trading center.

In Columbia, however, history marches in place. In this completely restored mining town, even people in sunglasses feel at home riding the stagecoach, drinking sarsaparilla, and eating Cornish pasties. Not too far away, Calaveras Big Trees State Park offers groves of giant sequoias and one of the loveliest rivers in California, the Stanislaus.

Daffodil Hill is a springtime (can we say it?) thrill. Over two hundred thousand of them trumpet spring. The competition from the wildflowers is stiff, though. Poppies, brodiaeas, lupines, larkspur, Mariposa lilies, mullein, and wild roses give their cultivated neighbors a run for their money.

To the southeast is California's gold mine of beauty, Yosemite National Park. Sheer walls of the glacier gorge rise almost vertically to four thousand feet above the peaceful meadows of the valley floor. In spring, plunging waterfalls veil chasms in perpetual mist. You walk tall in the high country, with its regal peaks and gem-like lakes, and feel small beneath the giant sequoias of the Mariposa Grove. One of the most spectacular spots for beauty in the country, Yosemite is a place for all seasons. The same could certainly be said of the Gold Country in general.

COLFAX

Bear River Mountain Farm   **(916) 878-8314**
21725 Placerhills Road, Colfax, CA 95713
(Two miles north of Highway 80)

   The delightful small farmhouse next to Lynne Lewis's home can accommodate up to eight guests. There are two upstairs bedrooms, one
downstairs bedroom, a bath, a living room, and a kitchen. A year-round
stream is within earshot and view, and a variety of flora and fauna share
the surrounding countryside. The Bear River is a mile from the farm, and
the American River, four miles, so swimming, fishing, rafting, picnicking,
hiking, and bicycling are practically at your doorstep. The woodland setting assures that you'll keep cool even in the warmest weather; firewood is
available for chilly evenings. Staying at Bear River Mountain Farm can be
totally relaxing, full of adventure, or a wonderful combination of both.
   Lots of animals on premises; guests' pets OK with $15 refundable
deposit; children welcome ($5 each); TV; kitchen; 1Q sofabed extra; air-
port pickup (Auburn, Nevada County). $45 for two rents the entire house
with complete privacy; rate is $5 less without breakfast, linens, or wood.

A	2T & 1Q	Pvt		2	$45 ($10)
	1K			1	

S - D (EP)

COLUMBIA

Mt. Holly Estate   (209) 532-0542
P.O. Box 787, Columbia, CA 95310
(One and one quarter-mile north of Columbia, off Parrotts Ferry Road)

Columbia has long been a favorite destination of anyone visiting the Mother Lode, especially private pilots. Now, in the vicinity of the airport and Columbia State Park, Mt. Holly Estate offers an opportunity to extend your stay long enough to get the full flavor of this quaint Gold Rush Town. Hosts Paul and Jean Schweizer love their location for its peaceful surroundings and feeling of seclusion. Their home is truly one of a kind. The Tudor-influenced exterior gives no clue as to what's inside. The interior has a rustic, baronial elegance that is partly inherent and partly created by the Schweizers' taste for unusual, large antiques, fascinating memorabilia, and paintings of historical significance. Cathedral ceilings make the living room and den seem vast. Old wood has been used extensively for walls and doors; brass sconces lend a warm glow. Lots of stone, brick, and tile give a heavily textured appearance. From the living room picture window, the scenic countryside is in full view. Sunsets from this vantage point are an inspiration. Lodging at Mt. Holly Estate is certain to make your visit to Columbia unforgettable.

No pets; no children; smoking outside only; TV; AC; swimming pool; picnics prepared for guests at extra charge; airport pickup (Columbia). Room B has a waterbed.

Room	Bed	Bath	Entrance	Floor	Daily Rates
A	1D	Shd*	Main	1	$43 - $48
B	1K	Shd*	Main	1	$43 - $48

S - D (EP)

DUTCH FLAT

Elmore Hill Mine   **(916) 389-2363**
P.O. Box 190, Dutch Flat, CA 95714
(Two miles from Highway 80 between Alta and Dutch Flat)

The town of Dutch Flat was the center of extensive mining in the 1850's and later was a strategic way point in the building of the transcontinental railroad. Secluded deep in the woods not far from Dutch Flat is the home of Sally and Nicolaas Pansegrouw. It is set on a ridge of forested land between the Bear and Little Bear Rivers and was built in 1902 by Sally's grandfather as headquarters for a hydraulic mine operation. Old diggings can still be found on the property. The house itself conveys a feeling of richness and permanence not found in newer homes. The Pansegrouws have finished off the upper floor of the pitched-roof house, creating a gallery lined with hundreds of books, a large bedroom, and a bath. There's extra sleeping space in the gallery, making ideal accommodations for a group or a family. Historical explorations, river recreation, hiking, and Nordic skiing can be enjoyed while staying at Elmore Hill. It's a wonderful getaway even if you do nothing more than sit back and take it easy on the vine-covered front porch.

Dog, cat, and parrot in residence; no guests' pets; families welcome; two extra twin beds in gallery.

ROOM	BED	BATH	ENTRANCE	FLOOR	DAILY RATES
A	3T	Pvt	Main	2	$30 - $35 ($5)

GRASS VALLEY

S - D (EP)

The Gunderson House   **(916) 272-2418**
415 West Main Street, Grass Valley, CA 95945
(Two blocks from the center of town)

The charming Queen Anne home of Martin and Barbara Gunderson looks like an ad for Grass Valley's unique Victorian Christmas. It's a large, two-story confection with gingerbread trim. Each room is enhanced by the use of bright colors, lace curtains, and antique furniture, reminding me of a fancy lady all dressed up. Breakfast at Gunderson House is graciously served on Limoges china. Many historical points are within walking distance, and a shuttle bus takes visitors on various routes around the area. People come to Grass Valley for a variety of reasons—to soak up some history, to visit the Empire Mine, to play golf, to experience a Victorian Christmas, to attend a Bluegrass Festival. Whatever your reason, the Gundersons would be pleased to have you as their guest.

Dog in residence; no guests' pets; no children; airport pickup (Nevada County). Guest golf privileges at Auburn Valley Country Club.

A	1Q	Pvt	Main	2	$55 - $60
B	1Q	Shd*	Main	2	$38 - $40
C	1D	Shd*	Main	2	$32 - $35
D	1Q	Shd*	Main	2	$38 - $40

MARIPOSA

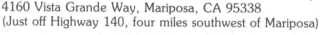

Doris & Michael Beccio   **(209) 742-6206**
4160 Vista Grande Way, Mariposa, CA 95338
(Just off Highway 140, four miles southwest of Mariposa)

The approach to the Beccios' home along sun-dappled Yaqui Gulch Road takes you through rolling cattle country dotted with live oaks. It's a world of remote beauty—a wonderful discovery. The Beccios offer guests the entire ground floor of their rustic cedar home. This includes a huge den with a wood-burning stove, a dining area, two bedrooms, a bath, and a utility room. As far as I'm concerned, though, the pièce de résistance is a small room with hand-crafted redwood walls that contains a large hydro-spa tub. Superb views are seen from the den, bedrooms, and deck. As a vacation headquarters or a short stopover, the Beccios' home has a lot to recommend it.

Dog in residence; dog run available; children over ten welcome; full breakfast; AC; den; deck; hydro-spa. *(EP rate for children is $5.)

ROOM	BED	BATH	ENTRANCE	FLOOR	DAILY RATES	
A	2T & 1D	Pvt	Sep	1G	$30 - $40	($10)*

S - D (EP)

MARIPOSA

Dick & Shirl's Bed & Breakfast   **(209) 966-2514**
4870 Triangle Road, Mariposa, CA 95338
(Five miles out of Mariposa enroute to Yosemite)

Hosts Dick and Shirley Fiester have found great contentment living on their fifteen forested acres. It's a quiet, secluded setting where you can slow down, unwind, and tune in to nature—most people leave completely refreshed. The home itself is rustic, commodious, and relaxing. On the main floor there's an open living area with a large stone fireplace and cathedral ceilings of warm polished redwood. An open kitchen is adjacent, and just off the kitchen is a guest suite that can be closed off for complete privacy. Large breakfasts and friendly conversation are part of the gracious hospitality to be found here. For country lodging on the way to Yosemite (forty miles away), you couldn't do better than Dick & Shirl's.

Dog and cat in residence; no guests' pets; TV; barbecue.

A	2T	Pvt	Main	1G	$25 - $35

MARIPOSA

Granny's Garden   (209) 377-8342
7333 Highway 49 N, Bear Valley, Mariposa, CA 95338
(Twelve miles northwest of Mariposa)

For as long as anyone in Bear Valley remembers, this small Victorian farmhouse has been known as "Granny's." Built in 1896, it was the home of Dave Trabucco's grandparents. After years of restoration work, Dave and his wife Dixie use the house for B&B lodging. There are two guest rooms downstairs that share a split bathroom (one room contains a clawfoot tub). A very private upstairs suite includes a bedroom, a bath, a sitting room, and a balcony—ideal for honeymoon couples. Many antiques in the house are original furnishings, and some are available for sale. Granny's bedroom (B) has a stitchery on the wall that reads "May This House To Every Guest Be A Place of Cheer And Rest." Dixie continues this hospitable tradition by providing elegant special touches, such as flowers, wine, and nice serving pieces set on a lace tablecloth. Bear Valley, home to five generations of Trabuccos, is a place where you can really get away from it all. See the home of General John Fremont, shop at the general store, and dine on French cuisine at the Bon Ton Café. The surrounding area is rich in Gold Rush lore; fishing is good at nearby Bagby. But if I were a guest, I think I'd spend a fair amount of time relaxing in a rocker on Granny's front porch.

Dogs, cats, and farm animals live on the farm; no guests' pets; no children; screened porch; front porch; airport pickup (Mariposa). OPEN MOTHER'S DAY TO HALLOWEEN.

A	2T	Shd*	Sep	1	$25 - $35
B	1D	Shd*	Main	1	$35
C	1D	Pvt	Sep	2	$45

125

MARIPOSA

Meadow Creek Ranch   **(209) 966-3843**
2669 Triangle Road, Mariposa, CA 95338
(At Highway 49 S and Triangle Road)

"A pleasant haven of rest" is the description given to this 1857 home in a Mariposa history book. It was once a stop on the Mariposa-Oakhurst stagecoach run that provided overnight lodging for weary travelers. Though many improvements have been made for the sake of comfort, guests today feel the same welcoming spirit of the early days. Hosts Michael and Nancy Hubert want you to feel completely at home here, whether you're relaxing by the living room fire or roaming freely over their eighty-five acres—"mostly meadows and pine trees, with a couple of ponds," according to Michael. Guests have a choice of three upstairs bedrooms that are the essence of country fresh simplicity. With Yosemite National Park and an abundance of river and lake activities so close at hand, you'll be glad to return to this "pleasant haven of rest."

Dog in residence; smoking on front porch only; TV; full breakfast; kitchen privileges by arrangement; barbecue; walking and hiking on premises; catfish and bass fishing on a "catch and release" basis; airport pickup (Mariposa-Yosemite).

A	1D	Shd*	Main	2	$30 - $35
B	1D	Shd*	Main	2	$30 - $35
C	2T	Shd*	Main	2	$30 - $35

PLACERVILLE

River Rock Home   (916) 622-7640
1756 Georgetown Road, Placerville, CA 95667
(Three miles from Placerville via Route 193)

Located directly on the South Fork of the American River, the home of Dorothy Irvin is very quiet and peaceful. From three of the lovely antique guest rooms, you can be at eye level with the river flowing by as you lie in bed. A one hundred and ten-foot deck stretches by each room, with patio doors opening onto it. Here deluxe breakfasts are served in summer, and there are plenty of lounge chairs for sunning. River rafting, fishing, and panning for gold are popular warm-weather activities. In winter there's still lots to do, such as exploring gold rush towns, wine-tasting in foothill wineries, and skiing at Sierra resorts. It's also nice to have breakfast in the warmth of the living room fire. Dorothy does everything possible to assure the pleasure and comfort of her guests.

Two dogs in residence; no guests' pets; children by special arrangement; full breakfast; TV; AC; laundry privileges; deck; rafting trips arranged; extra meals possible; airport pickup (Placerville). Rooms A, B, and D face the river; Room C has a vanity-sink.

A	1D	Shd*	Main	1	$45 - $50
B	1D	Shd*	Main	1	$45 - $50
C	1D	Shd*	Main	1	$45 - $50
D	1Q	Pvt	Main	1	$60

ROOM	BED	BATH	ENTRANCE	FLOOR	DAILY RATES

S - D (EP)

SONORA

Rosa Lee & Randy Maple   **(209) 532-0615**
20297 Sommette Drive, Sonora, CA 95370
(Five miles east of Sonora, off Highway 108 and Phoenix Lake Road)

Rosa Lee and Randy are very diverse people. She is an artist, photographer, and long-distance runner. He is a cross-country cyclist, runner, writer, and actor. The Maples' home has a large sun deck and is well situated for sweeping views of the surrounding countryside and dazzling sunsets. Guest accommodations are on a separate level of the house. There's a bedroom, a bath, and a large living room with a fireplace. The decor is attractive and soothing, with original works of art adorning the walls. Your hosts are well-versed on such matters as outdoor recreation, cultural events, and special restaurants in the area. It's easy to see why they thoroughly enjoy their location—it's a nice place to visit *and* a nice place to live.

No pets; no smoking; TV; one cot available; deck; airport pickup (Columbia).

A	1D	Pvt	Main	1G	$29 - $35	($2)

128

SONORA

S - D (EP)

Willow Springs Bed & Breakfast   **(209) 533-2030**
20599 Kings Court, Soulsbyville, CA 95372
(Seven miles out of Sonora via Highway 108)

Willow Springs is the kind of small country inn you'd hope to find snuggled in a tiny Sierra foothill town. It's an 1880's ranch house made into a
nostalgic retreat for travelers—a place to be pampered after an active day
in the Mother Lode. The cozy guest house (Unit A) has a full kitchen, a
bath, sleeping for four, and a woodstove. In the main house, each of three
guest rooms is named for an old mine in the area and is individually
decorated with special touches such as ceiling fans, fresh flowers, and
English and American country antiques. Several common areas are suited
to any occasion or weather: a living room with a crackling fire, a spacious
front porch, a country kitchen with a brick fireplace, a dining area where
sumptuous breakfasts are served, a patio under an ancient apple tree, and
a library packed with information about the wealth of attractions in the
area. Your hosts, Marty and Karen Wheeler, will make sure that your visit
to Willow Springs is an experience you'll warmly remember.

Cat in residence; no guests' pets; children welcome; smoking outside
only; TV and full kitchen in guest house; AC, living room, library, and
table games in main house; porch; patio. Adjacent park has summer
swimming lake, picnic tables, barbecue pits, tennis courts, and more. Airport pickup (Columbia). Add $10 to rates for Saturday night stays; dis-
counted rates for stays of more than two nights. Brochure available.

A	1Q & 1D	Pvt	Sep	1	$50 - $55	($10)
B	1D	Shd*	Main	1	$25 - $30	
C	1T & 1Q	Shd*	Main	1	$35 - $40	($10)
D	1Q	Pvt	Main	1	$43 - $48	

S - D (EP)

TAHOE CITY

Cedar Tree   **(916) 583-5421**
P.O. Box 7106, Tahoe City, CA 95730
(Between Route 89 and Lake Tahoe)

    Walt and Doris Genest make it easy for their guests to enjoy Lake Tahoe in a variety of ways. Cedar Tree, an aptly named mountain retreat, is just a short walk from a private beach and pier on the lake. You can try your luck at fishing with Walt in his boat, or at other games of chance in the North Shore casinos. Golfing, boating, biking on trails, hiking, rafting, skiing, and fine dining are all possible in the vicinity of Cedar Tree. The Genests' daughter Margret is even willing to babysit with children of guests. The second floor loft, with color cable TV and extra beds, is popular with the young set. Doris takes pride in serving nourishing homemade treats for breakfast. If you're looking for a vacation spot where the whole family gets a holiday, Cedar Tree hits the jackpot.

    Dog and two birds in residence; smoking outside only; TV; kitchen privileges by arrangement; barbecue; extra beds; deck; hot tub; private beach and pier; fishing by special arrangement; babysitting. Rooms A and B have sinks. CEDAR TREE IS AVAILABLE FOR B&B APRIL-NOVEMBER.

A	1Q	Shd*	Main	2	$30
B	2T	Shd*	Main	2	$30
C	1Q	Pvt	Main	1	$30

TAHOE CITY

Jon & Patty Graff   **(916) 583-7418**
P.O. Box 366, Tahoe City, CA 95730
(1255 Sequoia Avenue)

When the Graffs say their B&B unit is completely self-contained, they really mean it. It's been outfitted with all the essentials and many of the niceties that can make lodging an extra-special experience. The private guest residence consists of a living room, dining room/kitchen, bedroom, and bath. It's sparkling clean and unusually homey. It has knotty pine interior walls, carpeting, and very comfortable furniture. An old-fashioned woodstove (with plenty of wood) will keep you toasty in chilly weather. Glimpses of the lake can be seen through the trees from the rear deck or from the bedroom—what a glorious feeling to awaken to the sun rising over Lake Tahoe!

Color cable TV; FM stereo; living room; kitchen; sleeper sofa; deck; barbecue; bicycles available; bike path nearby.

A	1Q	Pvt	Sep	1G	$50	($5)

GENOA, NEVADA

Orchard House   **(702) 782-2640**
P.O. Box 77, Genoa, NV 98411
(One block south of main crossroads)

Located at the foot of the Eastern Sierra between Carson City and Gardnerville, Genoa is distinguished as the oldest town in Nevada. It is a national historic landmark and has two hundred proud residents. Genoa is the kind of town that remembers ice cream socials and holds a "Candy Dance" each September. The Falcke family home, now known as Orchard House, has been expanded from the original, but it still stands among ancient fruit trees and is surrounded by a white picket fence and century-old stone walls. A pine-paneled upstairs bedroom and private bath provide lodging for B&B guests. You are also welcome to enjoy the Falckes' huge living room; it has ample windows, comfortable seating, and a mammoth stone fireplace. As a guest at Orchard House, you can visit Tahoe's South Shore, Carson City, Virginia City, Gardnerville's Basque restaurants, and nearby Wally's Hot Springs. Whatever you do, try to soak up some of Genoa's history and ambiance. It's a treasure in itself.

TV; extra beds; babysitting possible; kitchen privileges; patio; large lawn and gardens. *(EP rate for children is $5.)

ROOM	BED	BATH	ENTRANCE	FLOOR	DAILY RATES	
A	1Q	Pvt	Main	2	$35 - $45	($10)*

Southern California

Southern California

California is a little like Shangri-La, a paradise that is sometimes hard to find. But visitors to Santa Barbara will feel that they have found it. Palm trees, sunny beaches, technicolor sails on blue water, red rooftops and white stucco against a gray-green backdrop of mountains—it's all here, the California of the travel posters. No wonder this was the place chosen as Shangri-La for the original movie version of *Lost Horizons*.

Santa Barbara is a city at home with itself, as a ramble along the terrazzo walks will convince you. A side trip through the County Courthouse buildings will make you feel as if you are in a Moorish castle. Turrets, arched doorways, and curving staircases have a regal air, a mood matched by the exquisitely manicured gardens. From the clocktower, a panorama of city and sea lies below. Another must-see is the "Queen of Missions," one of California's most beautiful, situated alongside a reflecting pool where mission Indians once bathed. Santa Barbara's peaceful pace makes it a good place to relax or gather your energies before heading south to L.A.

L.A. may be the only city in the country known by its initials. Somehow that fits. It expresses the adolescent charm of the unpredictable and offbeat that you find here. It makes this sprawling city of four hundred sixty square miles and three million people seem both down-home casual and fast-lane exciting.

Many people are not sure just where L.A. is—exactly. Is it downtown near the Civic Center and the Music Center's cultural constellation of theaters and auditoriums? Or is it more toward the soundstages of the satellite TV and movie studios? Maybe it's over near Chinatown, Little Tokyo, or Olvera Street, that delightful, brick-paved pedestrian street with its colorful wares of serapes and ollas, its taste-tempters of biznaga (candied cactus) or green corn tamales. Wait, isn't it somewhere over on Hollywood Boulevard near Grauman's Chinese Theater, where the stars leave footprints? It can't be far from Griffith Park, three thousand acres supporting a zoo, a planetarium, an outdoor theater, stables, playgrounds, and a mountain wilderness. Or is L.A., as some wags suggest, the La Brea Tar Pits where life-sized models of prehistoric animals (the real skeletons are in the Museum of Natural History) rise from the black murk, as Mercedes Benzes and Porsches whiz by on Wilshire Boulevard? But what about the beaches? Don't all of L.A.'s streets lead to the beach?

After you visit L.A., you will undoubtedly have your own opinion about its location. No one leaves L.A. without an opinion.

Northeast of L.A. is the San Gabriel Valley, lushest and plushest of the Los Angeles valleys. A highlight is the Huntington Library and Art Gallery, where you can see Gainesborough's "Blue Boy," a Gutenberg Bible, and two hundred acres of gardens, including the Shakespeare Garden, where the flora of the bard's plays flourish.

The San Gabriel Mountains stand sentinel to Glendale and other small cities, looking austere from the suburban streets. But a drive through these mountains reveals a wealth of waterfalls, rocky ravines, old gold mines, and Indian trails. Further east is Riverside, birthplace of the multi-million-dollar navel orange industry. You can see one of the two original trees brought from Brazil in 1873. It is still bearing fruit on the corner of Magnolia and Arlington Streets.

Good views of the green and golden orange groves and the scenic splendor of the San Bernardino Mountains can be had along the Rim of the World Drive. The road winds up to an elevation of seventy-two hundred feet and takes in the resort of Big Bear Lake. Here you can ski, hike, or fish, depending on the season.

The mountains meet the desert at Palm Springs. Sawtooth peaks guard the desert valley floor inhabited by survivors—tenacious plants, do-or-die wildlife, eroding rocks, and silent sand. Artist Robert Irwin once placed markers along the desert highway to urge people to *look,* really *look.* Then he took them away. He decided they weren't necessary after all.

South of L.A., from Huntington Beach to San Clemente, is the Gold Coast of California. Whether this coastline is named for the golden tans acquired here or the high price of real estate is in dispute. Either way, the Gold Coast offers a variety of beach topography. Wide, sandy stretches, cliff-clutched coves, tidepools, and balmy breezes delight the senses; swimming, boating, fishing, surfing, scuba diving, snorkeling, and windsurfing strain them to the limit. For your more artistic sensibilities, be sure to stop at the famous artists' colony in Laguna Beach.

For all its glory, the Gold Coast is actually the lesser-known side of Orange County, thanks to the magic wand of Walt Disney. In addition to Disneyland, which needs no description, there are three major amusement parks and seven specialty museums. The area roughly flanking Highway 5 is a never-ending world's fair. From Knott's Berry Farm (it was an actual farm once) north of Santa Ana down to Lion Country Safari, visitors will be amused, entertained, and informed. Aircraft, crocodiles, roller coasters, Wild West shows, chimps, antique cars—it's up to you to cry "Uncle."

Continuing oceanside to the south, you come—of course—to Oceanside. Watch the blue Pacific's lacy hem rise and fall, a slave not to fashion but to time. Oceanside is a good base for an exploration of San Diego's back country, a peaceful landscape including rambling hills, rocky peaks, and desert. Mission San Luis Rey, crowned "King of the Missions" as California's largest, dominates a hill overlooking a tranquil valley.

La Jolla, Jewel of the Pacific, has seven miles of coves, caves, and cliffs that are unsurpassed in the southland. On its northern boundary lies Torrey Pines State Park, where this Ice Age tree can be seen in abundance. Modern Icaruses in brightly colored wings hang-glide off the cliffs here.

La Jolla is the quiet edge of San Diego. In San Diego, the park came first; the city built up around it. Century-old Balboa Park is one of the country's greatest. Nine museums, the Old Globe Theater, and the renowned San Diego Zoo all lie within a public garden of fragrant eucalyptus trees and lush greenery. San Diego's other park, the Mission Bay Aquatic Park, is a water playground near downtown. Water sports and Sea World, a park within a park, are big attractions here. A stroll through Old Town is a stroll through San Diego's past. Nearby San Diego Mission was California's first.

With the diversity of natural and manmade attractions in Southern California, few generalizations apply. Only one seems certain: You will never run out of things to do.

S - D (EP)

ANAHEIM

Anaheim Bed & Breakfast   **(714) 533-1884**
1327 South Hickory, Anaheim, CA 92805
(Off Santa Ana Freeway, Ball Road Exit)

Anaheim is the obvious headquarters for anyone planning to visit Disneyland (less than a mile away) or Knott's Berry Farm. A guest at Anaheim Bed & Breakfast told me it was also easy to get to the beaches and L.A., as well as points south and east. (Clearly, he'd found the location ideal.) Margot Wright's suburban home exudes a welcoming and friendly quality that puts visitors at ease. She speaks German fluently and loves meeting people from all over the world. You'll be in good hands with this long-time resident of Anaheim—she knows the area intimately and can give you a real insider's view.

No pets; no smoking; TV, AC, and fireplace in den; full breakfast on weekends; German spoken; good public transportation and airport connections. Inquire about rates during the Olympics.

A	1D	Shd*	Main	1G	$25 - $35
B	1T	Shd*	Main	1G	$25
C	2T	Shd*	Main	1G	$25 - $35

CARPINTERIA

George & Jean Harris   **(805) 684-5629**
1483 Anita Street, Carpinteria, CA 93013
(One-half mile north of U.S. 101, Linden Exit)

The Harrises couldn't be happier living in Carpinteria. "Our climate is heavenly!" says Jean. Their home is in a small suburban area surrounded by rolling ranchlands where flowers, fruit, and nursery stock grow in profusion. There are mountains in the background, and "The World's Safest Beach" is only a mile away. Nearby Abbey Gardens has the largest display of cacti in the country. Guests are offered a bedroom and private bath in this comfortable, well-kept home. They're invited to use the croquet game on the back lawn and a spa that is set amidst ferns and flowers. Getting to know people as nice as the Harrises would be a plus to any vacation.

No pets; child over twelve OK; smoking outside only; full breakfast; TV; no RV parking; spa; lawn croquet.

ROOM	BED	BATH	ENTRANCE	FLOOR	DAILY RATES
A	1K	Pvt	Main	1G	$25 - $30

S - D (EP)

CARPINTERIA

Bev & Don Schroeder   **(805) 684-1579**
1825 Cravens Lane, Carpinteria, CA 93013
(Condo at 4902 Sandyland #245 in Carpinteria)

   The Schroeders welcome travelers to this vacation condo located directly across from "The World's Safest Beach." They'll be on hand to greet you, and if you wish, you may explore their nearby ranch; it provides seasonal fruits for breakfast. A beautiful beach, a park for picnicking, and a variety of restaurants are only steps away from where you'll be staying. Some visitors enjoy touring Carpinteria's noted orchid farm or attending weekend polo matches. Guest accommodations include a living area, kitchenette, bedroom, and bath; the complex has a swimming pool and laundry facilities. A scrapbook of articles about the area has been thoughtfully provided by your hosts.

   No pets; no smoking; color cable TV; living room; kitchenette; laundry facilities; swimming pool; beach; park; tennis club privileges at Polo & Racquet Club with $5 guest fee; Greyhound Bus stops nearby. July 28-August 12 rates are $100 per night.

A	2T & 1Q	Pvt	Sep	2	$45

ROOM	BED	BATH	ENTRANCE	FLOOR	DAILY RATES

S - D (EP)

CATALINA ISLAND

Gull House   **(213) 510-2547**
P.O. Box 1381, Avalon, CA 90704   **or 257-1281**
(A short walk from bay and town)

Whether you're discovering the romance of Santa Catalina for the first time or returning for the fiftieth, you'll find bed and breakfast at Gull House an experience unique on the island. Hosts Hattie and Bob Michalis offer two deluxe suites; each has a separate entrance, a large living room with a gas log fireplace, a morning room with a refrigerator and table, a bedroom, and a bath. Accommodations are immaculate and nicely decorated. Have breakfast at your leisure under an Italian umbrella on the patio, where there's a pool, a spa, and a gas barbecue. It's an easy walk to reach many of the sights and activities the island is known for. The distinct Mediterranean flavor of Catalina make it a feast for the senses. And the hospitality at Gull House adds an extra dimension of comfort to any visit.

No pets; no children; TV and stereo in each suite; pool; spa; barbecue; various tours, golfing, and horseback riding nearby; taxi service from ferry terminal included with full advance payment. Brochure available. *Rates vary according to season and minimum stays. Per diem double occupancy charges range from $40 for a five-day stay in winter to $90 for a two-day weekend in summer; most are somewhere in between. Call or write for rate schedule. **KNIGHTTIME PUBLICATIONS SPECIAL RATE: 15% discount with this book.

A	2T	Pvt	Sep	LL	*/**See notes above
B	2T	Pvt	Sep	LL	

ESCONDIDO

Halbig's Hacienda   **(619) 745-1296**
432 South Citrus Avenue, Escondido, CA 92027
(East of town, off Valley Parkway)

The Halbigs came to Escondido in the fifties and the town literally grew up around them. The home that they built by hand sits on a knoll, removed from the hustle and bustle, with wonderful views of the surrounding mountains. Fruit trees dot the property. Long verandas, adobe brick construction, and hand-hewn wooden doors recall the days of the early California ranchos. Life here is casual and unpretentious. Three rooms are offered for bed and breakfast; Room B has an heirloom brass bed. Ancestors of the Halbigs were dollmakers in Bavaria, and a few cherished antique dolls are on display. Escondido makes a good base for exploring San Diego's back country, fishing in nearby lakes, dropping by the Wild Animal Park, or paying a visit to Lawrence Welk's village and dinner theater. Beaches are only twenty minutes away, and San Diego forty-five.

Children and pets welcome; TV; some Spanish spoken; airport pickup (Palomar). Inquire about lower rates after first night.

A	1Q	Shd*	Main	1G	$35
B	1D	Shd*	Main	1G	$30
C	2T	Shd*	Main	1G	$15 - $30

GLENDALE

Geraldine & Spencer Shroff   **(818) 507-0774**
1114 Park Avenue, Glendale, CA 91205
(South of Ventura Freeway and east of Golden State)

The Shroffs' California-style Spanish stucco home is white with a red tile roof. It's on a residential street near a small business district; Glendale's major shopping area is less than three miles away. The home has been recently refurbished throughout, and one of the two bedrooms is offered as a B&B accommodation. It has a light and airy feeling, as does the bath down the hall. The large back yard contains a mini fruit orchard, producing an abundance of breakfast delights. Enjoy the rear patio and redwood gazebo, where large overhanging trees provide a cool, quiet respite for guests on lazy days. Glendale is a convenient base for visiting the many attractions on the north side of Los Angeles, such as motion picture studio tours, Forest Lawn Memorial-Park, and Huntington Library, Art Gallery, and Botanical Gardens. The famous Pasadena Rose Bowl is just a short drive from the Shroffs'. Your hosts are adept at supplying directions to these and other points of interest in the Los Angeles area.

No pets; full breakfast at extra charge for guests staying more than one night; TV; airport pickup (Burbank). An additional (large master) bedroom will be available from June 1 to September 1, 1984. It has three twin beds, a shared bath, and rates of $30 - $35 ($15, over 12 years; $10, under 12). Rates for both rooms will be higher during the Olympic season, July 25 to August 12, 1984.

| A | 1D | Shd | Main | 1 | $20 - $25 |

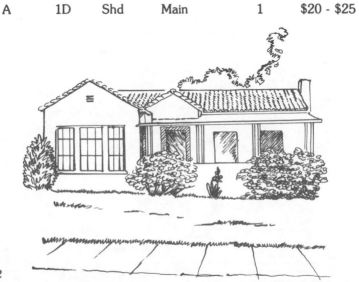

LA HABRA HEIGHTS

Marjorie & Bernie Arritt   **(213) 697-2924**
1854 Nueva Vista, La Habra Heights, CA 90631
(Fifteen miles east of L.A. via Pomona Freeway)

The Arritts' home is set on one acre in a semi-rural area east of L.A. and north of Disneyland (twenty minutes to each). The rooms and the outdoor entertaining area are huge and stunningly beautiful. It's a home that is meant to be shared and enjoyed to the fullest. As appealing as the interior is, it's the back yard that dazzles. There's a thriving garden, fruit trees, a vast patio, a pool, a spa, a barbecue/bar area, a rope hammock, and a tennis court. It's a full resort in itself, with lots of luxuries and personal touches. Once you're here to see it all firsthand, I doubt you'll want to set foot off the premises. The Arritts are experienced travelers with a genuine interest in people of all backgrounds. Being their guest is guaranteed to put some sunshine in your life in more ways than one.

No pets; no accommodations for children at present; no cigars or pipes preferred; TV; AC; kitchen privileges by arrangement; golf courses, malls, and good restaurants nearby; Spanish and some French spoken; tennis partners wanted; airport pickup (Ontario) or connections from LAX.

ROOM	BED	BATH	ENTRANCE	FLOOR	DAILY RATES
A	2T or 1K	Pvt	Main	1	$35 - 40

LOS ANGELES

Rusty Cantor   **(213) 663-9533**
4033 Holly Knoll Drive, Los Angeles, CA 90027
(Ten minutes from Hollywood and downtown L.A., near Los Feliz)

Rusty's home is an older Spanish stucco with lots of character. Business travelers will find it an ideal stop. The location has the quiet and greenery of a lovely residential area, yet it's only minutes from downtown and a long list of attractions that L.A. is famous for. Rusty is a professional fibre artist, and the pieces she creates are strikingly exotic. Some are on display in her home, giving a richly textured feeling to the decor. The guest area includes a bedroom with a private den adjacent—a good place to work, or just be alone. Anyone interested in L.A.'s exciting art scene will be especially pleased; Rusty knows it well, and she's willing to share her knowledge with interested guests.

No pets; TV; den; kitchen privileges by arrangement; barbecue; art-oriented tours by special arrangement at an additional charge; airport pickup (Burbank); connections possible from LAX. Inquire about rates during the Olympics. Entire house may be rented at times; ask for details.

| A | 2T or 1D | Shd | Main | 1 | $35 - $45 |

S - D (EP)

LOS ANGELES

Salisbury House   **(213) 737-7817**
2273 West 20th Street, Los Angeles, CA 90018
(Near Santa Monica Freeway and Western Avenue)

Experience the ultimate in bed and breakfast luxury at Salisbury House, L.A.'s first accommodation of its kind. Here you'll find all the amenities of a manor house in the country, yet you'll be only minutes from downtown and major freeways. This turn-of-the-century California Craftsman home is large and solid. An expert job of restoration has left its original integrity more than intact. Graciously proportioned rooms are exquisitely furnished with antiques and collectibles. Colors, fabrics, and nostalgia pieces have been imaginatively combined to give each room a distinct personality. The total effect is pure enchantment. The generous breakfasts served here are superb, the hospitality boundless. Hosts Kathleen and Bill invite you to treat yourself to the many charms of Salisbury House. I can't imagine a more relaxing or romantic getaway.

No pets; full breakfast and complimentary wine; weekly and monthly rates; Room A has a sink; brochure available. Beginning in June 1984, a two-room suite with 1D & 2T beds and a private bath will be available at $50 - $55   ($10). **KNIGHTTIME PUBLICATIONS SPECIAL RATE: 15% discount with this book.

Room	Bed	Bath	Entrance	Floor	Daily Rates
A	1Q	Pvt	Main	2	$50 - $55 **
B	1Q	Shd*	Main	2	$40 - $45 **
C	1T & 1K	Pvt	Main	3	$50 - $55 ($10)**
D	1Q	Shd*	Main	2	$40 - $45 **

S - D (EP)

NEWPORT BEACH

Villa Lido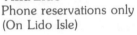

(714) 673-8335

Phone reservations only
(On Lido Isle)

Life on Lido Isle is California's version of life on the Riviera. After a vacation here, you'll understand why they call this part of Orange County the Gold Coast. The patio of Villa Lido is seventy-five feet from the yacht harbor and beautiful Newport Bay. An assortment of fine shops and restaurants is just steps away, across an auto and foot bridge that connects to the mainland. The natural tones used throughout the house create a calm and relaxing atmosphere. Two guest rooms with private baths have a common sitting area where breakfast can be taken at your leisure. You won't even need a car on Lido Isle—everything here, including the beach, is just a short walk or bike ride away. Anyone seeking a luxurious refuge from the cares of everyday life couldn't do better than Villa Lido.

Two dogs in residence; no guests' pets; no children; no RV parking; sitting room with TV, chess set, kitchenette, and exercycle; patio; barbecue; lawn croquet; bicycles; good public transportation and airport connections. Host is interested in exchanging homes with a family in Europe. Add $5 to rate for one-night stays.

A	1Q	Pvt	Main	2	$60
B	2T	Pvt	Main	2	$60

NORTHRIDGE

S - D (EP)

Hideaway House

(818) 349-5421

8441 Melvin Avenue, Northridge, CA 91324
(Just north of Ventura Freeway and west of San Diego Freeway)

A visit to Hideaway House feels like a true escape to the country. Once you're there, it's hard to believe that this one-and-a-quarter-acre estate is located so close to the L.A. freeway system, shopping malls, restaurants, universities, and public transportation. Hosts Dean and Dorothy Dennis love their woodsy setting and sprawling ranch-style home, and it's a cinch to see why. A wicker front porch swing, leaded and stained-glass windows, original art, and handsome antiques make it a home of great charm. Besides the two old-fashioned guest rooms, wonderful spots for relaxation include a large but cozy living room, an attached greenhouse with a bar, and a Jacuzzi soaking tub. The many windows keep the peaceful surroundings in view. Dorothy is an accomplished cook; she likes to serve breakfast by the fireplace or on the sunporch or patio, depending on the weather. She and Dean enjoy jazz, good books, good food, and good company. The casual atmosphere at Hideaway House makes it ideal for those seeking a leisurely pace.

No pets; one child over twelve welcome; no smoking in bedroom or bath; full breakfast; TV; AC; greenhouse bar; kitchen privileges by arrangement; Jacuzzi tub in master bath; airport pickup at extra charge (Burbank, Van Nuys, LAX). Tours, picnics, and extra meals optional at additional charge.

ROOM	BED	BATH	ENTRANCE	FLOOR	DAILY RATES
A	1D	Shd*	Main	1G	$50 - $55
B	1D	Shd*	Main	1G	$35

147

PALM SPRINGS

Elinor McMartin   **(619) 320-6136**
2285 Cardillo Avenue, Palm Springs, CA 92262
(North end of town, Tuscany area)

   In the Tuscany area of Palm Springs, homes tend to harmonize with the desert landscape. Elinor McMartin's home is surrounded by palms, pines, and other native flora. Mountains that line the Coachella Valley rise dramatically in the background. The atmosphere at Elinor's home is low-key and totally unpretentious, just as she is. Her appreciation for nature is evident throughout her home; rattan furniture, Indonesian fabrics, and an interesting collection of artifacts and seashells punctuate the decor. The private guest bedroom has sliding glass doors that lead to the patio and solar-heated pool with Jacuzzi. Anyone seeking solitude and rest will find it here. Should you care to explore, Palm Springs and environs are rich in natural wonders; Elinor especially likes the Palm Springs Desert Museum, the Living Desert Reserve, and Joshua Tree National Monument. Those seeking the Palm Springs of tennis, golf, shopping, and restaurants will find all of it only minutes away. Whatever you come here for, you're bound to return home enriched from your stay in the desert.
   Obedient, loving dog (Charlie, a standard poodle) in residence; no children; AC; shared cooking facilities by arrangement; patio; pool with Jacuzzi; public transportation nearby; French spoken; airport pickup (Palm Springs). CLOSED JUNE-SEPTEMBER. **KNIGHTTIME PUBLICATIONS SPECIAL RATE: 10% discount with this book.

ROOM	BED	BATH	ENTRANCE	FLOOR	DAILY RATES
A	2T	Pvt	Sep	1G	$40 - $45**

ROOM   BED   BATH   ENTRANCE   FLOOR   DAILY RATES

S - D (EP)

SAN DIEGO

Abigail   **(619) 583-4738**
6310 Raydel Court, San Diego, CA 92120
(Ten miles east of San Diego via I-8, College Avenue Exit)

If you're looking for a place in San Diego where you can really stretch out—both physically and mentally—this private apartment in the beautiful Del Cerro area (near San Diego State University) may be just the place for you. The second floor accommodation is separate from the home of hosts Felix and Pearl Ammar, though it's connected to the main residence by a staircase. It has large, carpeted rooms—a bedroom, bath, living room, and fully equipped kitchen. You may prepare your own breakfast whenever you choose. (If Pearl's been baking, watch out! This is no time for a diet.) You'll have a 360° view, a sundeck, and a private entrance. International visitors are welcome, for these well-traveled hosts speak many languages.

No pets; no children; no smoking; TV; living room; kitchen; deck; French, Greek, Hebrew, Arabic, some Italian, and some Spanish spoken; airport pickup at nominal charge (Lindbergh). Three-night minimum stay.

A   1D   Pvt   Sep   2 $46

S - D (EP)

SAN DIEGO

Bed & Breakfast in Del Cerro   (619) 466-2794
5649 Linfield Avenue, San Diego, CA 92120
(Ten miles east of San Diego via I-8, College Avenue Exit)

Paul & Libby Senecal provide a welcoming atmosphere for guests in their attractive suburban home. Two bedrooms with a connecting bath and a den/sitting area make for altogether pleasant B&B lodgings. Located near San Diego State University, the Senecals' home is a twenty-minute drive from downtown and beaches; it's about an hour's drive from beautiful mountain and desert scenery. For kind hospitality and nourishing breakfasts—both served in abundance—you couldn't ask for a nicer place to stay.

No pets; smoking on patio only; full breakfast; TV; den; kitchen privileges by arrangement; patio; French spoken; airport pickup at nominal charge (Lindbergh).

A	2T	Shd*	Main	1G	$20 - $30
B	1D	Shd*	Main	1G	$20 - $30

SAN DIEGO

The Cottage   **(619) 299-1564**
P.O. Box 3292, San Diego, CA 92103
(Hillcrest area, near Balboa Park)

The Hillcrest area is characterized by old homes and undeveloped canyons, offering an unhurried, isolated atmosphere. Conveniently located on a quiet cul-de-sac, this private cottage successfully recreates the feeling of a Victorian country home. It is furnished with beautiful antiques, including such nostalgic pieces as an oak pump organ and an old-time coffee grinder that still works. The cottage has a fully equipped kitchen, living room, bedroom, and bath—each uncommonly charming. Your hosts, Bob and Carol Emerick, have thought of everything a traveler might need while in residence, and their vast collection of helpful information about the area is yours to peruse at your leisure (history, architecture, restaurants, maps, directions, etc.). If ever a place could inspire affection, The Cottage does just that. You may find yourself returning sooner than you think.

TV; living room; woodstove; full kitchen; good public transportation.

ROOM	BED	BATH	ENTRANCE	FLOOR	DAILY RATES
A	1T & 1K	Pvt	Sep	1	$40 - $45 ($5)

SAN DIEGO

Barbara Farrell   **(619) 453-2982**
P.O. Box 2795, Del Mar, CA 92014-5795
(In San Diego, near La Jolla)

   To be a guest at Barbara Farrell's townhouse is to have the best of San Diego at your fingertips. Barbara is a travel agent, a tour guide, a supporter of the symphony and the arts, and an avid world traveler. She is thoroughly familiar with the unique and exciting aspects of the area and is happy to share them with visitors. Nearest her home is La Jolla; she seems to know every nook and cranny of this jewel of a town. Guest quarters consist of a large, sunny upstairs bedroom with private bath. It's attractively decorated in shades of blue and holds some of the special objects Barbara has found in her travels. Breakfast is usually served on the patio, which is surrounded by luxuriant foliage. For comfort, convenience, and a real insider's view of things, Barbara's townhouse is just the ticket.
   No pets; no children; no smoking; TV; patio; pool, Jacuzzi, and tennis courts in complex; French spoken. Women and couples only. Early morning or evening calls best.

| A | 1D | Pvt | Main | 2 | $35 - $40 |

SANTA ANA

S - D (EP)

The Craftsman **(714) 558-1067**
1711 North Bush Street, Santa Ana, CA 92706
(Two blocks west of Santa Ana Freeway)

Phil and Irene Chinn live in a Craftsman-style home built in 1910. Each room has been redecorated in the style of the era and furnished with American oak and Danish antiques. Staying at this handsomely restored home puts you close to many local attractions, including Disneyland, Knott's Berry Farm, Newport Beach, and Bowers Museum. Your cordial hosts will help you choose from the profusion of fine shops and restaurants in the area. The Craftsman is easy to reach by plane, train, bus, or car.

No pets; full breakfast; TV; kitchen privileges by arrangement; parks nearby; extra meals optional; airport pickup (John Wayne-Orange County) at extra charge. Evening calls, please.

| A | 1D | Shd* | Main | 2 | $30 - $35 |
| B | 1Q (sofa) | Shd* | Main | 2 | $30 - $35 |

S - D (EP)

SANTA BARBARA

The Cottage   **(805) 682-4997**
840 Mission Canyon Road, Santa Barbara, CA 93105   **or 682-4461**
(Near Mission Santa Barbara)

Hosts Ray and Sylvia Byers are offering the private cottage behind their home as a B&B accommodation. It is set among ancient trees and lush foliage, allowing only the songs of birds to awaken you each morning. Inside, it's paneled and nicely decorated in warm golds and browns. There's a bedroom, living room (with skylight), bath, and kitchenette. Within walking distance, Mission Santa Barbara and the botanical gardens are popular things to see. The downtown courthouse, harbor, and beaches are not too far away. Your hosts know the best beaches to send you to and the right restaurant for any occasion. For a homey feeling, complete privacy, and a convenient location, you really can't go wrong with The Cottage.

Three dogs in residence; no smoking; TV; living room; kitchenette; German spoken; airport pickup (Santa Barbara).

A	1D	Pvt	Sep	1	$40 - $45	($5)

S - D (EP)

SANTA BARBARA

Frank & Greta Hansen   **(805) 969-1365**
807 Cima Linda Lane, Montecito, CA 93108
(In hills overlooking Santa Barbara)

The view from this elegant home is simply intoxicating. Whether you're sunning by the pool or ensconced in your comfortable room, the expanse of sea and sky is yours to behold. Guests occupy either a first-floor bedroom that opens onto the patio or an upstairs bedroom with a private sitting room. Each guest area is tastefully appointed with decorator fabrics and coordinating wallpaper. For luxurious accommodations located only minutes from the beach and downtown Santa Barbara, the Hansens' home is the spot to pick.

Two dogs in residence; no children; TV and phone in each room; sitting room upstairs; kitchen privileges by arrangement; patio; swimming pool with Jacuzzi; airport pickup (Santa Barbara). Rates will be higher during Olympic season.

ROOM	BED	BATH	ENTRANCE	FLOOR	DAILY RATES
A	1Q	Pvt	Main	1	$60
B	1D	Pvt	Main	2	$60

SANTA BARBARA

Marie Miller   **(805) 569-1914**
435 East Pedregosa, Santa Barbara, CA 93103
(Two blocks from Mission Santa Barbara)

Marie Miller's Craftsman-style home was built in 1895. It has a brown
shingled exterior, mature shade trees, and commodious guest rooms with
fireplaces. The tone is calm and casual. Much of what you'll want to see in
Santa Barbara is quite close at hand. A short walk takes you to the Mission, the Museum of Natural History, beautiful parks, and downtown. The
wharf and beach are ten minutes away by bicycle. Make your plans over a
leisurely breakfast on the sunporch or patio. With a little luck, the rest of
the day will just fall into place.

Dog in residence; no guests' pets; balcony on Room A; fireplace in each
guest room; bicycles available. Rates $5 less September through May.

A	1Q	Shd*	Main	2	$45	
B	3T	Shd*	Main	2	$45	($10)

SANTA BARBARA

S - D (EP)

Ocean View House

(805) 966-6659

P.O. Box 20065, Santa Barbara, CA 93102
(Three blocks from the ocean)

    Bill and Carolyn Canfield have an attractive guest suite in their home. There's a bedroom, bath, and adjoining paneled den with its own entrance. The den sofa bed can accommodate extra guests. A complimentary drink and a generous Continental breakfast are served on the patio, a good vantage point for viewing sailboats and the Channel Islands against a background of vivid blue. Beaches and the lovely Shoreline Drive (popular with joggers, skaters, cyclists, and sightseers) are conveniently close by. The attractions of the harbor and downtown Santa Barbara are within three miles. The backyard playhouse is a big favorite with children. If you need a place to relax that the whole family can appreciate, Ocean View has all the necessary ingredients.

    Dog and cat in residence; smoking on patio preferred; full breakfast at small additional charge; TV; den; playhouse; bus or train station pickup. If den bed is used, the charge is $10 per extra person; Saturdays and holidays, add $10 to regular rate.

ROOM	BED	BATH	ENTRANCE	FLOOR	DAILY RATES	
A	1Q	Pvt	Sep	1G	$35 - $40	($10)

S - D (EP)

SANTA BARBARA

Valli's View   **(805) 969-1272**
340 North Sierra Vista, Montecito, CA 93108
(Montecito foothills)

Valerie Buckley has fashioned the house of her dreams on the site where her earlier home stood. It burned in the big fire of 1977, though no hint of that event remains now. She has reason to be proud: Valli's View is a beauty inside and out. Its ambiance of tranquility and comfort will soothe even the most frazzled nerves. There's a variety of places to relax outdoors—a spacious patio with lounges for sunning, a porch swing, or a deck with a view of the mountains. In the evening it's nice to sit in the living room around the grand piano and fireplace. There is one guest bedroom and bath (A) at one end of the house, and a master suite (B) at the other. Soft-colored fabrics, rich carpeting, and antique oak pieces enhance the charming decor. Valerie offers a choice of tempting breakfasts (fruits and vegetables from the garden, in season) which she'll serve you in bed, on the patio, or by the dining room fireplace. As a guest here, you'll feel that your every need has been anticipated—a satisfying experience indeed.

No pets indoors; no smoking; full breakfast; color TV in each room; extra bed; deck; patio; airport pickup (Santa Barbara).

A	1D	Pvt	Main	1G	$45 - $50	($10)
B	1Q	Pvt	Main	1G	$65 - $70	($10)

SOLVANG

El Ranchito
1451 Alamo Pintado, Solvang, CA 93463
(Between Solvang and Ballard)

**(805) 688-9517
or 688-9360**

The Santa Ynez Valley is gaining greatly deserved fame as the Wine Country of the South. Theatergoers flock here for the noted Theaterfest, and the Danish community of Solvang attracts a multitude of visitors year-round. El Ranchito, home of Don and Joan Speirs, offers a priceless opportunity to bask in the picturesque countryside just outside Solvang. The architecture and total feeling are strongly old-world Mediterranean. A small guest house on the property is newly constructed using old French windows and antiques in keeping with the recently restored main house. The Speirs family breeds llamas, and there's a small pond with waterfowl. The grounds are dotted with fruit trees and grape vines. The setting, the view, and the charm of El Ranchito are truly beyond compare.

Various outdoor animals are raised; no guests' pets; no smoking; no RV parking; TV; patio; airport pickup (Santa Ynez).

| A | 2T or 1K | Pvt | Sep | 2 | $75 |

S - D (EP)

WEST COVINA

Mary & George Hendrick   **(818) 919-2125**
2124 East Merced Avenue, West Covina, CA 91791
(Between Freeways 60 and 10, Azusa Exit)

The Hendricks' home in West Covina is guaranteed to give you an authentic taste of the California lifestyle. The large, rambling house was once photographed inside and out by *Life* magazine. It is enhanced by a gorgeous deck area with a swimming pool, a separate Jacuzzi, and nice outdoor furniture. The master suite (D), the guest room with rainbow motif (B), and one of the two living rooms face the deck. There's plenty of space to relax here, and the Hendricks' laid-back style will make you feel completely at ease. Genial conversationalists and inveterate travelers, Mary and George are happy to provide all manner of help to people unfamiliar with the area. They'll point you to special undiscovered spots or to the more popular attractions. Their home is centrally located for visiting Disneyland, L.A., mountains, and desert. If you don't catch some of the California spirit at the Hendricks', consider yourself immune.

No pets; school-age children welcome; TV; AC; two living rooms, each with fireplace; extra bed; deck; swimming pool; Jacuzzi; extra meals optional; good airport connections; maps and tourist information provided. Suite (D) is only available for stays of three days or longer. A beach home at Ensenada is available at times; inquiries welcome.

A	2T	Shd*	Main	1G	$35
B	1D	Shd*	Main	1G	$30
C	1T	Shd*	Main	1G	$25
D	1K	Pvt	Main	1G	$40

WEST COVINA

K.M. Pretzlik   (818) 919-8777
1418 Hollencrest Drive, West Covina, CA 91791
(Between Freeways 60 and 10, Azusa Exit)

Although the Pretzliks' home is in a populated area near freeways and the buzz of modern life, it is an island of tranquility. The lovely ranch-style home is situated below street level. Gently rolling hills extend behind the house, and there are no neighbors close by. In the beautifully landscaped yard, guests may picnic or use the spa under a redwood gazebo. Views of snow-capped Mount Baldy and the San Gabriel Mountains can sometimes be seen in the distance. The Pretzliks' German heritage is evident throughout the house; furnishings, art, and needlework are interesting reminders of their native land. Busy travelers will find the old-world atmosphere a haven of peace and quiet.

Two dogs on premises; no guests' pets; child over five OK; TV; AC; kitchen privileges by arrangement; extra bed; spa; extra meals optional; German, French, some Swedish and Spanish spoken. Large parties might consider the Pretzliks' and the Hendricks' homes for lodging in close proximity.

A	1D	Pvt	Main	1G	$30 ($5)

The traveler was active; he went strenuously in search of people, of adventure, of experience. The tourist is passive; he expects interesting things to happen to him. He goes "sight-seeing."

—Daniel J. Boorstin

The whole object of travel is not to set foot on foreign land; it is at last to set foot on one's own country as a foreign land.

—G.K. Chesterton

Oregon

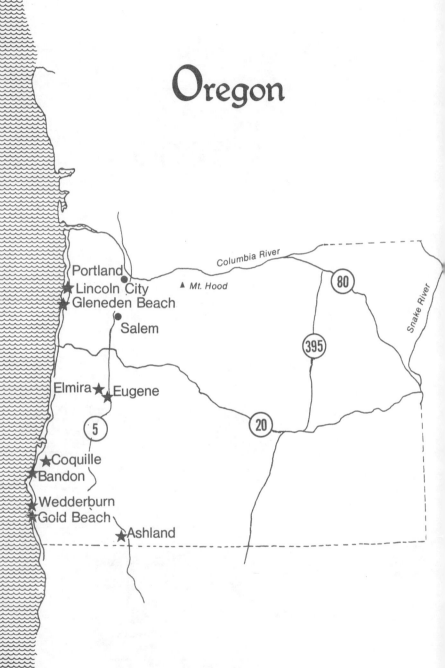

Oregon

Columbia River

Portland

Lincoln City

Gleneden Beach

Mt. Hood

Salem

Elmira

Eugene

5

Coquille

Bandon

Wedderburn

Gold Beach

Ashland

80

395

20

Snake River

From silken beaches to icy peaks to high desert plateaus to crumbled lava fields, Oregon is a state rich in contrasts. To travel Oregon is to experience both the astonishing power and the delicate beauty of nature.

The Oregon Coast alone is a dramatic confrontation of ocean, beach, and forest. To the west is the longest unimpeded expanse of open ocean on earth—neither islands nor reefs stand between Oregon and the beaches of Japan, six thousand miles away. To the east loom the mountains of the Coast Range, which rose gradually in a series of thunderous, continuous volcanic eruptions some forty million years ago. In between are the glorious beaches, some stretching for as many as ten miles, with jagged rocks dotting the surf like shaggy beasts looking for a home, spindrift blowing up from the restless waves, and cypress trees clutching at the wind with their tentacle-like branches. Highway 101 is a cliff-hanger, riding the tan shoulders of mountains up to two thousand feet above the water.

Oregon's coastline is by law "forever free," which means noncommercial and open to the public. There is a state park every five miles or so. In addition to spectacular scenery, fishing is the main attraction. Try some kaboodle fishing from the rocks (so called because on a good day you can catch "the whole kit and kaboodle") or rent a crab pot at one of the small towns, such as Gold Beach or Bandon, for some luscious Dungeness crab.

Gold Beach, at the mouth of the renowned Rogue River, is a favorite spot for the spring and fall runs of Chinook salmon and steelhead trout. If you're a sightseer, you might want to take a jet boat excursion through the Rogue's whitewater rapids. You can also explore this wilderness by foot, by car, or on horseback.

Further north lie some of the highest coastal dunes in the world, rising hundreds of feet above the water, sometimes burying whole spruce pine forests. For forty-five miles, the sandy hills and hollows of the Oregon Dunes National Recreational Area drift and change shape daily. Between Newport and Gleneden Beach, you may want to visit the Oregon State University Marine Science Center, which boasts seventeen saltwater aquariums. At Lincoln City, art lovers will find a host of galleries and shops to browse.

Roughly paralleling the coast, from its midpoint north, is Oregon's lush heartland, the Willamette Valley. The Eugene-Springfield area occupies its southerly pocket, only sixty miles from the coast.

Eugene, cradled in natural beauty, has all the advantages of a city—museums, shops, cultural and entertainment opportunities, and a major university—yet is also the gateway to unlimited outdoor recreation. Just a few miles to the west, near Elmira, the Fern River Reservoir invites boating, fishing, and swimming. To the east is the McKenzie River, famous for its scenery and watersports like kayaking. South is the Bohemia mining country, a primitive region of unfettered mountain streams, wildlife, shadowy gorges, cleavered scarps, and jagged peaks. You can navigate the narrow dirt roads yourself or take a landrover tour in search of ghost towns and lost mines.

The Willamette River flows generally north-south for the length of the valley, dissecting a city at one point, cutting through rolling hills or thick forests at another. You can go cruising down the river on a float trip or try some "shunpiking," a word that means motoring the backroads. Here classic covered bridges, pastoral picnic sites, and small towns whose streets are lined with well-preserved historic buildings will take you back in time.

The Willamette flows right through the center of Portland, where it joins the mighty Columbia, creating a waterfront setting for the city's skyline. Within sixty miles is the famous Columbia Gorge/Mount Hood area. The Gorge is the scene of sparkling waterfalls plunging over huge cliffs formed by the Columbia River as it cuts its path through the Cascade Mountain Range, the stony and spectacular backbone of the state. Toward the eastern end is the towering Mount Hood, the only peak in North America to offer year-round downhill skiing. With its gentle southern slope, Mount Hood is the most climbed mountain in the nation.

Further east is the Wallowa Range, Oregon's "Switzerland," known for its remarkable alpine scenery. On the eastern border of the Wallowa, the Snake River carves a gorge, Hells Canyon, that exceeds the depth of the Grand Canyon by as much as three thousand feet in some places. Here, east of the Cascades, you are in the sage-scented range land of the high desert plateaus.

A major feature of central Oregon is the "Lava Lands" near Bend. Four dramatic lava areas cover over four thousand square miles of Deschutes National Forest to make up the largest and most varied concentration of volcanic phenomena in North America—cinder cones, lava flows, ice caves, lava tubes, and craters.

Another volcanic attraction is Crater Lake National Park, high in the southern Cascades. The lake, the deepest in the United States, was formed when Mount Mazama blew its top more than six thousand years ago and collapsed into its own crater, forming a caldern six miles across. The exceptionally clear and brilliant water, looking like melted sapphires, is the result of accumulated snowmelt.

South of Crater Lake, nestled between the Cascades and the Coast Range is a delightful contrast of culture and natural beauty. In the country surrounding Ashland, you can enjoy Shakespeare, classical concerts, Gold Rush history, whitewater rafting, hiking, and skiing. Ashland's famous outdoor Shakespeare Festival is held from June through September, but the regular season runs from February through October. Nearby Jacksonville, a National Historic Landmark, preserves the Gold Rush atmosphere of the 1850's. Eighty homes and buildings have been restored, and you can ride a stagecoach in the Pioneer Village district. Jacksonville hosts the Peter Britt Music and Arts Festival in August for classical music lovers. Concerts for bluegrass and jazz fans are enjoyed here, too.

Rushing rivers, rugged peaks, cold blue lakes, stark and lovely deserts, unspoiled beaches . . . and the peace and quiet in which to enjoy it. Some people say Oregon has it all.

S - D (EP)

ASHLAND

The Miners Addition

(503) 482-0562

737 Siskiyou Boulevard, Ashland, OR 97520
(Walking distance to downtown and theaters)

Carolyn Morris invites you to "come and enjoy a bit of early Ashland history. Stay at The Miners Addition, a historic home built in 1900 and dedicated to the gold miners of Jackson County." She's made sure you can't miss it: an old ore car once used by the miners occupies a prominent position in the front yard. Two upstairs guest rooms are named for local mines, the Sterling and the Maltern. Both have a cozy, friendly feeling. There's a private half-bath with each room, and a separate, large, attractively-tiled shower. Breakfasts are substantial, hearty fare, such as sourdough pancakes. A lovely back yard is inviting for guests who wish to relax and enjoy the garden. Theaters, small shops, and a variety of restaurants await you at the end of a six-block stroll along the boulevard. The gold miners would be surprised at the Ashland of today. I'm certain they'd be pleased that their memory lives on at The Miners Addition.

No pets; children welcome; no smoking; full breakfast; crib available; garden, swing, and sandbox in back yard; toy box indoors; babysitting at reasonable rates; airport pickup (Ashland, or Medford at a nominal charge). Brochure available.

A	1T & 1Q	½ Pvt	Main	2	$40 - $45	($10)
B	1T & 1D	½ Pvt	Main	2	$40 - $45	($10)

THE MINERS ADDITION

ASHLAND

Parkside Cottage
(503) 482-2320

P.O. Box 721, Ashland, OR 97520
(171 Granite Street, adjacent to Lithia Park)

Susan and Rod Reid offer B&B accommodations in the fully furnished 1914 cottage beside their home. From there, it's a five-minute walk through beautiful Lithia Park to the Shakespearean theaters and plaza. Tennis courts and jogging trails in Lithia Park, as well as many other recreational opportunities in the area surrounding Ashland, make this a spot for year-round enjoyment.

No pets; kitchenette; rollaway bed available. Inquire about special weekly rates.

ROOM	BED	BATH	ENTRANCE	FLOOR	DAILY RATES
A	1Q	Pvt	Sep	1	$30 ($5)

ASHLAND

S - D (EP)

Wisteria House

(503) 488-2302

453 Allison Street, Ashland, OR 97520
(Three blocks from theaters; one block from town)

   Wisteria House is the kind of large, old-fashioned family home that is instantly endearing. It was built in 1910 and has retained its original feeling of country hospitality and comfort. The setting is as idyllic as the house itself: a quiet street lined with mature trees, a background of rolling hills, and a lovely view across the valley. The interior is furnished with some distinctive antiques and plenty of attention to the homey details that warm the heart and calm the spirit. Upstairs guest accommodations can be reached by a separate entrance. There's a single suite with a solid oak bed and a private bath; a double suite has two adjacent rooms and a bath. Partake of home-baked breakfast specialties around the kitchen table or out on the patio. A visit to Wisteria House confirms the message that hosts Victor and Nancy Wigginton express in their brochure: "Whether you are playing your favorite tunes on the old Victrola, or relaxing in the summer sun with an ageless classic from our library, we hope the memories and friends you make at Wisteria House will be the best ones ever."

   Dog, cat, chickens, parrot, and dove on premises; no guests' pets; no smoking; AC in Suite A; easy walk to town and theaters; German spoken; airport pickup by prior arrangement (Ashland, or Medford at a nominal fee). Brochure available. Phone before 9:00 a.m. or after 5:30 p.m.

A	1D	Pvt	Sep	2	$37	($5)
B	2D	Pvt	Sep	2	$50	($5)

S - D (EP)

BANDON

Cliff Harbor   **(503) 347-3956**
P.O. Box 769, Bandon, OR 97411
(Directly on Oregon Coast)

Cliff Harbor sits at cliff's edge overlooking the Coquille River harbor, the coastline, spectacular offshore rock formations, and the vast expanse of the Pacific Ocean. In Bandon, the pace of life is slow, and there is time for beauty, rest, and contemplation. Hosts Doris and Bill Duncan offer accommodations that are sure to enhance your experience of the coast. There's a ground-floor room with fine ocean views, a separate entrance, and a private bath; a room on the upper floor has a shared bath. A homey, casual atmosphere is felt throughout the house. Window seats on the ocean side of the living room invite relaxed communion with the sea. Doris is an avid photographer, beachcomber, and agate collector. Her knowledge can be a valuable resource for interested guests with enough time to explore. Whether you stop just overnight or stay for several days, you will be favored with special care as a guest at Cliff Harbor.

Dog (Janice) in residence; no guests' pets; smoking outside only; no RV parking; TV in Room A; ocean activities, nine-hole golf course, and good restaurants nearby; airport pickup (Bandon, or North Bend at an extra charge). Brochure available. A private studio apartment with ocean view, kitchen, bath, and separate entrance is also available at times for two-night minimum stays. Refrigerator is stocked for guests to prepare breakfast at their leisure. Apartment accommodates up to four people. Inquire about rates.

ROOM	BED	BATH	ENTRANCE	FLOOR	DAILY RATES
A	1T & 1D	Pvt	Sep	1G	$40 - $45 ($10)
B	2T	Shd	Sep	2	$28 - $32 ($5)

S - D (EP)

BANDON

Spindrift Bed & Breakfast   **(503) 347-2275**
2990 Beach Loop Road, Bandon, OR 97411
(Overlooking ocean)

Ocean lovers, rejoice! No more straining for a glimpse of blue from "ocean front" rooms. Witness the breathtaking beauty of the Oregon Coast at Spindrift Bed & Breakfast. This lovely home is perched on a bluff just forty feet above a long, sandy beach that is framed by massive offshore rock formations. Uninterrupted vistas are yours from floor-to-ceiling living room windows, from a large deck with direct beach access, or from one of the attractive guest rooms (A). You'll find the perfect vantage point for watching the ever-changing surf, sea animals, glorious sunsets, or even the approach of spectacular storms. There are two accommodations for guests. The Seaview has an expansive, open feeling, a magnificent view, a fireplace, and French doors to the deck; the Surfsound is a restful room with excellent twin beds. Guests are invited to enjoy the sunken living room with its vaulted, beamed ceiling, fireplace, and panorama of sea and sky. Breakfast is a real feast at Spindrift, so bring a hearty appetite. Afternoon refreshments are also served. Hosts Don and Robbie Smith are happy to share travel experiences, a game of bridge, and hobbies, such as spinning and weaving, rock polishing, and winemaking. They offer their friendship, but they can also provide relaxing privacy if that is your desire.

Friendly resident outdoor dog; family rates on request; full breakfast; deck; beach access; many visitor attractions in Bandon area; some French and Spanish spoken; airport pickup at extra charge (North Bend). 10% discount November 1-March 1. First guests to reserve have private bath and others share a bath with hosts at $3 off room rate. Brochure available.

ROOM	BED	BATH	ENTRANCE	FLOOR	DAILY RATES
A	1Q	Pvt	Main	1G	$40 - $45
B	2T	Shd	Main	1G	$35 - $40

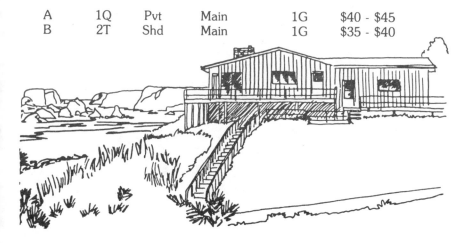

COQUILLE

Ginny Paseman   **(503) 396-3623**
Box 2840, Fairview Route, Coquille, OR 97423
(Twenty-six miles east of Coos Bay)

If Oregon's back roads intrigue you as much as they do me, then you'll appreciate the location of Ginny Paseman's home. It is so remote that you'll need help finding it, but once you do, you'll know you've really gotten away from it all. The setting is one of orchard and forest; Ginny's home, garden, and grazing cattle are the only signs of civilization. The entire lower-floor apartment—huge living room with wood-burning stove and fireplace, bedroom, bath, kitchen, and private entrance—is available to guests. It is a perfect place for people who know how to make the most of the great outdoors. There's fishing in the North Fork of the Coquille River, fishing or crabbing at the coast, hunting, berry-picking, and even golfing at the Coquille Elk's Club. Nearby LaVerne Park is popular with families; it has picnic tables, campsites, a swimming hole, a playground, and more. Whether you want a vacation that's full of outdoor activity or a chance to escape to utter stillness and relaxation, Ginny's home is a choice destination.

Dog, cat, and cattle on premises; no guests' pets; living room; kitchen; extra beds; barbecue; facilities for taking care of hunters' game; crab boiling facilities; help putting up berry jams and jellies.

ROOM	BED	BATH	ENTRANCE	FLOOR	DAILY RATES	
A	1D	Pvt	Sep	1G	$35 - $40	($5)

ELMIRA

S - D (EP)

Dick & Evelyn McGillivray   **(503) 935-3564**
88680 Evers Road, Elmira, OR 97437
(Off Highway 126, fourteen miles west of Eugene)

The McGillivrays' unique built-from-scratch log home is well-suited to its surroundings: five acres mostly covered with pine and fir trees. A lot of care and hard work have gone into this house, which combines the best of the past with the comforts of today. I was struck by the craftsmanship of the woodwork throughout the interior, where a variety of different woods have been used to beautiful advantage. A downstairs bedroom and bath comprise one guest area. An impressive stairway of half-logs leads to a balcony overlooking the living and dining areas. Doors lead from the balcony to a spacious bedroom with its own bath and small deck—another accommodation for guests. Old-fashioned breakfasts are prepared on the antique, wood-burning cookstove in the dining room, a good place to linger over coffee and plan your day. Whether you're on a quick stopover enroute to or from the coast (Florence is forty miles west), or settling in for a while, you're likely to be among those who, as Evelyn says, "fall in love with the quiet setting and the feel of the house." It's very easy to do.

No pets; families welcome; smoking on covered porches only; TV; AC; laundry privileges; extra beds; crib; winery touring and tasting nearby (Forgeron Vineyards); water recreation at Fern Ridge Reservoir; extra meals optional; wheelchair access; airport pickup (Mahlon Sweet).

ROOM	BED	BATH	ENTRANCE	FLOOR	DAILY RATES	
A	1K	Pvt	Main	1G	$25 - $30	($5)
B	1K	Pvt	Main	2	$25 - $30	($5)

ROOM   BED   BATH   ENTRANCE   FLOOR   DAILY RATES

S - D (EP)

EUGENE

Campus Cottage
(503) 342-5346

1136 East 19th Avenue, Eugene, OR 97403
(Near University of Oregon campus)

   Ursula Bates's Campus Cottage is a good example of the theory that "small is beautiful." Her 1925 blue shingled home has been renovated with its original character fully intact. Ursula is a decorating consultant; her sense of style and good taste are obvious throughout the cottage. Warm country furnishings create an interior of great charm and personality. The two guest accommodations are special indeed. The master suite (A) has a bedroom with a brass bed, a sitting room with a Jenny Lind bed, and a large bath with a hand-held shower. A cozy, south-facing bedroom (B) has an oak bed, a down-filled reading chair by the window, and a bath with a cedar-lined shower. You'll get the idea right away that you're meant to truly make yourself at home here, whether it means snuggling up by the living room fireplace, relaxing on the deck that overlooks the cottage garden, or taking the house bicycles on a jaunt around campus or town. Everything at Campus Cottage is geared to make your visit a memorable event.

   Dog (Annie) and cat (Gus) in residence; no guests' pets; older children OK; full breakfast; afternoon refreshments; TV available; bicycles; good public transportation and airport connections (Mahlon Sweet). Brochure available.

A	1T & 1Q	Pvt	Main	1	$53	($10)
B	1Q	Pvt	Main	1	$47	

EUGENE   S - D (EP)

Quigleyville, Population 2   **(503) 747-3543**
90072 Marcola Road, Springfield, OR 97478
(Five miles northeast of Springfield)

Quigleyville once boasted a higher population, but now Martha and Keith Quigley have this rambling country home all to themselves. Being family folk, however, they feel that home life is best shared with others. For guests, there are upstairs quarters that include two bedrooms and a bath. One of the rooms (B) is huge and is stocked with toys, games, and dolls of every description; children can amuse themselves for hours. The arrangement is ideal for a family of four or for two couples traveling together. The Quigleys invite guests to join them in the family room for talk and relaxation. The rural atmosphere provides peace and quiet, beautiful scenery, and plenty of room to spread out. Quigleyville is just the place for people who are keen on outdoor recreation and the smell of clean, fresh air.

Dogs and chickens on premises; no guests' pets; children welcome; no smoking; no alcohol; large fenced yard; TV; crib available; hiking, hunting, fishing, golf, and city of Eugene nearby; extra meals optional. For two unrelated parties, one has the private bath upstairs and one has a private bath downstairs. 10% discount to families and two parties traveling together.

Room	Bed	Bath	Entrance	Floor	Daily Rates
A	1D	Pvt	Main	2	$38 ($2)
B	2T	Pvt	Main	2	$32 ($2)

EUGENE

Joe & Isabel Wheeler   **(503) 344-1366**
P.O. Box 8201, Coburg, OR 97401
(Seven miles north of Eugene, off I-5)

The beautiful Cascades surround this green, fertile valley where the McKenzie and Willamette Rivers meet. Whether you're just passing through or staying long enough to explore the riches of the area, the Wheelers will be happy to share their comfortable home with you. Joe built the house himself, and guests are sure to find it as livable as he and Isabel do. They offer the entire upstairs as one unit; it has two spacious carpeted bedrooms, a bath, and a sewing room (with ironing board). It's separate enough from the rest of the house to afford complete privacy. Coburg is a small farming community with a unique atmosphere of antique stores and century-old homes. Dine at the renowned Coburg Inn (1877), where a fine meal can be yours just a short walk from the Wheelers'.

Full breakfast, if desired; TV; living room for guests; extra meals optional with advance notice; airport pickup (Mahlon Sweet).

A   2T & 1D   Pvt   Main   2 $25 - $30 ($5)

S - D (EP)

GLENEDEN BEACH

Ruth G. Strauss   **(503) 764-2045**
P.O. Box 514, Gleneden Beach, OR 97388
(5850 El Mesa, fifteen miles north of Newport)

Gleneden Beach is one of the most beautiful stretches of Oregon's dramatic coastline. The Salishan Lodge (with its new Market Place) is a widely known resort to which golfers and coast aficionados flock year-round. Located one mile south of Salishan and one block from the beach, Ruth's home in the pines is part of Coronado Shores, a private community. The constant sound of the surf and an ever-glowing fire in the hearth make this a restful ocean retreat. A gracious and helpful host, Ruth can recommend the best the area has to offer, from seaside restaurants to whale-watching sites.

No pets; children over ten OK; no RV parking; full breakfast; TV; washer and dryer; deck; golf courses. Lower rates off-season. Please phone after 7:00 p.m.

A	1Q	Shd	Main	1G	$30 - $35
B	1D	Shd	Main	1G	$30 - $35

GOLD BEACH

Bien Venue
(503) 247-2335

95629 Jerrys Flat Road, Gold Beach, OR 97444
(Nearly three miles east of U.S. 101)

Formerly Southern Californians, Forrest and Lucille Pendergast have come about as far from "life in the fast lane" as it is possible to get. Their home is in a natural, serene setting on the south bank of the Rogue River. Bed and breakfast guests may choose between a cozy cottage to the rear of the main house and a recently refurbished bedroom and bath inside. Each has a certain element of romance, depending on whether you prefer the feeling of a small, private vacation home or a charming, antique-furnished room that has its own little courtyard. Nature lovers will be pleased with the myriad wonders so close at hand. A short stroll down to the river bank, and you'll find an inviting bench where you can take in the peaceful, unspoiled beauty of the surroundings. Your hosts can suggest other special spots and things to do in the Rogue River—Gold Beach area. At Bien Venue, you'll be as welcome as the name implies. The Pendergasts bid you "à la Maison des Invité."

Two cats in residence; no guests' pets; children in cottage only; smoking outside only; TV; deck; queen-sized water bed in cottage; Rogue River, ocean, and forest recreation nearby; some French spoken; airport pickup (Gold Beach). Brochure available.

Room	Bed	Bath	Entrance	Floor	Daily Rates
A	1T & 1Q	Pvt	Sep	1G	$35 - $45 ($5)
B	1D	Pvt	Sep	1G	$30 - $35

S - D (EP)

GOLD BEACH

Endicott Gardens   **(503) 247-6513**
95768 Jerrys Flat Road, Gold Beach, OR 97444
(Four miles east of U.S. 101)

Endicott Gardens is the setting of a small nursery and the home of Stewart and Mary Endicott. Bed and breakfast accommodations have been created in a private wing of the house, consisting of four guest rooms, each with its own bath. Rooms C and D open onto a deck that allows gorgeous views of the forest and mountains. As one might imagine, the grounds are spectacular with flowers and shrubs. Breakfast on the deck is a thrill, but if the weather is cool, Mary delights guests with hearty fare graciously presented in the dining room, as the nearby fireplace crackles and warms. The welcoming spirit, touches of humor, and thoughtful amenities found at Endicott Gardens make it a place you'll remember with a smile.

No pets; full breakfast; TV available; deck; Rogue River, ocean, and forest recreation nearby; airport pickup (Gold Beach). Brochures available. Garden wedding receptions by arrangement.

A	2T	Pvt	Sep	1G	$35 - $45	($10)
B	1Q	Pvt	Sep	1G	$30 - $45	($10)
C	1T & 1Q	Pvt	Sep	1G	$35 - $45	($10)
D	1Q	Pvt	Sep	1G	$35 - $45	($10)

S - D (EP)

GOLD BEACH

Wedderburn House   (503) 247-6126
P.O. Box 592, Wedderburn, OR 97491
(South coast of Oregon, thirty-seven miles from the border)

Wedderburn House, built in the 1890's, occupies a prime site overlooking the point where the Rogue River meets the sea. A popular choice for visitors is a ride by jet boat up the wild and scenic Rogue. Ocean and River fishing for salmon and steelhead will tempt anglers to the limit. A one-half mile walk to a jetty and beach provides hours of beachcombing, sea lion and bird watching, and driftwood gathering. Ken and Lea Leonard invite you to enjoy all this as their guest at Wedderburn House. After a day full of activity and perhaps a hearty seafood dinner (just steps away at Jot's Rod 'n' Reel), you're welcome to join Ken and Lea around their large living room fireplace. And it's a virtual certainty that you'll sleep comfortably in the lovely old-fashioned guest suite on the first floor—a perfect ending to a perfect day.

Dog in residence; children and pets welcome; no smoking in bed; no RV parking; TV; extra bedroom upstairs; airport pickup (Gold Beach). OPEN MAY 15-OCTOBER 1. Brochure available.

A	1D	Pvt	Main	1	$40

LINCOLN CITY

Shirlee & Bud Sherman   (503) 994-9409
1736 NW 37th, Lincoln City, OR 97367
(Two blocks west of U.S. 101)

The Shermans have made their home away from home in the small coastal town of Lincoln City, where people come to enjoy the myriad activities that flourish here: lake, stream, and ocean fishing; crabbing; boating; beachcombing; kite-flying; golfing; craft and antique shopping; good dining. Located in a residential area two blocks from the beach, the house is also within easy walking distance of the main attractions of Lincoln City. There is a separate wing for guests, consisting of two bedrooms and a bath—an ideal situation for families. It's safe to say that there's something to suit everyone's idea of fun in this vacation spot.

One dog in residence; no smoking; full breakfast; TV; kitchen and laundry privileges; deck; golf course and municipal pool nearby; children's and adults' bicycles available; children's games. *(EP rate applies to children only. Rate for both bedrooms if used by two couples is $45.) Advance reservations at: 4048 SW Hewett Boulevard, Portland, OR 97221, (503) 297-2965. (Best to call between 8 and 9 a.m.) Drop-ins can be accommodated if the Shermans are at the beach; call (503) 994-9409 to check.

ROOM	BED	BATH	ENTRANCE	FLOOR	DAILY RATES
A	2T & 2D (bunk)	Pvt	Sep	1G	$28 ($ 5)*

I never travel without my diary. One should always have something sensational to read in the train.

—Oscar Wilde

Voyage, travel, and change of place impart vigour.

—Seneca

Washington

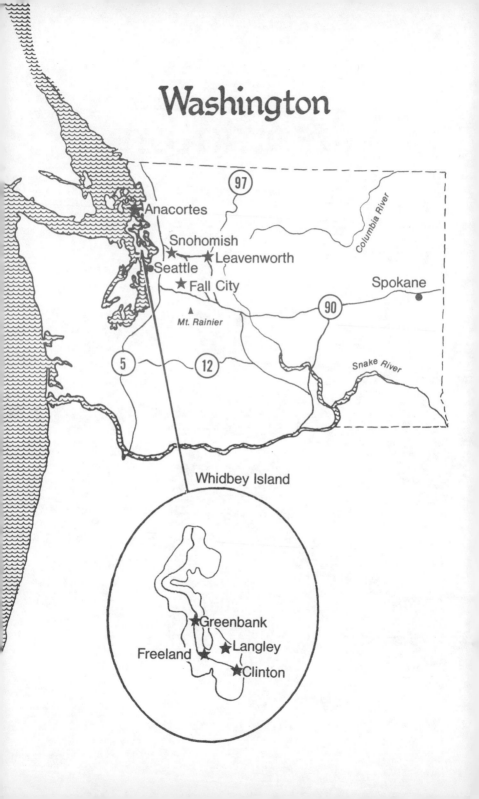

Washington

97

Columbia River

Anacortes

Snohomish

Seattle ★ ★Leavenworth

★ Fall City

Spokane

▲
Mt. Rainier

90

5

12

Snake River

Whidbey Island

★Greenbank

Freeland ★ ★Langley

★Clinton

Washington wears two faces. On the west is a panorama of timbered mountains, deep canyons with rushing streams, fertile valleys, and shimmering, island-dotted bays. On the east lie black lava formations, the silver-green sagebrush plains, and rolling wheat country. The dividing line is the jagged, snowy crest of the majestic Cascade Range, which separates the mild, wet coastal climate from the drier east, where the mighty Columbia River carves a great arc, providing both water and power through its dam system.

Not far from the Interstate 5 mainline is Mount St. Helens, Washington's most famous performing mountain, which dominates the southern end of the Cascades. After losing thirteen hundred feet of its peak in the recent eruption, Mount St. Helens now stands at eighty-three hundred feet. Visitors to this national monument can learn a lot about volcanos from the daily interpretative programs. You can even call ahead for a volcanic activity report—just in case Mount St. Helens decides to blow again.

Further north, Washington's most famous mountain, glacier-mantled Mount Rainier, towers nearly three miles above sea level. A network of state and forest roads and three hundred miles of hiking trails provide access to this stately, pristine mountain. With thirty-four square miles of glaciers, it is the United States' largest single-peak glacier system outside of Alaska.

Travelers going north on Highway 101 will most likely be headed for the wild, wet, and wooded Olympic Peninsula. The Olympic Mountains rise seven thousand feet above the Pacific and overlook some of the last wilderness beaches in the country. The national park is comprised of nearly a million acres of untouched wilderness. Within it are six hundred miles of hiking trails that take you from icy crags to driftwood-strewn beaches. Clamming, crabbing, and fishing are all rewarding along the impressive coastline. Hurricane Ridge, almost a mile high, provides the most accessible view of the Olympic Range. This knife-edged mountain ridge explodes with color when the wildflowers bloom in the summer. The Sol Duc Hot Springs testify to the region's volcanic origins.

Yearly rainfall on the peninsula exceeds one hundred forty inches, promoting the growth of skyscraping trees and the only coniferous rain forest in the world. The centuries-old spruces and hemlocks seem to possess the wisdom of their years, giving this dim emerald forest cathedral a striking solemnity. The park contains the largest known specimens of Douglas fir, red cedar, western hemlock, and Alaskan cedar. Imaginative hikers might look for elves hiding beneath the immense ferns or dancing on the moss-carpeted forest floor.

The largest of Puget Sound's islands is Whidbey, approximately fifty miles long, where homes of the early settlers still dot the shore. Coupeville,

Directly east is Puget Sound, a saltwater arm of the Pacific. Its hundreds of bays and inlets provide a total of no less than eighteen hundred miles of shoreline, much of it tree-lined and unspoiled. Getting around is sure to involve Washington's fleet of ferries, part of the state highway system.

one of the oldest towns in the state, has been restored and features Victorian buildings and picturesque shops. There are several parks on the island, including one of the state's finest at Deception Pass, where a bridge spans a gorge that is notorious for its unpredictable tidal currents.

From here it is a short distance to Mount Erie, about five miles south of Anacortes, where you can get a good view of Mounts Baker and Rainier, the Olympic Peninsula, the Cascades, and the San Juan Islands. A paved road ascends its thirteen hundred-foot summit.

A more intimate view of the San Juans can be had on a spectacular ferry ride, which leaves from Anacortes and weaves its way through this archipelago of one hundred seventy-two isles. The recreational opportunities in the San Juans are many—boating, water skiing, scuba diving, fishing, hiking, and bicycling.

Seattle, a city of hills and lakes, offers a number of attractions, including Pioneer Square, the Space Needle, the Pike Place Open-Air Market, and the waterfront. Southeast of Seattle, near Fall City, is Snoqualmie Falls, which plunge a hundred feet farther than those of Niagara. A trail leads into the canyon. An antique steam engine chugs along a seven-mile loop, enabling railroad buffs to visit the falls by train.

Further east, the Wenatchee National Forest stretches along the eastern slope of the Cascades. Leavenworth, near its eastern boundary, is modeled after a Bavarian village and offers art and music activities in the summer, skiing in the winter. Scenic Tumwater Canyon is about six miles to the west, while glacier-fed Lake Chelan lies to the east. This unique elongated lake stretches like a smooth blue ribbon for fifty-five miles and is very popular with fisherfolk. Surrounded by the peaks of the Cascades, the lake's bottom drops to four hundred feet below sea level.

Lake Chelan National Recreation Area, noted for its beauty and recreational opportunities, marks the southern boundary of the North Cascades National Park, one of the wildest and most rugged sections of the United States. There are three hundred living glaciers in the park. Largely a backcountry wilderness area, the hardy will encounter breathtaking scenery—granite towers, glacier-sculpted pinnacles, precipitous (and avalanche-prone) slopes, jewel lakes, cascading rivers, and dense forests, as well as mountain goats, bald eagles, and other wildlife. The North Cascade Highway, which links the Puget Sound area to the North Cascades, offers some of the most astonishing vistas of mountains and alpine meadows anywhere. (The eastern section of the highway is closed in winter.)

If you're looking for unspoiled beauty, you are sure to find it in Washington. Here sea, mountain, and desert converge to provide enough natural diversity to satisfy the most restless of spirits.

S - D (EP)

ANACORTES

The Channel House   **(206) 293-9382**
2902 Oakes Avenue, Anacortes, WA 98221
(Overlooking Guemes Channel, five minutes from ferry docks)

The Channel House is a joyous discovery for anyone traveling to this corner of the country. It's a home of unusual character, uniquely situated for gazing out at the channel and the San Juan Islands from all rooms. Shiny wooden floors covered with Oriental rugs, fine antique furnishings, a library, and three fireplaces create an atmosphere of classic European elegance. Hosts Sam and Kathy Salzinger have added other special features to make your visit memorable: outdoor hot-tubbing with a view of island sunsets, sailing Puget Sound (as weather permits), and having your breakfast served beside a crackling fire. Being a guest at Channel House is an experience to be savored.

No pets; no children; no smoking in bedrooms; honeymoon room with four-poster canopied bed; hot tub; possible sailboat trips; some German spoken; airport pickup (Anacortes). Brochure available.

Room	Bed	Bath	Entrance	Floor	Daily Rates
A	1D	Shd*	Main	2	$38 - $45
B	1D	Shd*	Main	2	$38 - $45
C	1D	Shd*	Main	2	$38 - $45
D	1D	Shd*	Main	2	$38 - $45

FALL CITY

John & Patricia Koba   **(206) 222-5185**
32511 SE Redmond-Fall City Road, Fall City, WA 98024
(Thirty miles east of Seattle)

The Kobas' home is located in the heart of the picturesque farmland lying east of Seattle. Excellent bus service can put you in downtown Seattle in about forty minutes, but if you feel more at home in the country, basing yourself at the Kobas' will be a pleasure. Some regional attractions near their home are well worth exploring: Snoqualmie Falls, Lodge, and fish hatchery; Carnation Farms; Lake Sammamish. Bellevue is close enough for shopping and dining, while Snoqualmie Pass lures skiers, campers, and anglers in the other direction. The Kobas are used to hosting foreign visitors and especially enjoy families. Their rear deck and hot tub are ideal for long, relaxed conversation under a starry country sky. Upstairs guest quarters consist of two bedrooms and a half-bath; there's a full bath downstairs. Extensive remodeling has put the entire home in top condition. Warm and hospitable hosts look forward to sharing it with you.

Dog (Bosley) in reidence; pets and children welcome; TV; kitchen and laundry privileges; deck; hot tub; some Japanese spoken; airport (Sea-Tac), bus, or train pickup.

| A | 1D & 1Q | 1½ Shd | Main | 2 | $25 | ($5) |
| B | 2T | 1½ Shd | Main | 2 | $20 | ($5) |

LEAVENWORTH

S - D (EP)

Brown's Farm, A Bed & Breakfast Home Place   **(509) 548-7863**
11150 Highway 209, Leavenworth, WA 98826
(One and one-half miles north of town on the road to Plain)

Leavenworth is a picturesque Bavarian village that overlooks the Wenatchee River and is outlined by snowcapped Icicle Ridge. Each season brings its special celebration, and each year thousands of visitors are touched by the welcoming spirit that abides here. In the Chumstick Valley just north of town is Brown's Farm, A Bed & Breakfast Home Place. Steve and Wendi Brown, their three children (Jennifer, Emily, and Peter), and the resident animals make staying at this large country farmhouse in the woods a rare experience in homespun hospitality. The family worked together to build the house; it has exposed log beams, walls of local timber, a huge fireplace made of stones from the Icicle Valley, multi-paned windows, and stained-glass accents created by Steve and Wendi. Everyone helps out with the bed and breakfast guests. Two bedrooms and a bath on the main floor make wonderfully cozy guest quarters. The simplicity of the decor is refreshing. Nothing about the ambiance is contrived—the charm is all natural, an outgrowth of the way the Browns live. I can't imagine a healthier atmosphere for children growing up. It has a lot to offer the rest of us, too.

Dogs, cats, horses, chickens, and rabbits on premises; families welcome (crib provided for children under four at no charge; other children should bring sleeping bags); no smoking in bedrooms; full country breakfast; some cross-country skis and snowshoes available; hiking, swimming, rafting, and sleigh rides nearby. Brochure available. Room A has a sink.

ROOM	BED	BATH	ENTRANCE	FLOOR	DAILY RATES	
A	1T & 1Q	Shd*	Main	1	$45	($6)
B	1Q	Shd*	Main	1	$40	($6)

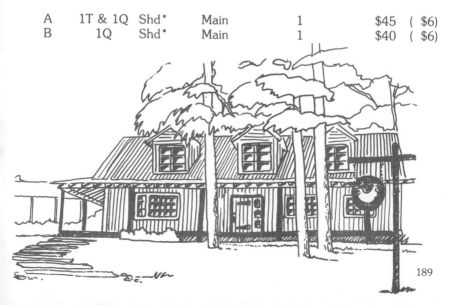

SNOHOMISH

Bud & Ethel Adams   **(206) 568-9070**
6001 96th Drive SE, Snohomish, WA 98290
(Two miles west of downtown)

The founding of Snohomish dates back to 1859, making it one of the oldest communities in the state. This old river town once thrived as a center for dairy farming and logging. An impressive assortment of frame houses remains from the turn of the century, showing visitors why Snohomish is proud of its past. Tour the historic district and then shop in "The Antique Capital of the Northwest"—over ninety antique dealers are within a four-block area! Whether you're interested in the town's history or just like its scenic location at the "Gateway to the Cascade Loop," pleasant overnight lodgings can be found at the home of Bud and Ethel Adams. It's an attractive and well-maintained house with a split entry; guests are offered two bedrooms on the upper level. A master bedroom has its own bath and a lovely view of the backyard garden, fruit trees, and distant mountains. The other guest room has a private bath down the hall. If you're smart, you'll time your arrival for just after Ethel's been putting up jam or baking an apple pie. A taste of genuine Northwestern hospitality awaits you here.

No pets; teenagers OK; no smoking; guided ski outings or hikes by arrangement; good public transportation; airport pickup (Snohomish, or Sea-Tac at extra charge).

A	2T or 1K	Pvt	Main	2	$30 - $35	($10)
B	1D	Pvt	Main	2	$25 - $30	($10)

WHIDBEY ISLAND — CLINTON

Home By The Sea   **(206) 221-2964**
2388 East Sunlight Beach Road, Clinton, WA 98236
(On Useless Bay, South Whidbey)

The Fritts-Drew family finds their Home By The Sea simply too wonderful to keep all to themselves. You may *arrive* here in a stressful state, but you're certain not to leave that way. It's hard to say just what magic is at work; it's a unique combination of things. The seaside setting on a fjord-like bay offers scenes of boats on the Sound, the Olympic Mountains, and Mount Rainier. All manner of waterfowl inhabit the area, a natural bird sanctuary. Beachcombing and beach fires provide balm for the spirit. Inside the house, an international flavor prevails. There are Persian carpets, American antiques, and treasured souvenirs from Sharon Fritts-Drew's world travels. The beauty of the seashore can be seen from every room. High antique beds in both the Seabreeze Suite (A) and the Sunset Room (B) allow soothing views as you take it easy. Your generous hosts are casual, relaxed people who have a way of making you feel that way, too.

Two cats in residence; no guests' pets; children over twelve OK; no smoking in bedrooms; private sitting room with Seabreeze Suite; deck; airport pickup (Oak Harbor). Brochure available. Whidbey Island cottages (seashore and woodland) and private accommodations with fireplaces can be arranged.

ROOM	BED	BATH	ENTRANCE	FLOOR	DAILY RATES S - D (EP)	
A	1D	Pvt	Main	2	$55	($5)
B	1D	Pvt	Main	2	$45	

S - D (EP)

WHIDBEY ISLAND—FREELAND

Pillars By The Sea   **(206) 221-7738**
1367 East Bayview Avenue, Freeland, WA 98249
(Eleven miles north of Mukilteo Ferry, right at Book Bay Bookstore)

The neat yellow home of Walker and Ellen Jordan has white pillars, white trim, and pure turn-of-the-century charm. Geraniums in window boxes and pretty stained-glass panels flanking the front door add lively splashes of color. Huge shade trees and a back yard that slopes down to historic Holmes Harbor complete the picture. The 1907 home has been restored to mint condition inside and out. Two handsomely appointed guest rooms with private baths occupy the upper floor. Room A has a view of the Sound; Room B features down comforters and pillows. There is access to the upstairs through a door leading from the rear deck. Ellen's tasty breakfasts are served with the Harbor in sight. Walk to beaches or nearby Freeland Park, or visit the quaint seaside towns of Langley and Coupeville. What you're likely to remember most, though, are the serene beauty and unfailing graciousness of Pillars By The Sea.

No pets; no smoking; full breakfast; porch; deck; airport pickup (Oak Harbor). Brochure available.

A	1Q	Pvt	Sep	2	$40 - $45	($10)
B	1D	Pvt	Sep	2	$40 - $45	($10)

WHIDBEY ISLAND — GREENBANK

Guest House Bed & Breakfast   **(206) 678-3115**
835 East Christenson Road, Greenbank, WA 98253
(Sixteen miles north of Mukilteo Ferry)

Don and Mary Jane Creger's yellow 1920's farmhouse is set back from the road in quiet, pastoral surroundings. Two bedrooms formerly occupied by daughters Sara and Peggy now accommodate B&B guests. Still referred to by the girls' names, each room is as pretty as a picture. Sara's (A) is papered in a blue country print and Peggy's (B) in pink roses. The living room is a natural gathering place for fireside conversation. Like Whidbey Island in general, Guest House is small-scale, unspoiled, and largely undiscovered. Once you've found it, your first visit probably won't be your last.

No pets; no children; smoking outside only. Also available on the fifteen wooded acres are three hideaway cottages (children over fourteen welcome) and a luxurious log lodge—all with rustic charm and modern conveniences. Brochure available.

ROOM	BED	BATH	ENTRANCE	FLOOR	DAILY RATES
A	1D	Shd*	Main	1	$30
B	1D	Shd*	Sep	1	$35

S - D (EP)

WHIDBEY ISLAND – LANGLEY

The Orchard Bed & Breakfast   (206) 221-7880
619 Third Street, Langley, WA 98260
(South Whidbey Island)

Picture a vintage farmhouse, with a large wrap-around porch and a hanging swing, standing in the midst of an old orchard. It has been remodeled to perfect condition in accord with Martha Murphy's vision of a warm, family place where everyone can feel at home. There's a wholesome quality about The Orchard that reminds me of fresh apples and home-baked bread. Bountiful country breakfasts are served in a solarium that's been added to the rear of the kitchen. Two upstairs bedrooms are as pretty as they are comfortable; they make ideal accommodations for a family of four or for two couples. People who live in or visit South Whidbey appreciate the simple pleasures of a slow-paced life. There are forests to roam, berries to pick, and quaint spots to explore; Puget Sound is at your feet, and the Cascade Mountains loom in the background. At The Orchard, you might enjoy reading a book in the front porch swing or helping yourself to the fruits and nuts on the surrounding trees. Everything about Martha's home inspires pure relaxation and doing as you please.

Children welcome; smoking outside only; full breakfast; TV; kitchen privileges; piano; cradle; lots of toys and games; babysitters available. Room A has a covered balcony. Brochure available. OPEN SEVEN DAYS A WEEK JUNE 15-LABOR DAY; REST OF YEAR, OPEN FRIDAY, SATURDAY, AND SUNDAY ONLY. Weekly rates; special $70 rate for a family of four in two rooms; small child, no charge.

| A | 1Q | Shd* | Main | 2 | $35 - $40 |
| B | 1D | Shd* | Main | 2 | $35 - $40 |

WHIDBEY ISLAND – LANGLEY

Sally's Bed & Breakfast Manor　　　　　　　　　**(206) 221-8790**
P.O. Box 459, Langley, WA 98260
(South Whidbey Island)

In creating her bed and breakfast establishment, Sally DeFelice had a specific idea in mind: "A Home Retreat in Country Elegance." And *elegant* it is. A dedicated group of artisans and craftspeople have made the spirit of this 1929 farmhouse come alive. The creamy soft colors used throughout the house contribute to its feeling of peace and serenity. From the custom woodwork and cabinetry to the coordinated designer fabrics, wallpaper, and furnishings, the quality of workmanship and materials is unsurpassed in every detail. A view of Langley, the Cascades, and Puget Sound's Saratoga Passage is yours from either of the two country suites and from most rooms in the house. A fieldstone fireplace in the living room beckons guests to cozy up to the crackling fire and sip a cup of hot cider. Sumptuous breakfasts made from choice natural ingredients are served in the dining room or in the solar sunroom. From Sally's, it's an easy stroll to the seaside village of Langley where you'll find a variety of shops, galleries, and restaurants. A restful and romantic holiday awaits you at Sally's Bed & Breakfast Manor.

No pets; no smoking; no children; full breakfast; hot tub. Brochure and gift certificates available. Rates for longer stays are negotiable.

ROOM	BED	BATH	ENTRANCE	FLOOR	DAILY RATES
A	1Q	Pvt	Main	2	$60 - $65
B	1D	Pvt	Main	2	$60 - $65

195

APPENDIX

SOURCES FOR OBTAINING TOURIST INFORMATION

CALIFORNIA

California Office of Tourism
1030 13th Street, Suite 200, Sacramento, CA 95814   (916) 322-1396

North Coast

Eureka Chamber of Commerce
2112 Broadway, Eureka, CA 95501   (707) 442-3738

Fort Bragg Coast Chamber of Commerce
P.O. Box 1141, Fort Bragg, CA 95437   (707) 964-3153

Mendocino County Chamber of Commerce
P.O. Box 244, Ukiah, CA 95482   (707) 462-3091

Superintendent, Point Reyes National Seashore
Point Reyes Station, CA 94956   (415) 663-1092

Central Coast

Cambria Chamber of Commerce
767 Main Street, Cambria, CA 93428   (805) 927-3624

Carmel Business Association
P.O. Box 4444, Carmel-by-the-Sea, CA 93921   (408) 624-2522

Monterey Peninsula Chamber of Commerce
P.O. Box 1770, Monterey, CA 93940   (408) 649-3200

Morro Bay Chamber of Commerce
P.O. Box 876A, Morro Bay, CA 93442   (805) 722-4467

Pacific Grove Chamber of Commerce
P.O. Box 167, Pacific Grove, CA 93950   (408) 373-3304

San Luis Obispo Chamber of Commerce
1039 Chorro Street, San Luis Obispo, CA 93401   (805) 543-1323

San Simeon Chamber of Commerce
P.O. Box 1, San Simeon, CA 93452   (805) 927-3500

Santa Cruz County Convention & Visitors Bureau
P.O. Box 1820, Santa Cruz, CA 95061   (408) 423-6927

San Francisco & the Bay Area

Berkeley Chamber of Commerce
P.O. Box 210, Berkeley, CA 94701   (415) 845-1212

Los Gatos Chamber of Commerce
P.O. Box 1820, Los Gatos, CA 95031   (408) 354-9300

Marin County Chamber of Commerce & Visitors Bureau
30 North San Pedro Road, Suite 150
San Rafael, CA 94903   (415) 472-7470

Novato Chamber of Commerce
P.O. Box 824, Novato, CA 94947   (415) 897-1164

Oakland Convention & Visitors Bureau
1330 Broadway, Suite 1105, Oakland, CA 94612   (415) 839-9000

Palo Alto Chamber of Commerce
Two Palo Alto Square, Suite 150
El Camino Real at Page Mill Road
Palo Alto, CA 94304   (415) 494-2150

San Francisco Convention & Visitors Bureau
1390 Market Street, San Francisco, CA 94102   (415) 626-5500

San Jose Convention & Visitors Bureau
One Paseo de San Antonio, San Jose, CA 95113   (408) 998-7000

San Mateo County Convention & Visitors Bureau
888 Airport Boulevard, Burlingame, CA 94010   (415) 347-7004

Walnut Creek Area Chamber of Commerce
1395 Civic Drive, Walnut Creek, CA 94596   (415) 934-2000

Wine Country

Anderson Valley Chamber of Commerce
P.O. Box 275, Boonville, CA 95415

Geyserville Chamber of Commerce
P.O. Box 276, Geyserville, CA 95441

Lake County Chamber of Commerce
875 Lakeport Boulevard, Lakeport, CA 95453   (707) 263-6131

Napa Chamber of Commerce
1900 Jefferson Street, Napa, CA 94558   (707) 226-7455

Napa Valley Tourist Bureau & Wine Tours, Inc.
6488 Washington Street, Yountville, CA 94599   (707) 253-2611

Petaluma Area Chamber of Commerce
314 Western Avenue, Petaluma, CA 94952   (707) 762-2785

Russian River Region Visitor Information Center
P.O. Box 255B, Guerneville, CA 95446   (707) 869-9009

St. Helena Chamber of Commerce
1508 Main Street, St. Helena, CA 94574   (707) 963-4456

Santa Rosa Chamber of Commerce
673 First Street, Santa Rosa, CA 95404   (707) 545-1414

Sonoma Valley Chamber of Commerce
453 First Street East, Sonoma, CA 95476   (707) 996-1033

Central Valley to Mount Shasta

Merced Chamber of Commerce
505 West 20th Street, Merced, CA 95340   (209) 384-3333

Mount Shasta Chamber of Commerce
P.O. Box 201, Mount Shasta, CA 96067   (916) 926-4865

Oroville Area Chamber of Commerce
1789 Montgomery Street, Oroville, CA 95965   (916) 533-2542

Sacramento Convention & Visitors Bureau
1100 14th Street, Sacramento, CA 95814   (916) 449-5291

Gold Country & the Sierra

Carson City Chamber of Commerce
1191 South Carson Street, Carson City, NV 89701   (702) 882-1565

El Dorado County Chamber of Commerce
542 Main Street, Placerville, CA 95667   (916) 626-2344

Grass Valley Area Chamber of Commerce
151 Mill Street, Grass Valley, CA 95945   (916) 273-4667

Mariposa County Chamber of Commerce
P.O. Box 425, Mariposa, CA 95338   (209) 966-2456

North Lake Tahoe Chamber of Commerce
P.O. Box 884, Tahoe City, CA 95730   (916) 583-2371

Placer County Chamber of Commerce
661 Newcastle Road, Newcastle, CA 95658   (916) 663-2061

Tahoe North Visitors & Convention Bureau   (California) (800) 822-5959
P.O. Box 5578, Tahoe City, CA 95730   (Other) (800) 824-8557

Truckee-Donner Chamber of Commerce
P.O. Box 361, Truckee, CA 95734   (916) 587-2757

Tuolumne County Chamber of Commerce
P.O. Box 277, Sonora, CA 95370   (209) 532-4212

Southern California

Anaheim Area Visitor & Convention Bureau
800 West Katella Avenue, Anaheim, CA 92802   (714) 999-8999

Carpinteria Valley Chamber of Commerce
P.O. Box 956, Carpinteria, CA 93013   (805) 684-5479

Catalina Island Chamber of Commerce
P.O. Box 217, Avalon, CA 90704   (213) 510-1520

Escondido Visitor & Information Bureau
720 North Broadway, Escondido, CA 92025   (714) 745-4741

Greater Los Angeles Visitors & Convention Bureau
505 South Flower Street, Los Angeles, CA 90071   (213) 628-3101

San Diego Convention & Visitors Bureau
1200 Third Avenue, San Diego, CA 92101   (714) 232-3101

Pathfinder Visitor Information Center
2688 East Mission Bay Drive, San Diego, CA 92109   (619) 276-8200

Palm Springs Convention & Visitors Bureau
Municipal Airport Terminal
Palm Springs, CA 92262-6993   (619) 327-8411

Greater Santa Ana Chamber of Commerce
P.O. Box 205, Santa Ana, CA 92702   (714) 541-5353

Santa Barbara Chamber of Commerce
P.O. Box 299, Santa Barbara, CA 93102   (805) 965-3021

Solvang Chamber of Commerce
P.O. Box 465, Solvang, CA 93463   (805) 688-3317

OREGON

Oregon Travel Information Section
Department of Transportation
Salem, OR 97310   (Toll free, outside Oregon) 1-800-547-7842

The Oregon Coast Association
P.O. Box 670, Newport, OR 97365   (503) 265-2611

The Ashland Chamber of Commerce
P.O. Box 606, Ashland, OR 97520   (503) 482-3486

Bandon Chamber of Commerce
P.O. Box 1515, Bandon, OR 97411

Eugene Springfield Convention & Visitors Bureau, Inc.
P.O. Box 10286, Eugene, OR 97440   (503) 484-5307

Gold Beach-Wedderburn Chamber of Commerce
P.O. Box 55, Gold Beach, OR 97444

Lincoln City Chamber of Commerce
P.O. Box 787, Lincoln City, OR 97367   (503) 994-3070

Newport Chamber of Commerce
555 S.W. Coast Highway, Newport, OR 97365   (503) 265-8801

Greater Portland Convention & Visitors Association, Inc.
26 S.W. Salmon Street, Portland, OR 97204   (503) 222-2223

WASHINGTON

Washington State Department of Commerce & Economic Development
101 General Administration Building   (WA) 1-800-562-4570
Olympia, WA 98504   (Other) 1-800-541-9274

Cascade Loop Association
P.O. Box 225, Chelan, WA 98816   (509) 682-LOOP

Anacortes Chamber of Commerce
1319 Commercial, Anacortes, WA 98221   (206) 293-3832

Lake Chelan Chamber of Commerce
P.O. Box 216, Chelan, WA 98816   (509) 682-2022

Seattle-King County Convention & Visitors Bureau
1815 Seventh Avenue, Seattle, WA 98101   (206) 447-7273

Snohomish Chamber of Commerce
P.O. Box 135, Snohomish, WA 98290   (206) 568-2526

Whidbey Island

   North Whidbey Chamber of Commerce
   P.O. Box 883, Oak Harbor, WA 98277   (206) 675-3535

   Central Whidbey Chamber of Commerce
   P.O. Box 152, Coupeville, WA 98239   (206) 678-5305

   Langley Chamber of Commerce
   P.O. Box 403, Langley, WA 98260   (206) 321-6765

Wenatchee Area Visitors & Convention Bureau
P.O. Box 850, Wenatchee, WA 98801   (509) 662-4774

INDEX OF CITIES & TOWNS

CALIFORNIA

Alameda 44
Alamo 45
Anaheim 137
Anchor Bay 14
Avalon . . . . See Catalina Island
Baywood Park . . . . See Morro Bay
Berkeley 46
Burlingame 49
Calistoga 85
Cambria 27
Carmel-by-the-Sea 30
Carpinteria 138
Castro Valley 50
Catalina Island 140
Clearlake 87
Colfax 119
Columbia 120
Concord 51
Davenport 33
Dutch Flat 121
Escondido 141
Eureka 15
Fremont 52
Geyserville 89
Glendale 142
Grass Valley 122
Gualala 17
Inverness 18
La Habra Heights 143
Little River . . . . See Mendocino
Los Gatos 53
Los Angeles 144
Lower Lake . . . . See Clearlake
Mariposa 123

Martinez 54
Mendocino 19
Merced 107
Middletown 90
Mill Valley 56
Montecito . . . . See Santa Barbara
Monterey 34
Moraga 57
Morro Bay 35
Mount Shasta 108
Napa 91
Newport Beach 146
Northridge 147
Novato 58
Oakland 59
Oroville 110
Pacifica 60
Pacific Grove 36
Palm Springs 148
Palo Alto . . . . See Stanford
Pebble Beach 38
Pescadero 39
Petaluma 93
Piedmont 61
Placerville 127
Pleasant Hill 62
Point Reyes Station 20
Roseville 111
Sacramento 112
St. Helena 95
San Diego 149
San Francisco 63
San Jose 72
San Mateo 74
San Rafael 75
Santa Ana 153
Santa Barbara 154
Santa Cruz 40
Santa Rosa 98

Solvang 159
Sonoma 100
Sonora 128
Soulsbyville . . . . See Sonora
Stanford 76
Sunol 77
Tahoe City 130
Tiburon 78
Walnut Creek 79
West Covina 160
Westport 21
Yorkville 102

NEVADA
Genoa 132

OREGON
Ashland 167
Bandon 170
Coburg . . . . See Eugene
Coquille 172
Elmira 173
Eugene 174
Gleneden Beach 177
Gold Beach 178
Lincoln City 181
Springfield . . . . See Eugene
Wedderburn . . . . See Gold Beach

WASHINGTON
Anacortes 187
Fall City 188
Leavenworth 189
Snohomish 190
Whidbey Island
    Clinton 191
    Freeland 192
    Greenbank 193
    Langley 194

ORDERING THE 1985 SUPPLEMENT

BED & BREAKFAST HOMES DIRECTORY is updated annually by either a supplement or a new edition. A supplement to this edition is scheduled for publication by May 1, 1985. It will contain new host home listings and any changes in information stated in this book. In order to have the most current information possible, just clip and send in this form to receive the supplement *at no additional charge*—the cost is included in your $7.95 purchase price.

NOTICE TO MAIL ORDER CUSTOMERS: You do not need to send in this form, as our record of your order entitles you to receive the supplement *automatically* upon publication. Anyone ordering the book after May 1, 1985, receives both the book *and* the supplement. (You may use this form for a change of address if necessary; please also indicate the name and address to which book was sent.)

---------------------- FOLD HERE ----------------------

BOOKSTORE CUSTOMERS: Please fill in the form below and mail to us following your purchase of *BED & BREAKFAST HOMES DIRECTORY*.

NAME _____

ADDRESS_____

CITY/STATE/ZIP _____

COMMENTS_____

_____

_____

_____

CUT HERE

From: _____

_____

_____

Diane Knight
Knighttime Publications
P.O. Box 591
Cupertino, CA 95014

---------------------- FOLD HERE ----------------------

CUT HERE

STAPLE OR TAPE

B&B TRAVELER'S REPORT

Knighttime Publications would like to receive any comments you may have about your experiences while using this directory. Please report any comment, suggestion, compliment or criticism as indicated:

Name and location of host home _____

_____

Date of visit _____Length of stay _____

Comments_____

_____

_____

_____

_____

_____

_____

_____

_____

_____

_____

Your name_____

Address _____

City/State/Zip _____

Telephone _____

CUT HERE

From: _____

_____

_____

FIRST
CLASS
POSTAGE
HERE

Diane Knight
Knighttime Publications
P.O. Box 591
Cupertino, CA 95014

---------------------- FOLD HERE ----------------------

CUT HERE

STAPLE OR TAPE

B&B TRAVELER'S REPORT

Knighttime Publications would like to receive any comments you may have about your experiences while using this directory. Please report any comment, suggestion, compliment or criticism as indicated:

Name and location of host home _____

_____

Date of visit _____Length of stay _____

Comments_____

_____

_____

_____

_____

_____

_____

_____

_____

_____

_____

_____

_____

Your name_____

Address _____

City/State/Zip _____

Telephone _____

- - CUT HERE - -

From: _____

_____

Diane Knight
Knighttime Publications
P.O. Box 591
Cupertino, CA 95014

-------------------- FOLD HERE -------------------- CUT HERE

STAPLE OR TAPE

B&B TRAVELER'S REPORT

Knighttime Publications would like to receive any comments you may have about your experiences while using this directory. Please report any comment, suggestion, compliment or criticism as indicated:

Name and location of host home _____

_____

Date of visit _____ Length of stay _____

Comments _____

_____

_____

_____

_____

_____

_____

_____

_____

_____

_____

Your name _____

Address _____

City/State/Zip _____

Telephone _____

CUT HERE

From: _____

_____

_____

Diane Knight
Knighttime Publications
P.O. Box 591
Cupertino, CA 95014

------------------------- FOLD HERE -------------------------

CUT HERE

STAPLE OR TAPE

APPLICATION TO BECOME A B&B HOST

Name(s) _____

Mailing address _____

City/State/Zip _____

Telephone _____

Best time to phone you _____

Brief description of your home and room(s) available:

_____

_____

_____

_____

_____

_____

_____

_____

_____

_____

There is a listing fee which is equal to the highest (double) rate you charge for one night's lodging. Hosts must maintain clean, comfortable accommodations and a hospitable manner toward guests.

Signature _____

Date _____

Note: Amount of listing fee is subject to change for future editions.

CUT HERE

From: _____

_____

_____

FIRST
CLASS
POSTAGE
HERE

Diane Knight
Knighttime Publications
P.O. Box 591
Cupertino, CA 95014

-------------------------- FOLD HERE ----------------------------

CUT HERE

STAPLE OR TAPE

ORDER FORM

Please send me_____additional copies of the West Coast Edition of BED & BREAKFAST HOMES DIRECTORY. I enclose $7.95 (tax and handling included) for each copy ordered.

Name _____

Address _____

City/State/Zip _____

Send as a gift to: (Use extra paper for additional gifts.)

Name _____

Address _____

City/State/Zip _____

Gift card should read: _____

KNIGHTTIME PUBLICATIONS, P.O. Box 591, Cupertino, CA 95014

CUT HERE

ORDER FORM

Please send me_____additional copies of the West Coast Edition of BED & BREAKFAST HOMES DIRECTORY. I enclose $7.95 (tax and handling included) for each copy ordered.

Name _____

Address _____

City/State/Zip _____

Send as a gift to: (Use extra paper for additional gifts.)

Name _____

Address _____

City/State/Zip _____

Gift card should read: _____

KNIGHTTIME PUBLICATIONS, P.O. Box 591, Cupertino, CA 95014